basic mathematics

basic mathematics

by NORMAN H. CROWHURST

Engineering Consultant

Formerly: Senior Mathematics Lecturer
S. E. London Technical College
and
Beckenham Technical College
London, England

VOL. 1

Developing

ARITHMETIC

as an outgrowth of learning to count

JOHN F. RIDER PUBLISHER INC., NEW YORK

Library of Congress Catalog Number 61-7327

Printed in the United States of America

SIXTH PRINTING, 1966

PREFACE

Ask any mathematician and he'll tell you mathematics is easy. To show you, he'll demonstrate some calculation, leaving out half the steps, which he does in his head. This leaves the uninitiated viewing him with a sense of awe: mathematics is something you must have a "bent" for.

But this just isn't true. The mathematician isn't trying to be smart—he doesn't understand why many people find it difficult, when he finds it so easy. It's not because the others lack the right kind of brain. In 99 cases out of 100, it's because nobody bothered to give them the right start.

Even addition is too often wrongly taught. You mustn't use your fingers. You are asked what 3 and 5 make, and you should know. You guess 7 or 9 and get marked wrong. Eventually you manage to *memorize* that 3 and 5 are 8.

Then comes subtraction, where the same process of memorizing is continued. In multiplication, there are the tables to be learned. Then division, with its divisor, dividend, quotient, and remainder. As well as learning not to confuse these words, you have to learn to divide, *by following rules.* Fractions, decimals, and the things that follow compound the injury. How can anybody possibly memorize so many calculations? Oddly enough, the few people who *can* rarely make good mathematicians.

You may have seen those "stump the memory man" programs, where a person with what is called a "photographic memory" can recite who won the world series in 1928, the names of the players on both teams, their ages at the time, their individual scores at that game, and so on, with similar information about any event within living memory you care to pick.

If such a person happens to have memorized multiplication tables up to 1,000 times 1,000, he could tell, like a flash, the result of 371 times 542. But if you asked him for 2 times 1,001, he'd be stumped because he never memorized beyond 1,000 times 1,000!

There you have it. Mathematics, including arithmetic, should *not* be learned *by memory*. True, in learning arithmetic, you will get to *remember* what 5 times 7 are. But memorizing tables is asking for trouble. If you forget what 5 times 7 are, you are stumped. You either give up or guess. That's the mistake most people make in learning arithmetic.

As you work through this book, you will find that arithmetic is really an extension of learning to count. It's quite alright to use your fingers, or counters, or anything handy, to help you add. After a while you'll get to remember without having to use your fingers (or take your shoes off). Multiplication is really only extended addition. So learn it that way.

Then, if you forget what 5 times 7 are, you can find out again for yourself, without fear of "showing your ignorance."

When you learn arithmetic by memorizing numbers and ways of using them, you generally have trouble with problems. How on earth do you find what piece of arithmetic will solve this particular problem? By learning arithmetic the practical way, this difficulty does not arise. You don't have to worry about which formula or method to use; you just go ahead and figure it out.

That's really what arithmetic is—ways of figuring things out. So go ahead and do it; don't worry about the formalities of whether you are using "the way teacher wants it done." Any way that is correct will find you the right answer. Some ways are easier than others, and you naturally want to find the easiest ways. That's exactly how we go about it in this book.

Perhaps you manage addition, subtraction, multiplication, and division fine, but you get into trouble with fractions. What you may not realize is that your trouble with fractions started because you never really *understood* what came before them. So I suggest that you start at the beginning—at least reading through. If you don't find it new, you'll find it interesting, *and* you'll be ready for fractions when you get to them.

People tell us that never before has math been so important in our lives; never before has there been so much need for people who have mastered math. This is true. But mathematics has always been intimately connected with everyday life. The problems it helps us with now are only up-to-date versions of problems that confronted man from the dawn of time.

This is mentioned because it may help you to remember the *essentially practical* nature of the subject. Each form of calculation has developed from its forerunners as a step to make the work easier—not to give school kids a harder time learning it! Keeping this in mind will help you see a useful purpose in each progressive step, instead of leaving you wondering, "Why on earth do I have to learn all this?"

While grade school children may find that this book helps them approach arithmetic with more understanding than they get from other texts, it is also written to help the millions of people whom school failed to give an effective and confident background in arithmetic and mathematics.

New York, N. Y. NORMAN H. CROWHURST
February 1961

CONTENTS

VOL. I—BASIC MATHEMATICS

Counting

The easiest way to count a number of things is to arrange them in groups and then move them from one group to another, one at a time, giving each one a number: "One, two, three, four . . ." as we move it over.

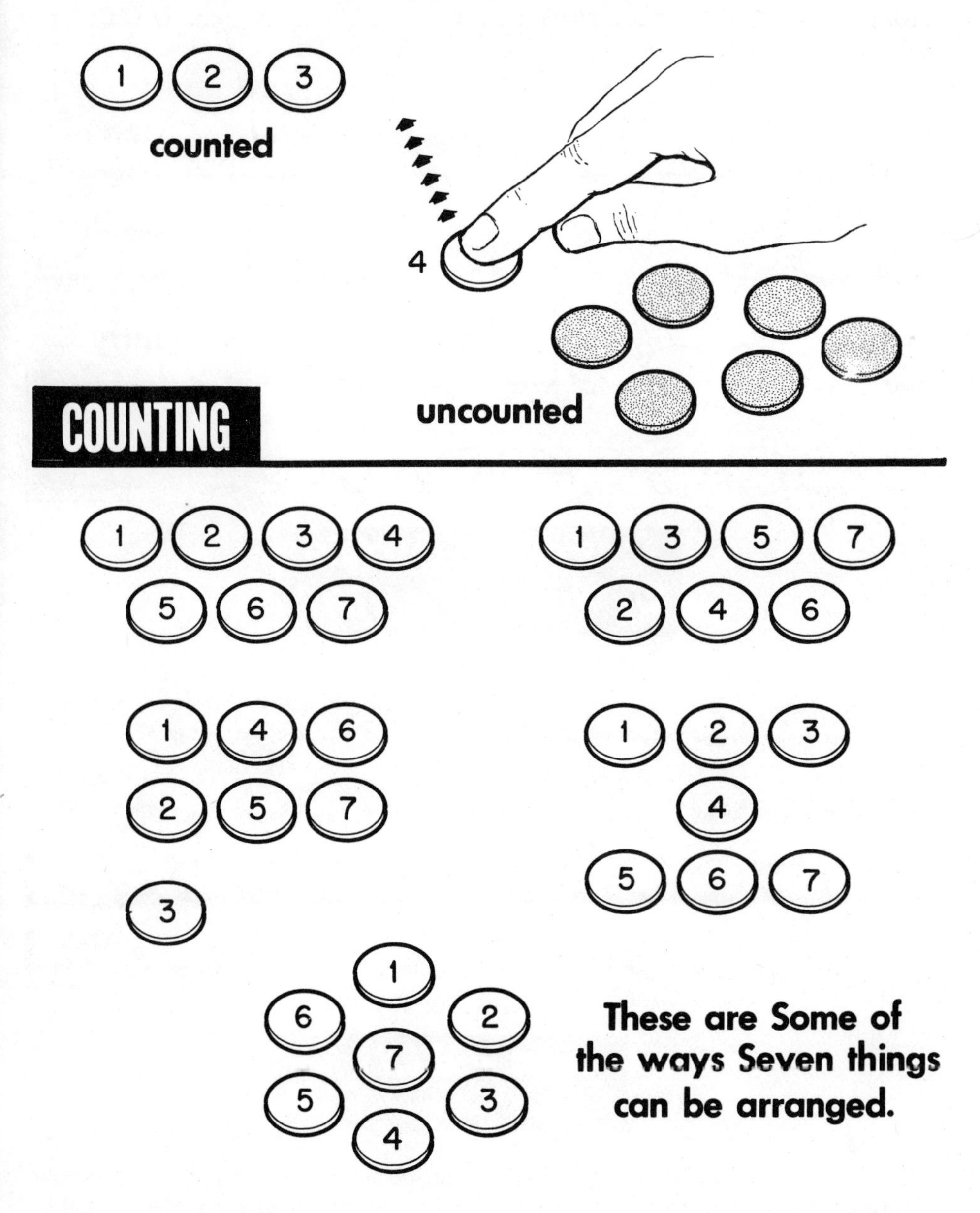

It does not make any difference how a number of things are arranged (we have used circles, which could be coins). There will still be the same number. In this example, there are 7 circles in each group.

Counting into Tens and Dozens

When we have a large number of things to count, it is more convenient to arrange them into regular groups. This way the number is more easily recognized. Our common numbering system uses groups of *ten.* Thus 2 groups of ten are 20; 3 are 30; 4 are 40; etc. This use of tens is called the *decimal system.*

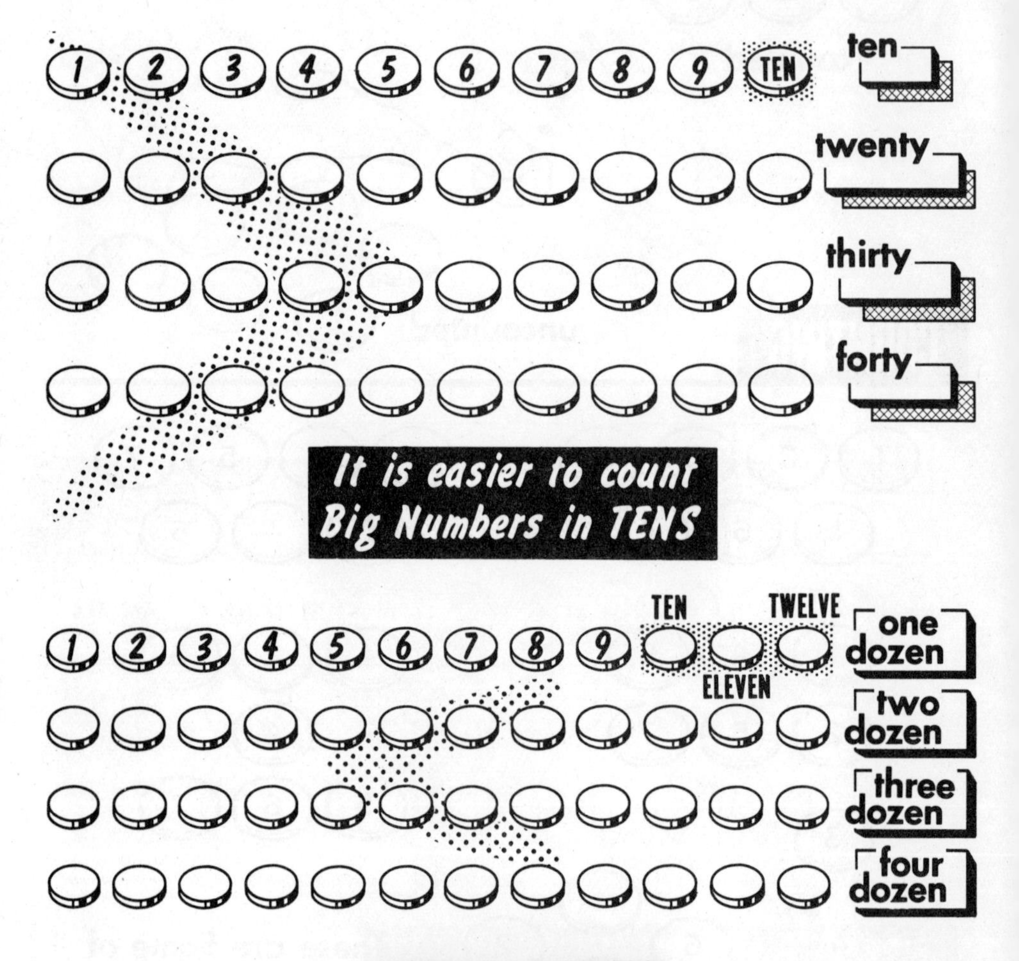

Tens are not the only size group that can be used for a numbering system. At one time, many things used to be counted in dozens, or *twelves.* This use of dozens is called the *duodecimal system* and is still used for counting some things, such as eggs. The decimal system, however, is the more common.

Writing Numbers Bigger Than Ten

When we have a number bigger than ten, we can state it in the number of complete-ten groups with the extra number left over. Thus *thirty five* means 3 tens and 5 left over. By writing these numbers side by side, we show that the left-hand number stands for complete-ten groups, and the right-hand number for the extras, called the "ones" number.

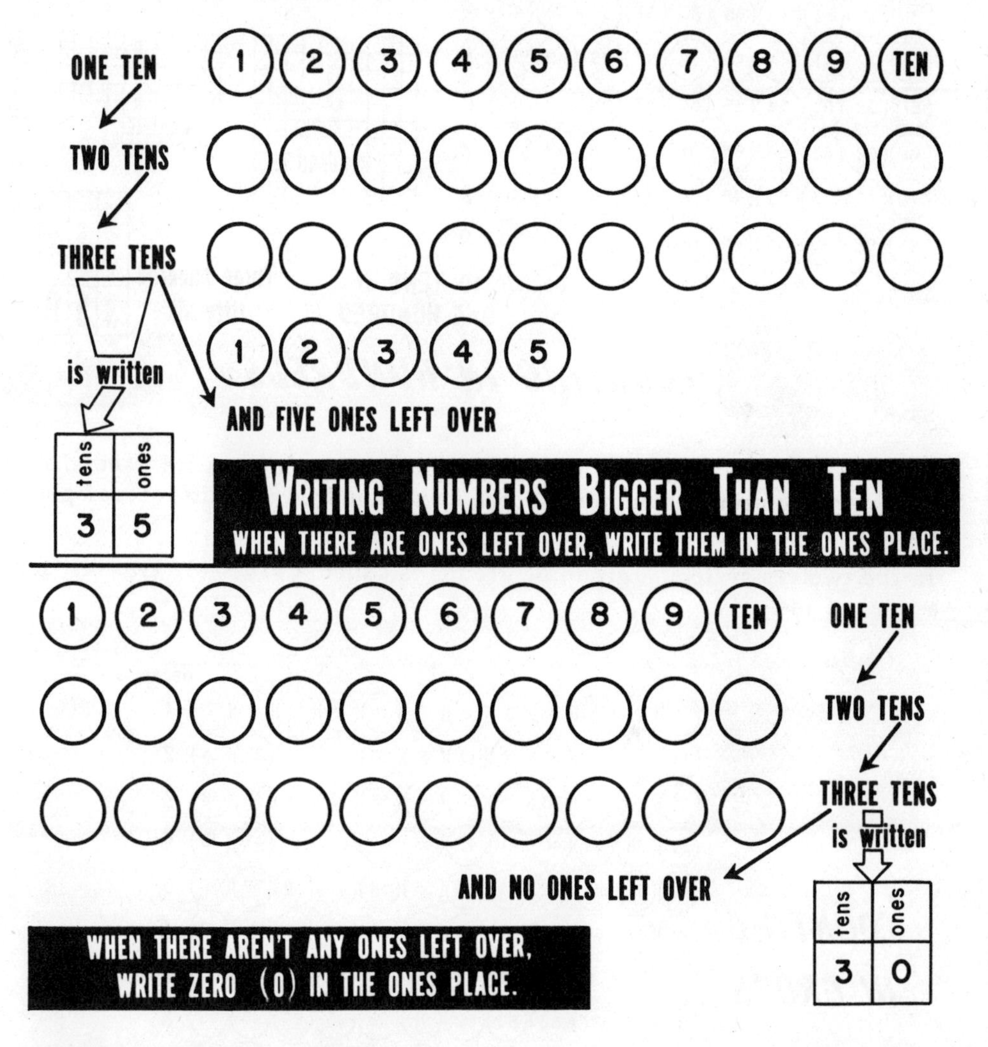

Why Zero Is Used in Counting

If we have an exact number of tens, we still need to show that the number we write means *tens* and not ones. This we do by writing a zero (0) as the right-hand number in the *ones* place, showing that we have an exact number of tens, because there is nothing left over to put in the ones place. Zero means "none."

Groups of Groups — Hundreds

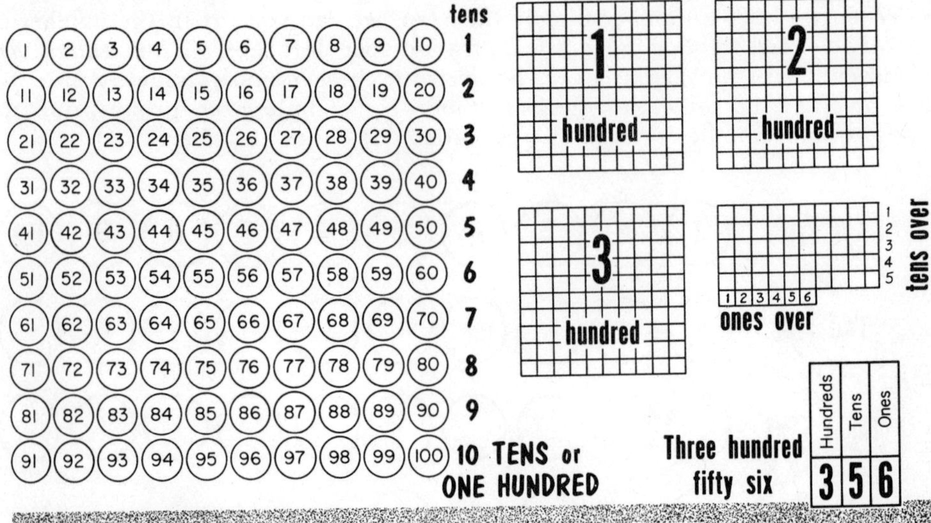

When we complete 10 tens, we have a group of groups called a *hundred,* and start counting again toward the next hundred. Counts of complete hundreds are written to the left of the tens figure.

In the twelves system, a group of groups is called a *gross*—12 twelves, for a total of 144.

COUNTING IN GROSS

												dozens
1	2	3	4	5	6	7	8	9	10	11	12	1
13	14	15	16	17	18	19	20	21	22	23	24	2
25	26	27	28	29	30	31	32	33	34	35	36	3
37	38	39	40	41	42	43	44	45	46	47	48	4
49	50	51	52	53	54	55	56	57	58	59	60	5
61	62	63	64	65	66	67	68	69	70	71	72	6
73	74	75	76	77	78	79	80	81	82	83	84	7
85	86	87	88	89	90	91	92	93	94	95	96	8
97	98	99	100	101	102	103	104	105	106	107	108	9
109	110	111	112	113	114	115	116	117	118	119	120	10
121	122	123	124	125	126	127	128	129	130	131	132	11
133	134	135	136	137	138	139	140	141	142	143	144	12 DOZEN OR 1 GROSS

By Hundreds to Thousands

In the same way, when we get to 10 hundreds in our counting, the number reaches another group category called *thousands*. If each layer in a package contains 10 rows of ten, or 1 hundred, 10 layers make up 1 thousand.

COUNTING IN THOUSANDS

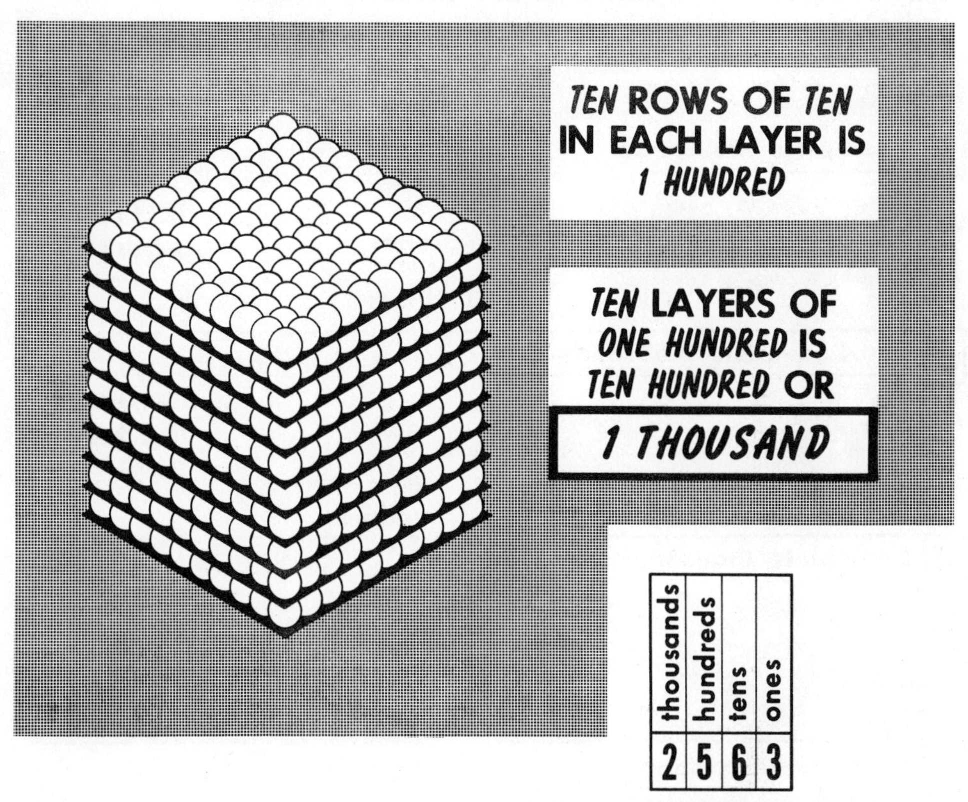

thousands	hundreds	tens	ones
2	5	6	3

Two thousand five hundred sixty three

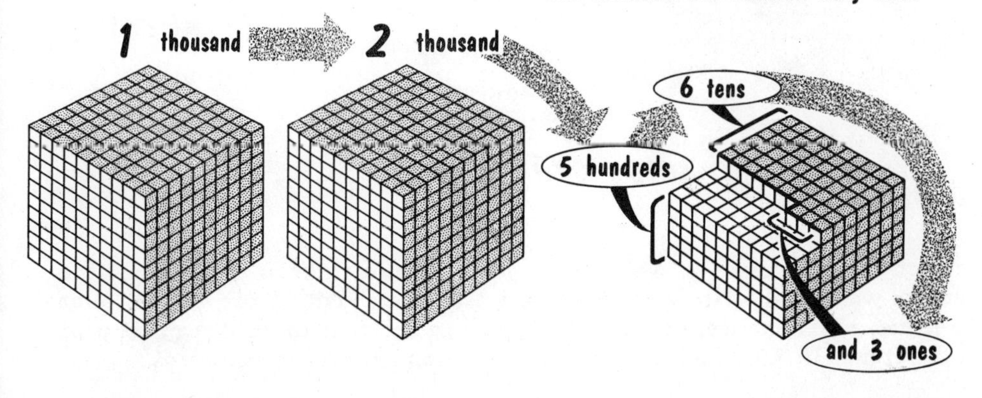

Don't Forget To Use Zeros

When a count has left-over layers, rows, and parts of rows, using this systematic arrangement idea, there will be numbers in each column. But if there are no complete-hundred layers after the last complete-thousand layer, the hundreds (A) will be zero. Part (B) shows four complete-thousand layers, three complete-hundred layers, seven complete-ten layers, and no ones left over, so the ones figure will be zero. Part (C) shows a count with no complete-tens layer and Part (D) with neither complete-hundred nor complete-ten layers.

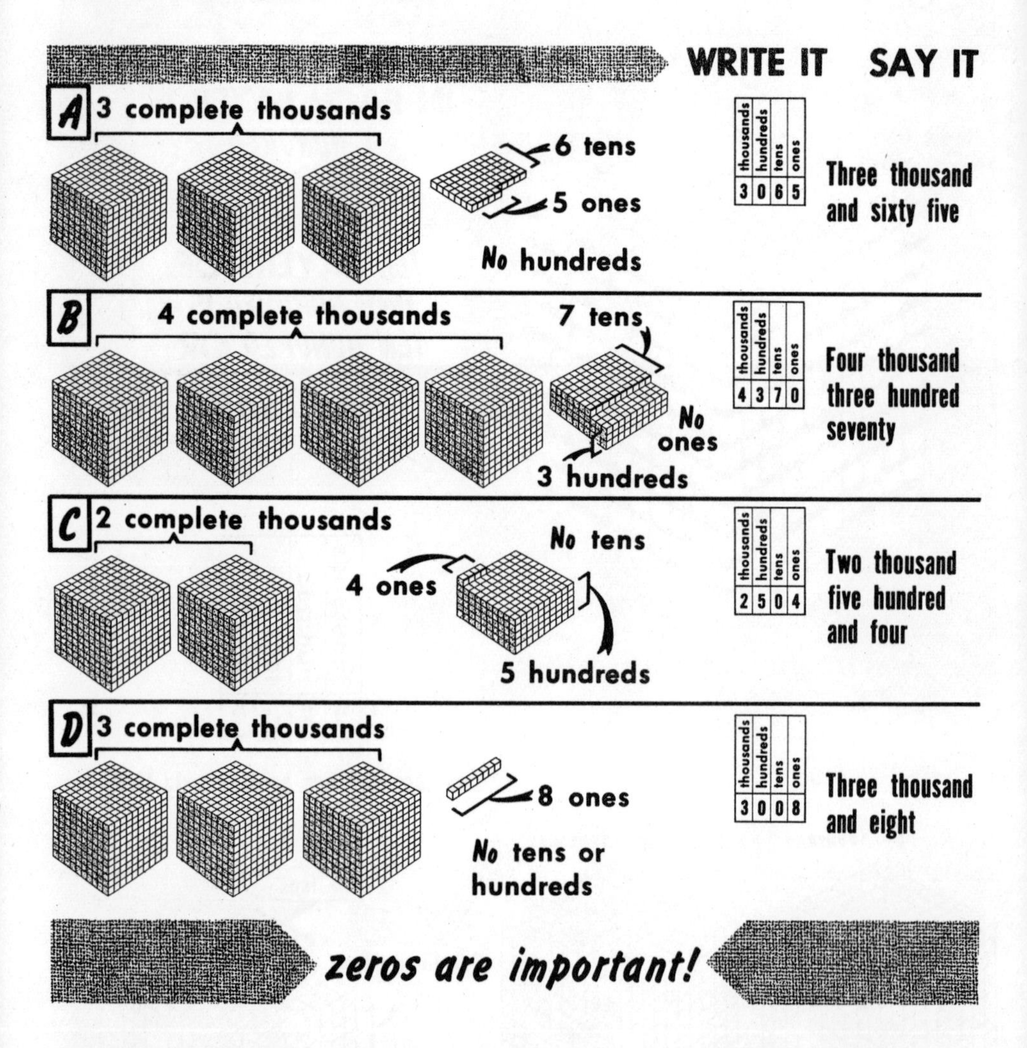

In each of these cases, if we had not put a zero in to keep the "place," the number we would write would not be a true statement of the actual count we made. For instance, in Part (D), you can see that there is a great deal of difference in 3,008 and 38; so we repeat: *don't forget to use zeros.*

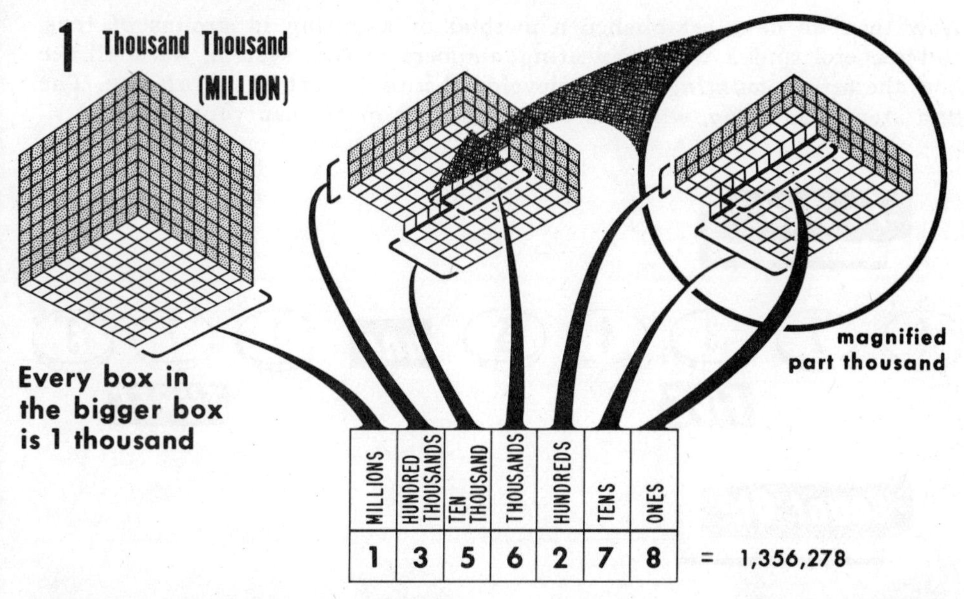

1 THOUSAND THOUSANDS IS 1 MILLION - 1,000,000
1 THOUSAND MILLIONS IS 1 BILLION - 1,000,000,000

Counting up to a thousand makes a "box," 10 in a row, 10 rows, and 10 layers of 10 rows. We can now go on up to even bigger numbers by starting over, using these boxes of 1 thousand each as "units," which are terms of stating what we mean, to build up a new arrangement of rows and layers. In this way, we can count on up to 1,000 thousands, which is called a *million.*

There is no limit to how high we can count using this system. We can start over again, using millions as units, until 1,000 millions make up a *billion.* Going on in this way, 1,000 billions make a *trillion,* 1,000 trillions make a quatrillion, etc.—but that will be enough for now.

To mark off each "start-over" point, or the point at which we begin to speak in terms of another *unit,* above hundreds, we put a comma between the numbers. Thus we count up to 1 thousand without commas (999). Above 1 thousand, we separate the complete thousands in our count toward 1 million from the part of a thousand (complete hundreds, tens, and ones) left over, by the first comma (1,000—999,999). When we pass 1 million (more than 999,999), we use another comma to separate complete millions from the part of a million (complete thousands, hundreds, tens, and ones) left over (1,999,999), etc.

This means that *we use a comma to mark off every three numbers, starting from the right.*

Adding — Counting On

Now that we have established a method of counting in groups of tens, 10 tens, etc., and a way of writing numbers in this system, we shall see how the art of *counting* can be developed into the art of *calculating*. The first step is *addition*, which is really nothing more than counting on.

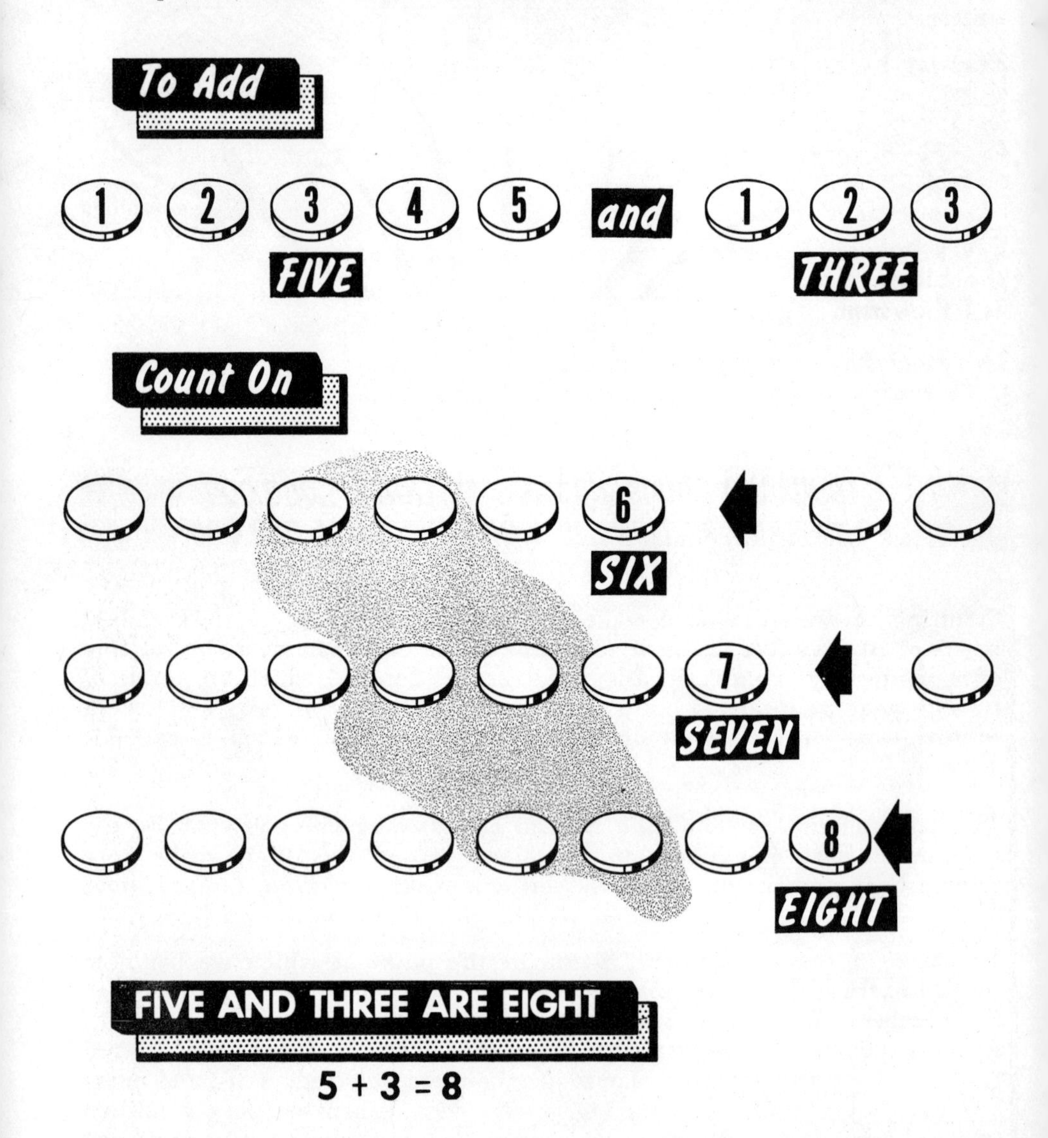

Suppose we have two numbers—say 5 and 3. When we write it down, we put 5 + 3, using the plus sign (+) to show that we are to *add* the numbers. We want to know how many this makes altogether. We put down our two groups of objects by counting them out. Now we count on the second group as we add it to the first, and find that the total is 8.

Making an Addition Table

Every time we add, we could follow this counting-on method. But it would take quite a lot of time for the more complicated calculations; so we find a way of doing the same thing more quickly. There are two ways to do this, and it really doesn't matter which one you use; the end result will be the same—you'll learn to add quickly.

The way we shall show you is to make a table of what every combination of two numbers between 1 and 9 makes, by performing the counting-on method for each. Notice that it does not matter whether we add 5 and 3 or 3 and 5; the result is 8 either way Also, you will notice that there are several interesting patterns of odd (1, 3, 5, etc.) and even (2, 4, 6, etc.) numbers in the table. These patterns make a good way to check that your table is right.

If you make such a table, you can then use the table for all your calculations, until by constant use, you get to know them all from memory.

The other way is to do the counting on every time you have an addition to do, until you get to remember all the combinations.

ADDITION TABLE

	1 and	2 and	3 and	4 and	5 and	6 and	7 and	8 and	9 and
1 are	2	3	4	5	6	7	8	9	10
2 are	3	4	5	6	7	8	9	10	11
3 are	4	5	6	7	8	9	10	11	12
4 are	5	6	7	8	9	10	11	12	13
5 are	6	7	8	9	10	11	12	13	14
6 are	7	8	9	10	11	12	13	14	15
7 are	8	9	10	11	12	13	14	15	16
8 are	9	10	11	12	13	14	15	16	17
9 are	10	11	12	13	14	15	16	17	18

Adding Three or More Numbers

When we have more numbers to add, we proceed in just the same way. We never add more than two numbers together at once. But when we have added two together, we can then add another one to this single total for the three numbers, etc.

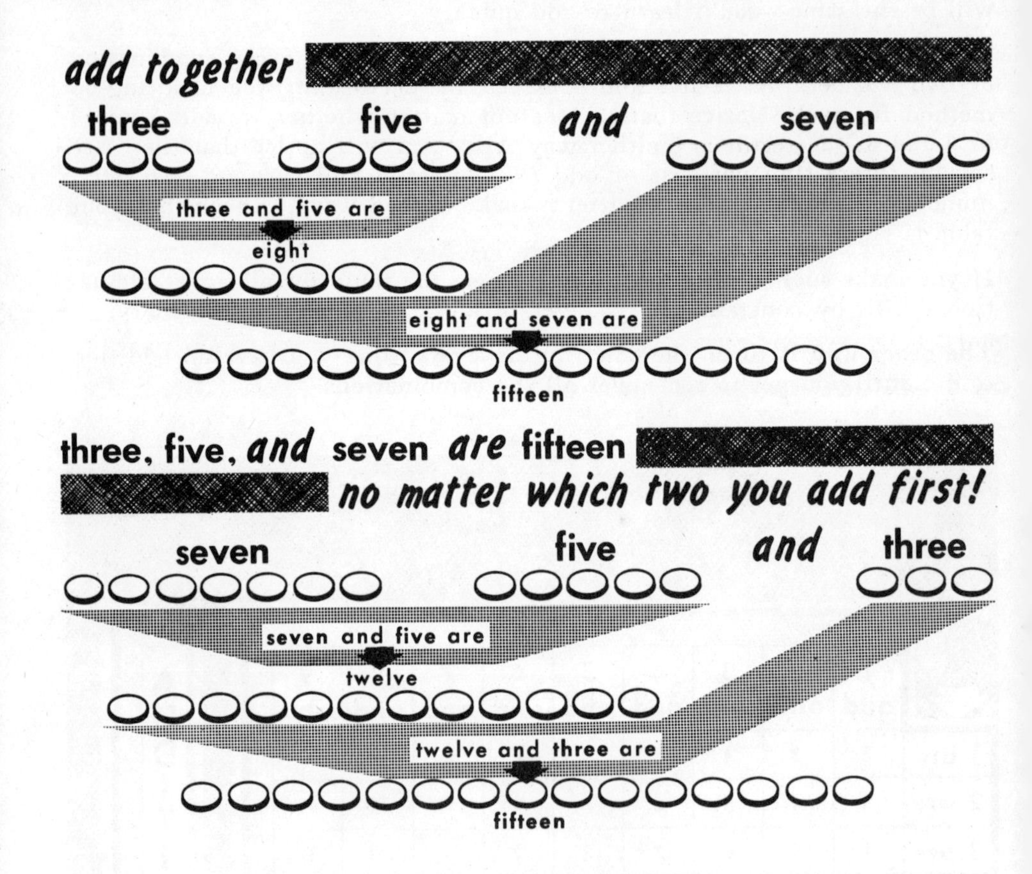

Suppose we have to add 3, 5, and 7 together. 3 and 5 are 8; 8 and 7 are 15. It doesn't matter what order we take the numbers in; the result will be the same. We could take 3 and 7 are 10; then 10 and 5 are 15. Or 5 and 7 are 12; then 12 and 3 are 15. The last two we could do by counting on, although they are not in the table. But 2 and 3 are 5; and the ten part of 12 does not change, so 12 and 3 are 15.

We can extend this to as many numbers as we choose. For example, add together 6, 7, 9, 3, and 2. Taking them in that order: 6 and 7 are 13; 13 and 9 are 22 (3 and 9 are 12, and now we have the second ten); 22 and 3 are 25 (the 2 tens are unchanged); 25 and 2 are 27. This would produce the same result with the five numbers taken in any order. Let's take them backwards: 2 and 3 are 5; 5 and 9 are 14; 14 and 7 are 21; 21 and 6 are 27—the same answer.

Adding Larger Numbers

So far we have only added numbers with a single figure—ones. But bigger numbers can be added in the same way. Suppose we want to add 125 and 324: each of these numbers has three figures—hundreds, tens, and ones.

Just as 1 and 1 are 2, so 10 and 10 are 20, 100 and 100 are 200. We can use the counting-on method or the addition table for any group of numbers, so long as all in the group *belong*—that is, all are in the same "place." A figure from the tens place cannot be added to a figure from the ones place.

Taking the *ones* first: 5 and 4 are 9. So the ones total is 9. Next take the *tens:* 2 and 2 are 4. Finally the *hundreds:* 1 and 3 are 4. Now we put all this together, with each total written in its proper place: 4 hundreds, 4 tens, and 9 ones: 449.

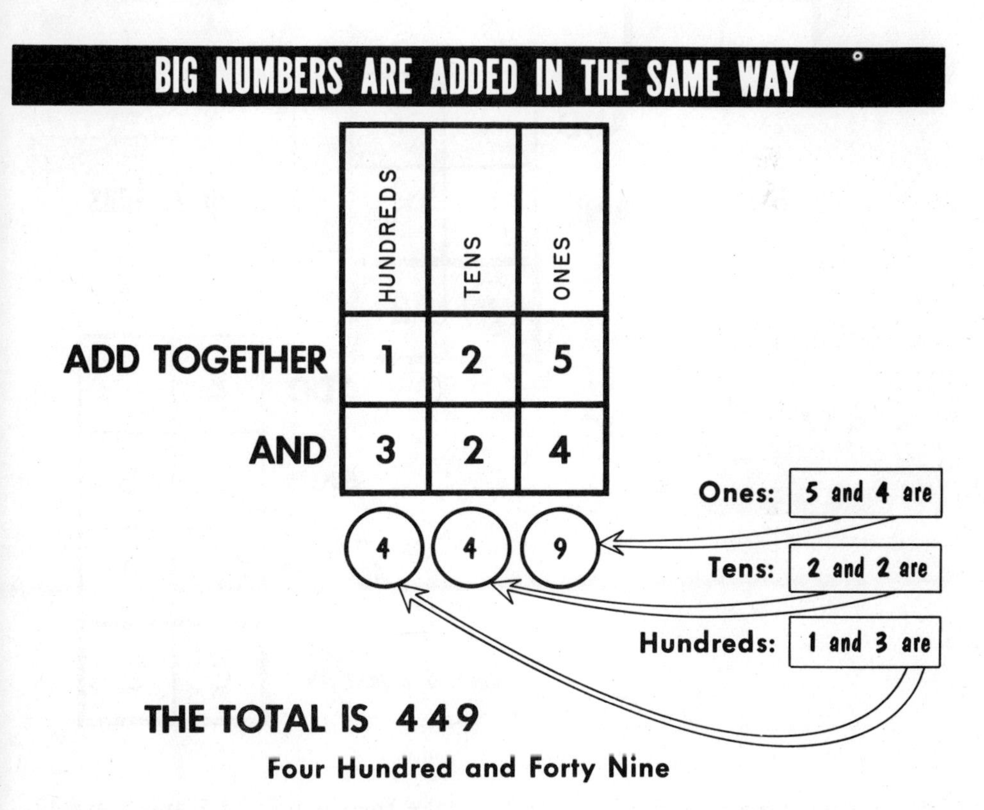

Notice that we are now taking quite a few short cuts: we no longer count tens and hundreds one at a time. To add 125 and 324 by counting on all of the 324 would take a long while, and the chances of skipping one or of counting one twice are great in so large a count. Therefore the short cut not only saves time but also cuts down the chances of error.

Carrying

We deliberately chose an easy example of big numbers to add. Conveniently, the addition in each group—ones, tens, and hundreds—did not come over 10. But sometimes it does, and then we have to "carry."

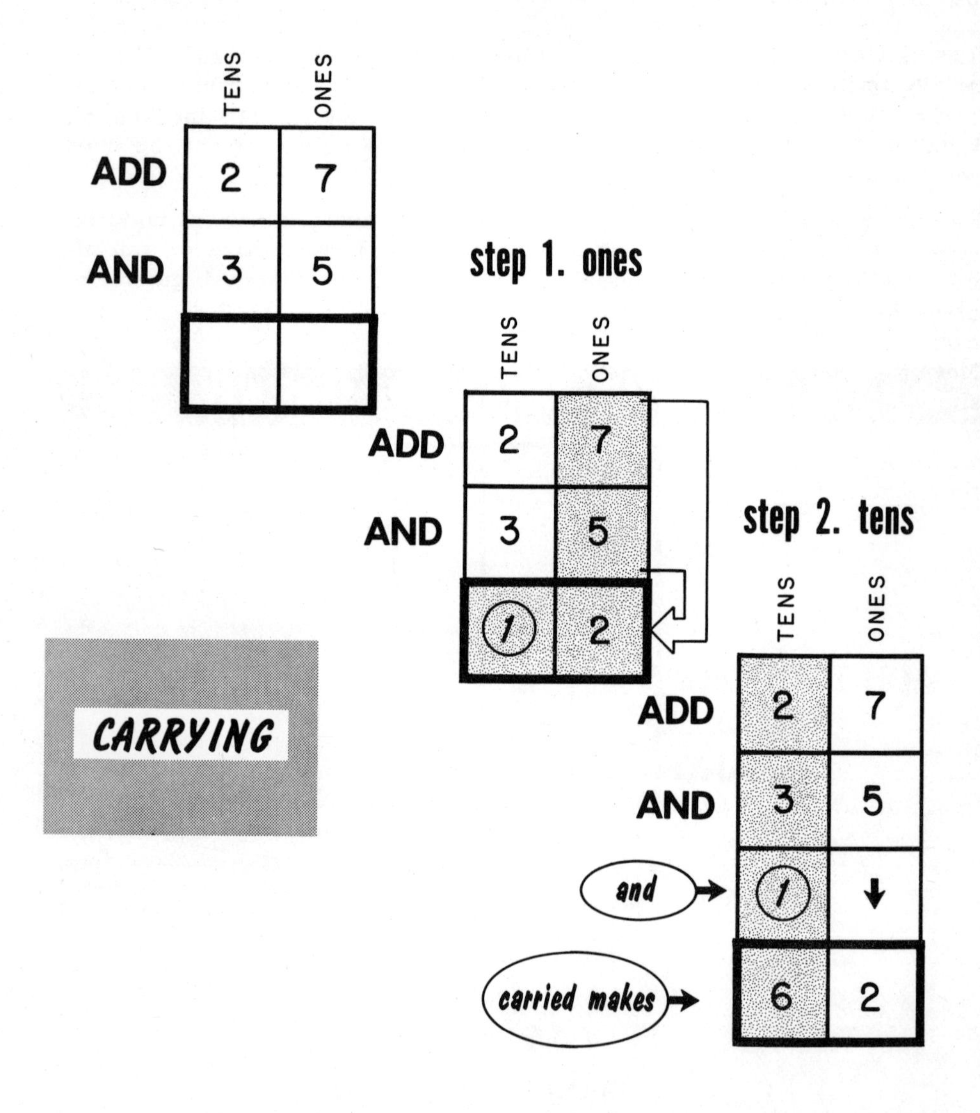

Suppose we have to add 27 and 35: we take the *ones* first: 7 and 5 are 12. But we can only write the 2 in the ones place; the 1 of the 12 belongs in the *tens* place because 12 is really $10 + 2$. So now we have the original 2 and 3 in the tens place to add, as well as the 1 that resulted from adding the ones. This is just like adding 2, 3, and 1 in the tens place, which comes to 6 however you do it. The 1 is said to be *carried* from the ones place.

Carrying (contd.)

This carrying goes on any time the total at a certain place runs over ten. For example let us add 7,358 and 2,763:

Starting with the *ones:* 8 and 3 are 11; we write 1 in the ones place and carry 1. Now the *tens:* 5 and 6 are 11, and 1 carried from the ones makes 12; we write 2 in the tens place and carry 1. Now the *hundreds:* 7 and 3 are 10, and 1 carried from the tens makes 11; write 1 in the hundreds place and carry 1. Finally the *thousands:* 7 and 2 are 9, and 1 carried from the hundreds makes 10; as there are no ten thousands in the original numbers, we just write down 10 and the addition is finished: 10,121.

Let us take another example: add 7,196 and 15,273. Starting with the *ones:* 6 and 3 are 9; we write this in the ones place. Now the *tens:* we have none carried from ones this time, so it is just 9 and 7 are 16; we write 6 in the tens place and carry 1. Now the *hundreds:* 1 and 2 are 3, and 1 carried from the tens makes 4; we write this in the hundreds place. Now the *thousands:* we have none carried from the hundreds, so it is simply 7 and 5 are 12; write 2 and carry 1 to the ten thousands. In the *ten thousands,* the first number does not have any, the second has 1, and we have 1 carried. So this gives us 1 and 1 are 2 to write in the ten thousands: 22,469.

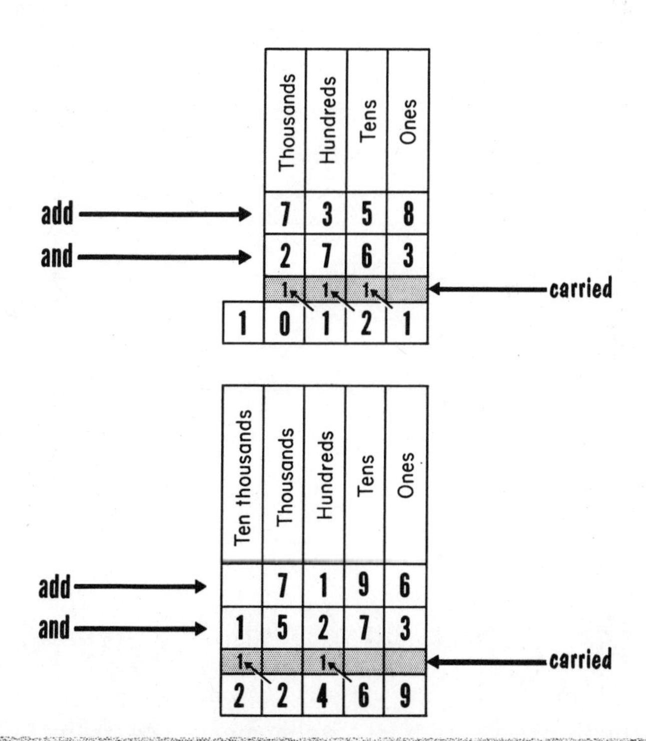

CARRY LEFT-OVER NUMBERS TO THE "PLACE" AT THE LEFT

Successive Addition

When we have a lot of larger numbers to add together, there are several ways to do it, but each, done correctly, will give the same answer. First we shall use the method employed by any adding machine. It adds each whole number to the next, one at a time. For an example, we shall take the numbers: 13,476; 25,523; 43; 6,542; and 376.

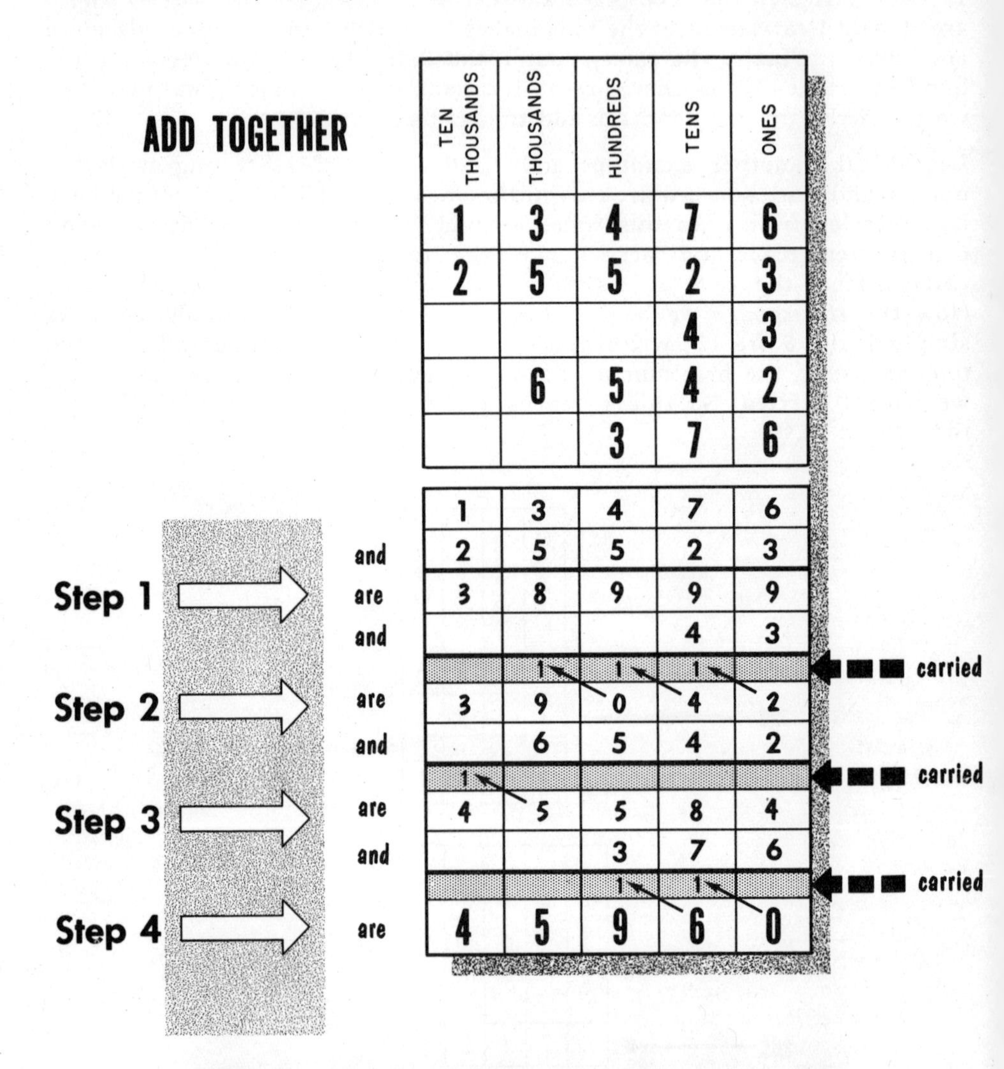

This is how an ADDING MACHINE adds.

Taking them in order, the first two numbers add to make 38,999. Now we take this with the next: 38,999 and 43 make 39,042. And the next: 39,042 and 6,542 make 45,584. Finally the last: 45,584 and 376 make 45,960.

Successive Addition (contd.)

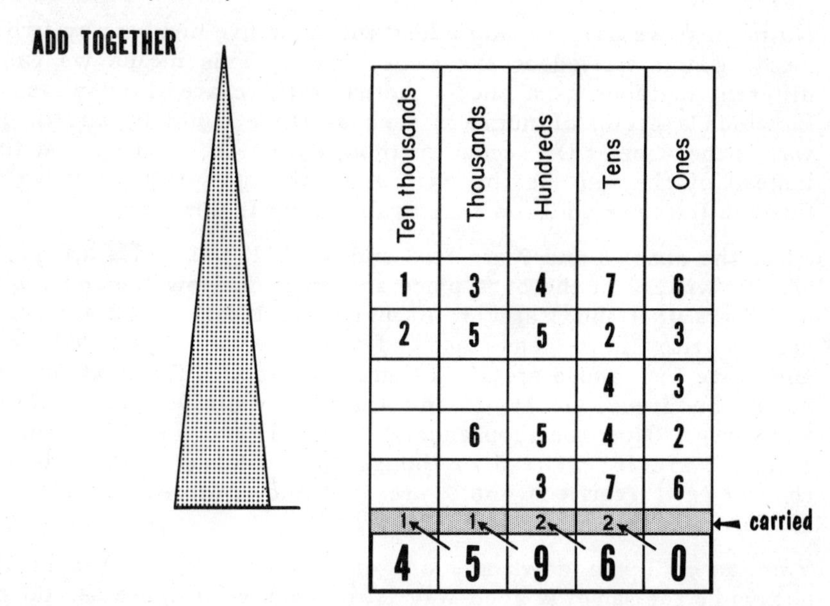

Or you can add the same numbers this way.

The second method is to add each place for the whole group of numbers, starting at the ones and working left to the highest numbers. Take the same five numbers for an example: 13,476, 25,523, 43, 6,542, and 376.

First the *ones:* 6 and 3 are 9; 9 and 3 are 12; 12 and 2 are 14; 14 and 6 are 20; write 0 in the ones place and carry 2. Now the *tens:* it is best to add in the carried figure first, so we don't forget it; 2 (carried) and 7 are 9; 9 and 2 are 11; 11 and 4 are 15; 15 and 4 are 19; 19 and 7 are 26; write 6 in the tens place and carry 2. Now *hundreds:* 2 (carried) and 4 are 6; 6 and 5 are 11; 11 and 5 (skip the next number, which has no hundreds figure) are 16; 16 and 3 are 19; write 9 in hundreds place and carry 1. Now *thousands:* 1 (carried) and 3 are 4; 4 and 5 are 9; 9 and 6 are 15 (the others have no thousands figures); write 5 and carry 1. Now *ten thousands:* 1 (carried) and 1 are 2; 2 and 2 are 4 (that's all in the ten thousands); write 4: 45,960.

When you use this method of adding, there is an advantage to writing the numbers one under each other, so the places—ones, tens, hundreds, etc.—line up. This makes it less likely for you to add a figure from the wrong place. It will also aid you in checking your result to write in the number carried as a small figure above and between the numbers where it is carried.

Checking Answers

Notice that we have already added the same five numbers by two different methods and arrived at the same answer. This means we can use the different methods as a check. Actually there are three ways (at least) in which a group of numbers such as these could be added. The third way is the same as the second method, except that you start at the bottom instead of the top. As the written result looks the same, we shall run through the same addition once again, doing it this way.

First the *ones:* 6 and 2 are 8; 8 and 3 are 11; 11 and 3 are 14; 14 and 6 are 20; write 0 in the ones place and carry 2. Now the *tens:* 2 (carried) and 7 are 9; 9 and 4 are 13; 13 and 4 are 17; 17 and 2 are 19; 19 and 7 are 26; write 6 in the tens place and carry 2. Now the *hundreds:* 2 (carried) and 3 are 5; 5 and 5 are 10; 10 and 5 (skipping the next number which has no hundreds) are 15; 15 and 4 are 19; write 9 in the hundreds place and carry 1. Now the *thousands:* 1 (carried) and 6 are 7; 7 and 5 are 12; 12 and 3 are 15; write 5 in thousands place and carry 1. Now the *ten thousands:* 1 (carried) and 2 are 3; 3 and 1 are 4; that's all—write 4: 45,960.

You can go up or down any one of the columns, and the result should always be the same. A good way is to check each figure as you go. Count the ones first up, then down; if you get the same result both ways, proceed. If not, double check your counting. Then do the same with the tens, hundreds, etc. That way you find your mistake as you make it.

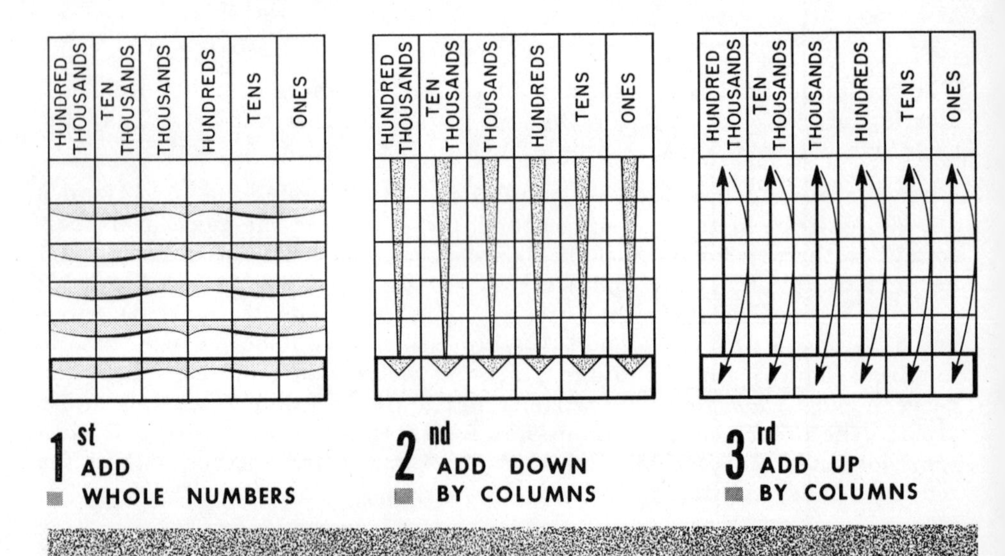

Three Ways to Add — Two Ways to Check your Answer

Adding Cash

Adding cash is just the same, except for the division of a *dollar* into *cents.* This means, starting from the right, that you have two figures to represent ones and tens of cents. Then there is a decimal point, rather than a comma, after which dollars are written just like any other numbers, but with the $ sign at the extreme left. Let us add the figures shown. We shall do it down, and you can check it by doing it up.

Ones of *cents:* 9 and 8 are 17 (skip the 0); 17 and 9 are 26; 26 and 5 are 31; write 1 and carry 3. *Tens* of *cents*: 3 (carried) and 4 are 7; 7 and 9 are 16; 16 and 3 are 19; 19 and 9 are 28; write 8 and carry 2. This 2 carried is $2, from cents into whole dollars. *Ones* of *dollars*: 2 (carried) and 5 are 7; 7 and 3 are 10; 10 and 6 are 16; 16 and 9 are 25; write 5 and carry 2. *Tens* of *dollars:* 2 (carried) and 5 are 7; 7 and 2 are 9; 9 and 5 are 14; 14 and 2 are 16; write 6 and carry 1. *Hundreds* of *dollars:* 1 (carried) and 3 are 4; 4 and 3 are 7; write 7, none carried. *Thousands* of *dollars:* just write the single figure 2, as none have been carried to add to it: $2,765.81.

ADDING MONEY IS LIKE ADDING ANYTHING ELSE – EXCEPT NOW WE ALSO HAVE CENTS

	DOLLARS					CENTS		
	THOUSANDS	HUNDREDS	TENS	ONES		TENS	ONES	
	2	3	5	0	.	4	9	
			2	5	.	9	8	
				3	.	0	0	
		3	5	6	.	3	9	
			2	9	.	9	5	
		1	2	2		3		carried
$	2	7	6	5	.	8	1	

Adding Weight

Once we learn to count and add, it does not matter what the numbers relate to; the method is the same. That is, it is the same provided the recognized method of counting follows the decimal system: tens, hundreds, thousands, etc. The European metric system—meters for measurement, grams for weight, etc.—follows the decimal system. But the English system, more commonly used in England and the United States, is not so convenient.

The commonest weights in everyday use are the dram, ounce, and pound. In this system, called *avoirdupois,* there are 16 drams to each ounce, and 16 ounces to each pound. So to add to this system, we need a two-figure column each for ounces and drams, to the right of the normal numbering. Big weights go by tons, which are usually 2,000 pounds. In England the ton (called the "long ton" in America) is 2,240 pounds, and is divided into twenty "hundredweights" of 112 pounds each. That can get quite complicated, but we shall leave it to people who have to deal with it.

Suppose we have to add together 12 ounces and 5 drams; 1 pound 11 ounces; 1 ounce and 7 drams. Forming three columns, reading from left to right—pounds, ounces, and drams—we start by adding the *drams:* 5 and 7 are 12. As this is not enough to make 1 ounce, we write this in the drams column. Now *ounces:* 12 and 11 are 23; 23 and 1 are 24; this is 1 pound (16 ounces) and 8 ounces over (which you can find by counting on from 16); write 8 in the ounces column and carry 1 to the pounds column. Finally *pounds:* 1 (carried) and 1 are 2: 2 pounds, 8 ounces, 12 drams.

In the United States, we use the avoirdupois system of weights.

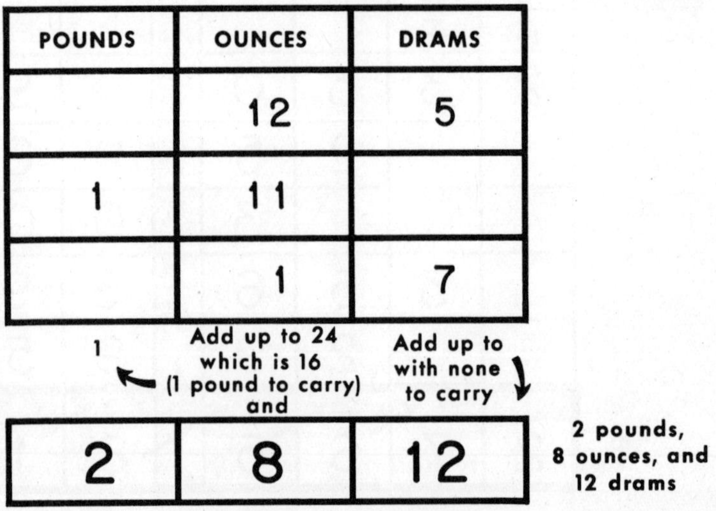

POUNDS	OUNCES	DRAMS
	12	5
1	11	
	1	7
1 ←	Add up to 24 which is 16 (1 pound to carry) and	Add up to with none to carry ↓
2	8	12

2 pounds, 8 ounces, and 12 drams

Weighing

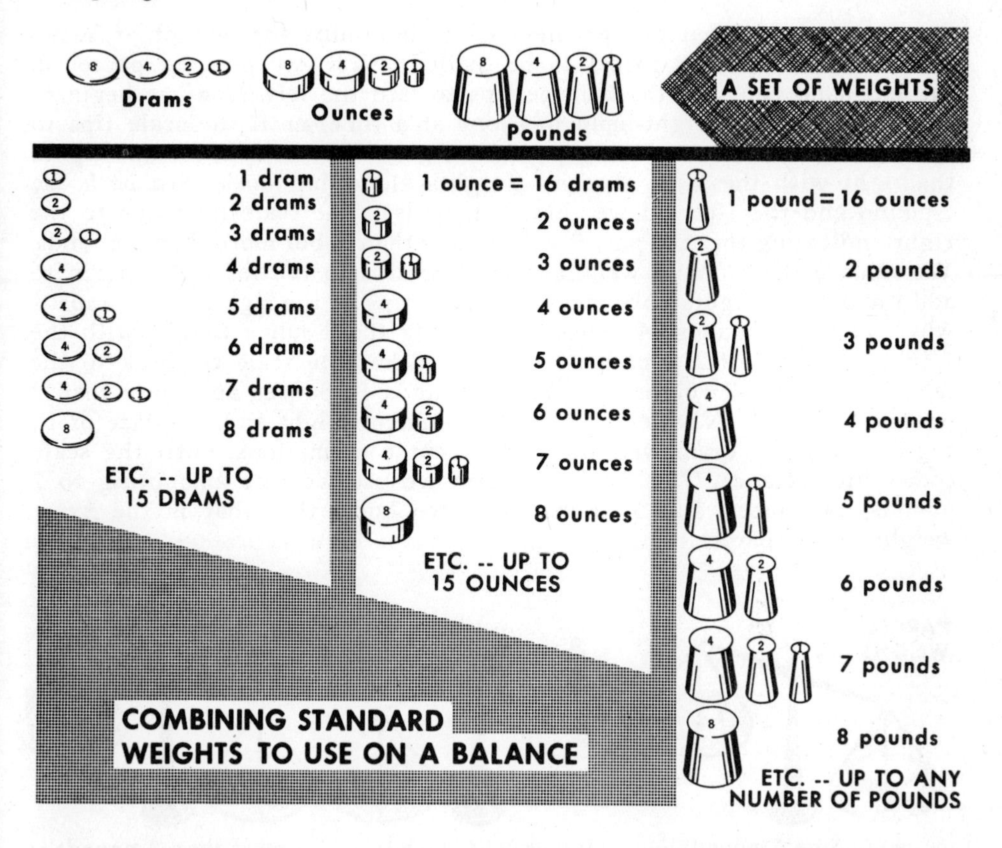

With most modern scales, we place the article to be weighed on the scales and an indicator marks off the exact weight for us. But before these "automatic" scales were invented, we had to use scales with balancing pans and weights. Knowing how to use this type of scale—also called a "balance"—is useful for precise chemical work and, as well, provides the basis for some types of computer work.

The weights which are used on a balance come in steps, each of which is exactly twice the previous one: 1, 2, 4, and 8 drams; then 1, 2, 4, and 8 ounces; finally 1, 2, 4, 8, and 16, etc., pounds. With a set of these weights, we can make up any required weight exactly to a dram: for 1 dram, we use that weight alone; for 2 drams we use that one; for 3, the 2 and 1; for 4, that one alone; for 5, the 4 and 1; for 6, the 4 and 2; for 7, the 4, 2, and 1; for 8, that one alone; for 9, the 8 and 1; for 10, the 8 and 2; for 11, the 8, 2, and 1; for 12, the 8 and 4; for 13, the 8, 4, and 1; for 14, the 8, 4, and 2; for 15 the 8, 4, 2, and 1—all the dram weights. The next dram makes an ounce, so we start using ounce weights. Now we can use ounce weights in the same way to make up any number of ounces up to a pound, then similarly with the pound weights. This way the weight can be assembled in any combination, exactly to the smallest unit of measure.

Weighing (contd.)

Suppose, though, that our problem is to determine the weight of something—for instance, a parcel to be mailed. First, we put the parcel in the left-hand pan, and the balance tips toward the left. Now we begin to add weights to the right-hand pan, one at a time, until the scale tips to the right. We begin by using pound weights. The scale does not tip to the right with the 1- or 2-pound weights alone, but does with *both* the 2-pound and the 1-pound weights (3 pounds). The scale now tips to the right, indicating that the parcel weighs less than 3, but more than 2 pounds. We remove the 1-pound weight (the scale tips to the left) and begin to add the ounce weights until the scale again tips to the right. This happens when we use 2 pounds 14 ounces. Replacing the 2-ounce weight with the 1-ounce (a total of 2 pounds 13 ounces) makes the scale tip back to the left, so the parcel weighs less than 2 pounds 14 ounces and more than 2 pounds 13 ounces. Now we remove the 1-ounce weight and, in place of it, begin to use the dram weights in different combinations, until the scale comes into balance. This happens when we use weights amounting to 2 pounds, 13 ounces, and 3 drams. Now we know that that is the exact weight of the parcel.

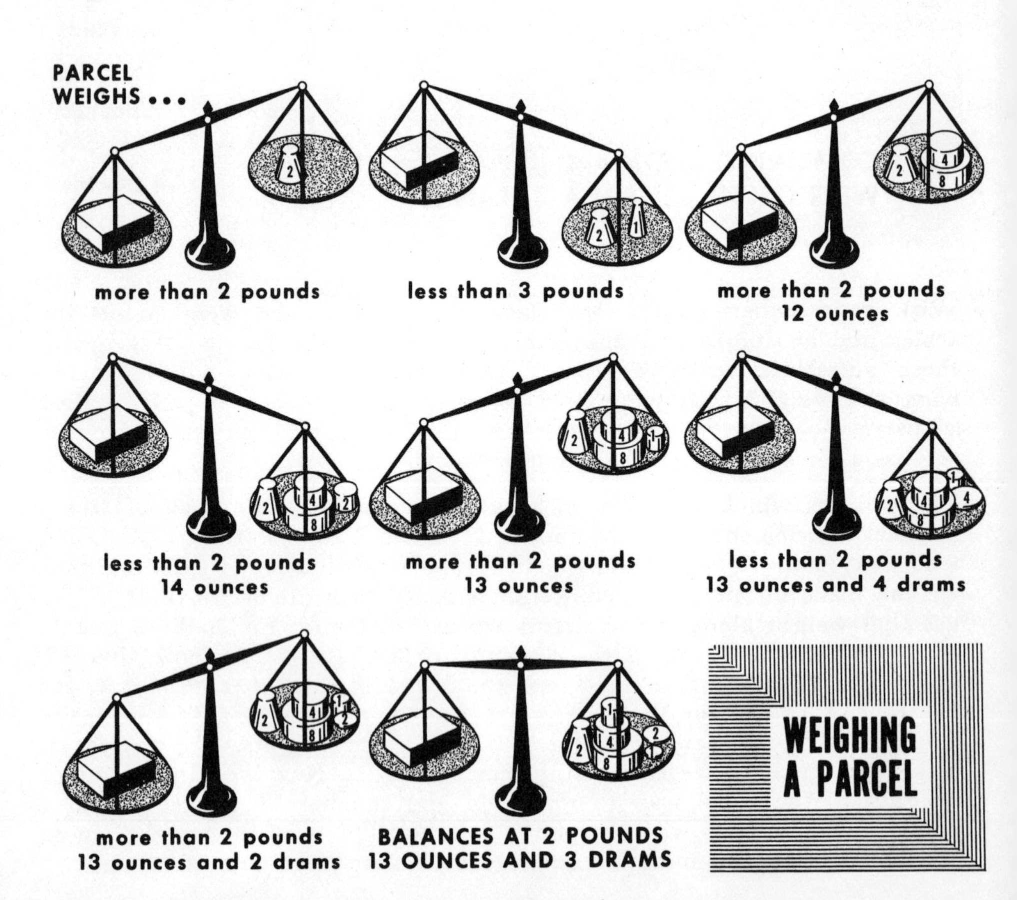

Measures of Length

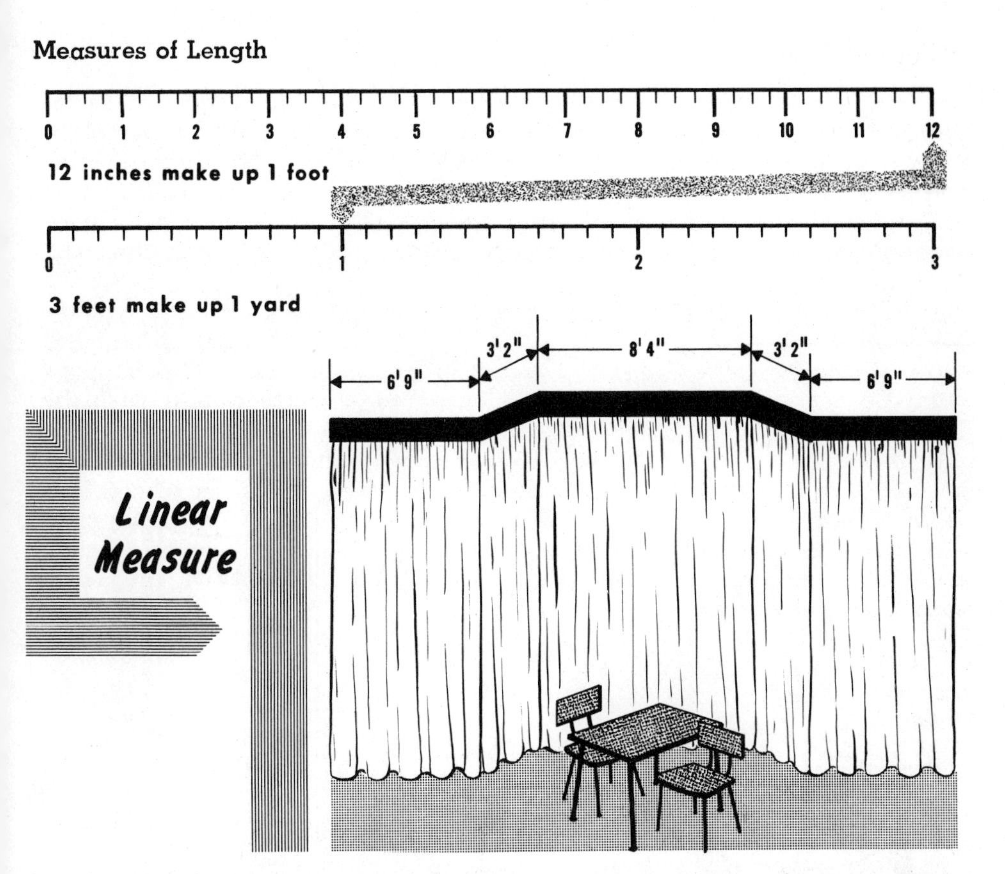

The metric system of measures follows the decimal system, so that each column represents a group containing tens of the next smaller group. But again, the English system is not so convenient. It uses inches, feet, yards, and miles, sometimes including an extra: furlongs. There are 12 inches to a foot; 3 feet to a yard; and 1,760 yards (5,280 feet) to a mile. A furlong is 220 yards (660 feet) and there are 8 furlongs to a mile.

Suppose we are having new drapes made and must find the total length of a wall with an alcove. The different areas are 6 feet 9 inches, 3 feet 2 inches, 8 feet 4 inches, 3 feet 2 inches, and 6 feet 9 inches. First, add the *inches:* 9 and 2 are 11; 11 and 4 are 15; 15 and 2 are 17; 17 and 9 are 26. This is over 1 foot, which is 12 inches. Counting on from 12, we find that all the inches add up to 2 feet and 2 inches, so we write 2 in the inches column and carry 2 feet. Now add the *feet:* 2 (carried) and 6 are 8; 8 and 3 are 11; 11 and 8 are 19; 19 and 3 are 22; 22 and 6 are 28. This total can be written either as 28 feet 2 inches or as 9 yards, 1 foot, and 2 inches.

Whether to give measures in feet or yards depends largely on what we are measuring. Lumber, for example, is usually measured in feet, however long the piece may be, whereas real estate may be given in terms of yards or of feet.

Adding Liquid and Dry Measures

The common measures of quantity (bulk)—dry or liquid—use the units *pint, quart,* and *gallon.* For various purposes there are other larger and smaller units, but these are the common ones. There are 2 pints to the quart and 4 quarts to the gallon.

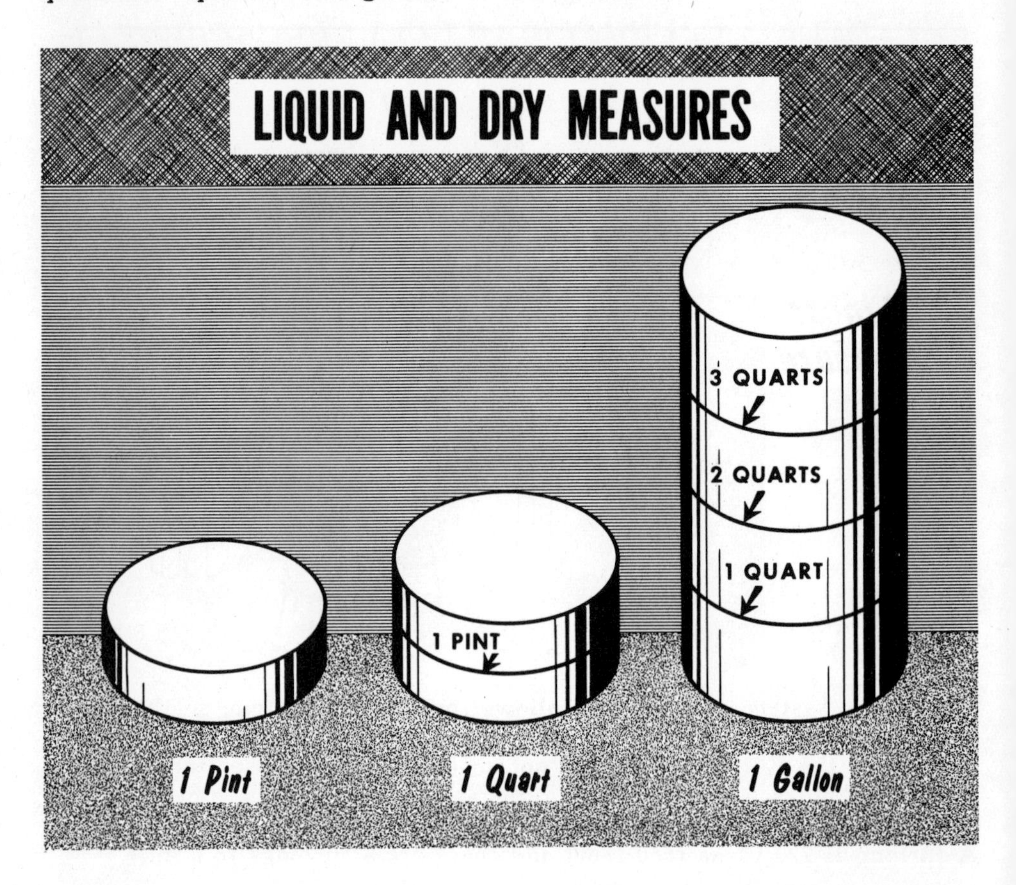

As there are 2 pints to a quart, 1 pint is half a quart. Similarly, as there are 4 quarts to a gallon, 1 quart is one quarter of a gallon (which is probably why it's called a quart). For this reason, and because the subdivisions are closer to the same size than the standard decimal or ten system, we do not often find a quantity stated as so many gallons, so many quarts, and so many pints. It is much more usual to use only one unit to state the quantity. Thus 3 pints could also be called $1\frac{1}{2}$ quarts, or 6 quarts might be called $1\frac{1}{2}$ gallons.

Milk, for example, is usually sold to the consumer by the quart; so however many quarts there may be, they will still be listed as quarts. However, the retailer buys his milk in gallons, because this is a more convenient unit. Gasoline is sold by the gallon, and lubricating oil by the quart.

1. Does it make any difference, in the final answer, (how many articles or objects there are) whether they are counted: (a) one by one; (b) in groups of ten; (c) in groups of twelve?
2. Why are bigger numbers counted in hundreds, tens, and ones, instead of one at a time?
3. The figure zero (0) means there are not any. Why then should we bother to write down this number?
4. What are (a) 10 tens; (b) 12 twelves?
5. What are 10 hundreds?
6. What are 1,000 thousands?
7. By counting on, add the following groups of three numbers together; then check your results by adding them together in the reverse order; finally, use your addition table as a check:

(a) 3 + 6 + 9
(b) 4 + 5 + 7
(c) 2 + 7 + 3
(d) 6 + 4 + 8
(e) 1 + 3 + 2
(f) 4 + 2 + 2
(g) 5 + 8 + 8
(h) 9 + 8 + 7

8. Add together the following groups of five numbers; use each of the three methods shown on page 1-16 to be sure you have the right answer. If you get different answers, work over each one carefully, until you find your mistake or mistakes.

(a) 35,759 + 23,574 + 29,123 + 14,285 + 28,171
(b) 235 + 5,742 + 4 + 85,714 + 71,428
(c) 10,590 + 423 + 6,129 + 1 + 2
(d) 12,567 + 35,742 + 150 + 90,909 + 18,181
(e) 1,000 + 74 + 350 + 9,091 + 81,818

9. How does adding money differ from adding numbers?
10. Add together the following weights: (a) 1 pound, 6 ounces, and 14 drams; (b) 2 pounds, 13 ounces, and 11 drams; (c) 5 pounds, 11 ounces, and 7 drams. Check your result by adding them in at least three ways. If you get different answers, find your mistakes.
11. What weights would you use to weigh out each of the quantities named in question 10, using the system of weights on page 1-19? Check your answers by adding up the weights you name.
12. In weighing a parcel, when the 4 pound weight is put on, it tips the weight pan down; when the 2- and 1-pound weights, with all the ounce weights in the set (page 1-19) are put on, the weight pan tips down. (It does not tip until the *last* ounce weight is put on.) What would

you do next to find the weight of the parcel (a) if you want to know it to the nearest dram; (b) if you have to pay postage on the number of ounces, or fractions of an ounce?

13. How many inches are there in 2 yards? (First add together the inches in 3 feet, to make 1 yard, then add together the inches in another yard to make 2).

14. Add together 130 yards, 270 yards, 400 yards, 530 yards, and 427 yards. Check your result by adding the numbers three ways.

15. The distances stated in question 14 are the frontage measurements of adjoining properties along a highway. They start from a certain mile post and end just three yards before another post. What post is this?

16. A man has a fleet of cars that need oil changes. Three of them take 5 quarts each, two of them 6 quarts each, four of them a gallon each. How many gallons of oil does he need? Write down the number of quarts for each car (4 for the ones using a gallon). This will add up to the number of quarts needed. Then count off 4 quarts for every gallon.

17. In question 16, there are some odd quarts over the complete gallons needed. If he buys the oil for $1 a gallon, and each quart costs him 35¢, to be economical, how much oil will he buy?

18. In question 16, if he can get 12 gallon drums of oil for $10, how much do you think he would buy?

19. In making an itinerary for a journey, a man has to cover the following distances: 25 miles, 35 miles, 75 miles, 83 miles, 62 miles, 14 miles, and 10 miles. Find his total distance traveled.

20. A women buys three dresses at $12.98 each, spends $3.57 on train fare to get to town, and $2.50 on a meal while she is there. How much did she spend altogether?

Subtraction Is Counting Away

Just as addition is counting *on,* so subtraction is counting *away.* We start with the total number, count away the number to be subtracted, and see how many of the original number are left.

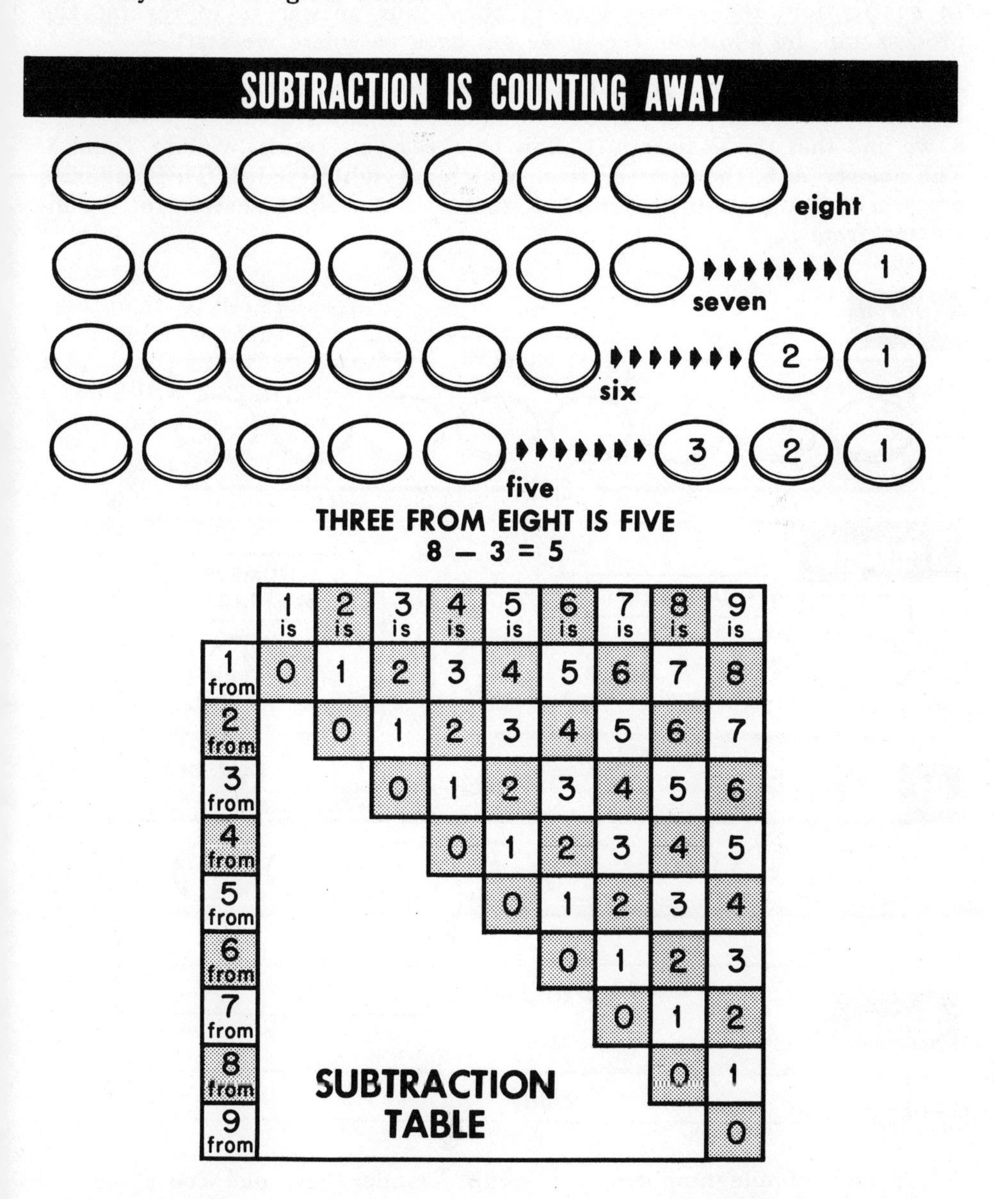

	1 is	2 is	3 is	4 is	5 is	6 is	7 is	8 is	9 is
1 from	0	1	2	3	4	5	6	7	8
2 from		0	1	2	3	4	5	6	7
3 from			0	1	2	3	4	5	6
4 from				0	1	2	3	4	5
5 from					0	1	2	3	4
6 from						0	1	2	3
7 from							0	1	2
8 from								0	1
9 from									0

As with addition, we can learn the different combinations either by counting away every time until we get to remember them all, or we can make a table of them. Of course, we can only subtract a smaller number from a larger one.

Checking Subtraction by Addition

One of the most important things in working mathematics is to know that you have the right answer. That is why we used at least two ways in adding, so we could check the results and make sure they are right. In subtraction, the easiest way to check our answer is to reverse the process and, by addition, see if we get back to where we start.

We have to subtract 3 from 8. We write this $8 - 3$, using the minus sign ($-$) to show that we are to *subtract* instead of add. Counting away from 8, we find that the answer is 5. Now to check this result, we add 3 and 5. The answer is 8, the number from which we subtracted 3. This confirms our work, and we can be confident that 5 is the right answer for 3 subtracted from 8.

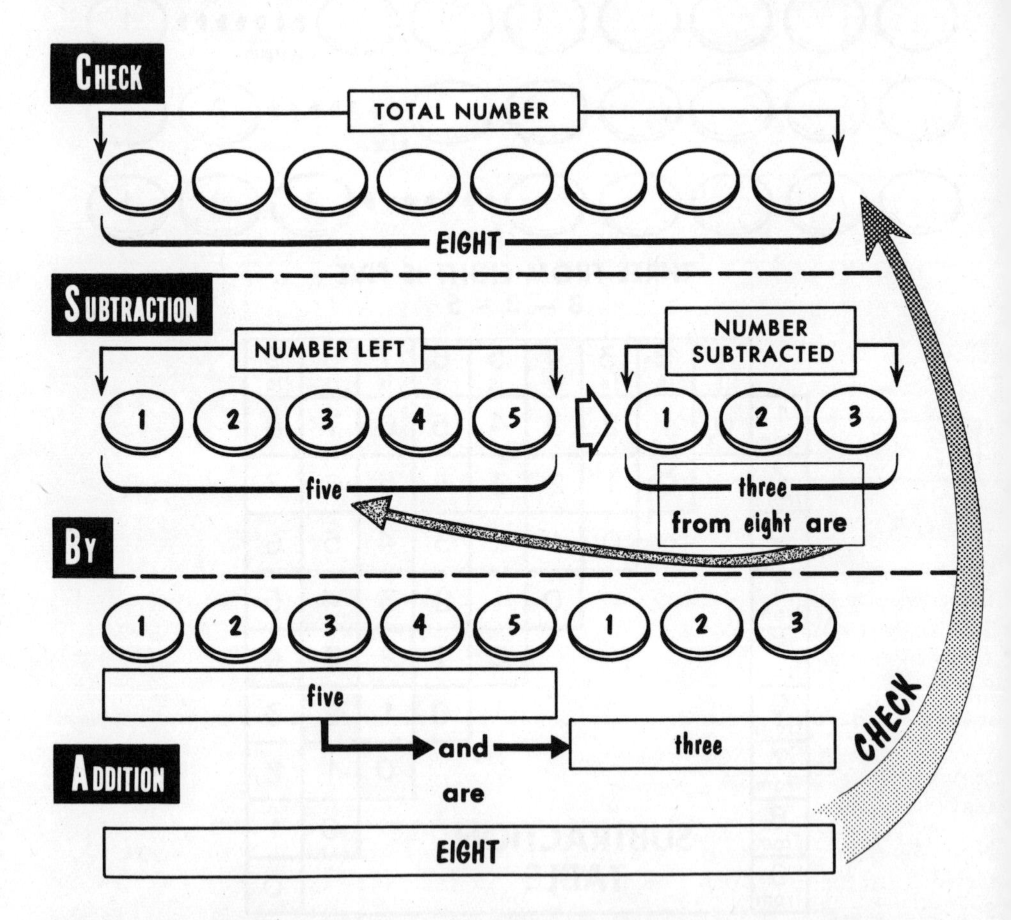

With such simple numbers, you might wonder how one could make a mistake. It's much less likely than with more complicated numbers. But if we get the good habit of checking our work while it is easy to do, then we shall be less likely to make mistakes when the work is more difficult.

Borrowing

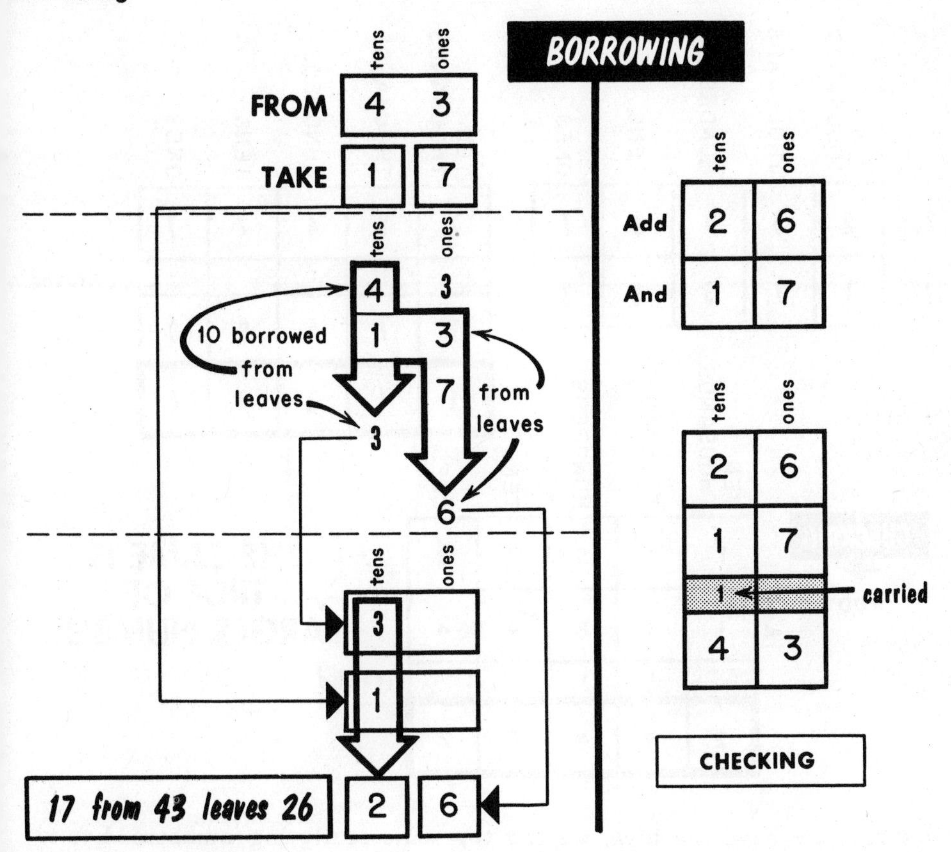

In addition, when the ones figures came to ten or over, we carried into the tens figures, and so on. In subtraction, we have to reverse the process. Suppose we have to subtract 17 from 43. First we subtract the *ones*. But 7 is bigger than 3. We have to subtract 7 from 13. This is "borrowing" 1 ten from the *tens* figure. It now leaves 6 as the ones figure in the answer So far we have subtracted 7 from 43. 7 from 13 leaves 6, so 7 from 43 leaves 36. Because we borrowed 1 from the tens figure, the 1 representing ten of 17 must be subtracted, not from the 4 of 43, but from the 3 of 36, leaving 2 as the tens figure in the answer. So subtracting 17 from 43 leaves 26.

Now we check the result by adding 26 and 17. In the ones, 6 and 7 are 13; write 3 in the ones place and carry 1. In the tens 1 (carried) and 2 are 3; 3 and 1 are 4; write 4 in the tens place. 26 and 17 are 43, which checks back to the number we started with. We have taken away 17, and put it back, and have the same number we started with; so our answer should be right. We'd have to make two mistakes for this to happen for a wrong answer—and two very special ones. Usually the more mistakes we make, the further we get from right.

Subtracting with Larger Numbers

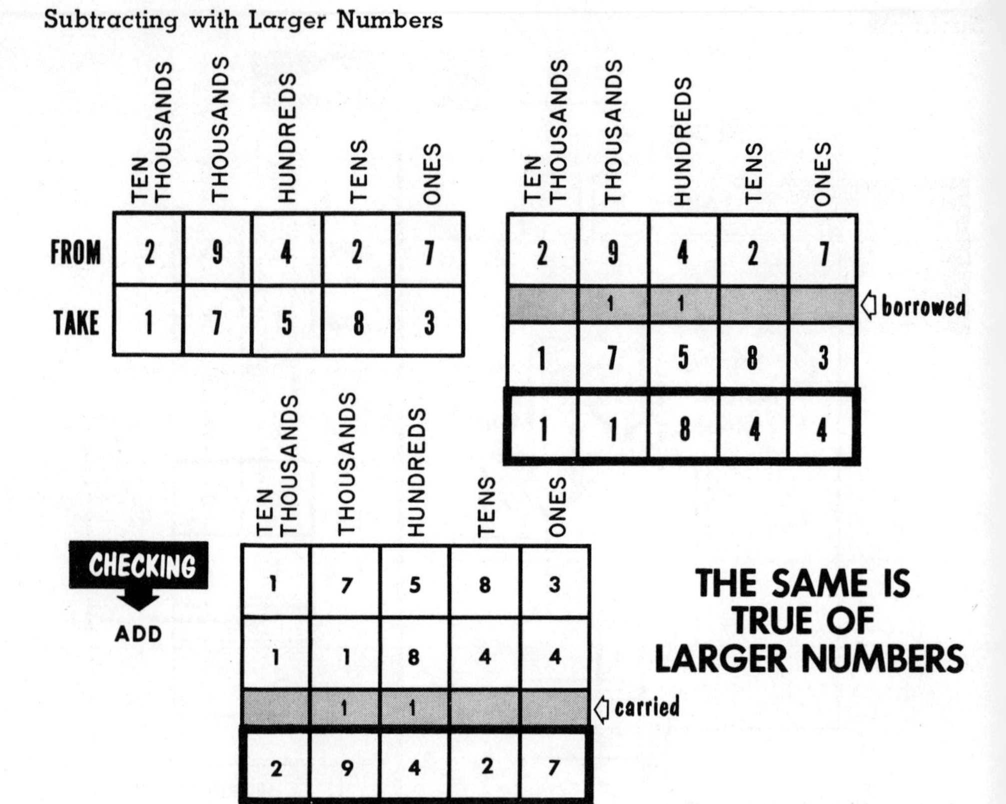

Now that we have the idea, we can try some really big numbers. Let us subtract 17,583 from 29,427. We should arrive at an answer which, when added to 17,583, will give 29,427 again.

Starting with *ones:* subtract 3 from 7, leaving 4, without borrowing. Now *tens:* 8 does not subtract from 2, so we have to borrow and subtract 8 from 12, leaving 4. Now *hundreds:* the borrowing reduced the hundreds figure from 4 to 3, requiring 5 to be subtracted from 3 which again calls for borrowing from the thousands. 5 from 13 leaves 8. Now the *thousands:* the thousands figure is reduced from 9 to 8; subtracting 7 from 8 leaves 1 without borrowing. Finally, the *ten thousands:* 1 from 2 leaves 1. The answer is 11,844.

Now to check: add 11,844 and 17,583. First the *ones:* 4 and 3 are 7 with nothing to carry; write 7. Now the *tens:* 4 and 8 are 12; write 2 and carry 1. Then the *hundreds:* 1(carried) and 1 are 2; 2 and 7 are 9; write 9. Last, the *ten thousands:* 1 and 1 are 2; write 2. The answer is 29,427, which is what we started with.

Notice that carrying occurs exactly where we borrowed: between tens and hundreds, and between hundreds and thousands. This is because we exactly reversed the process.

Subtracting Cash

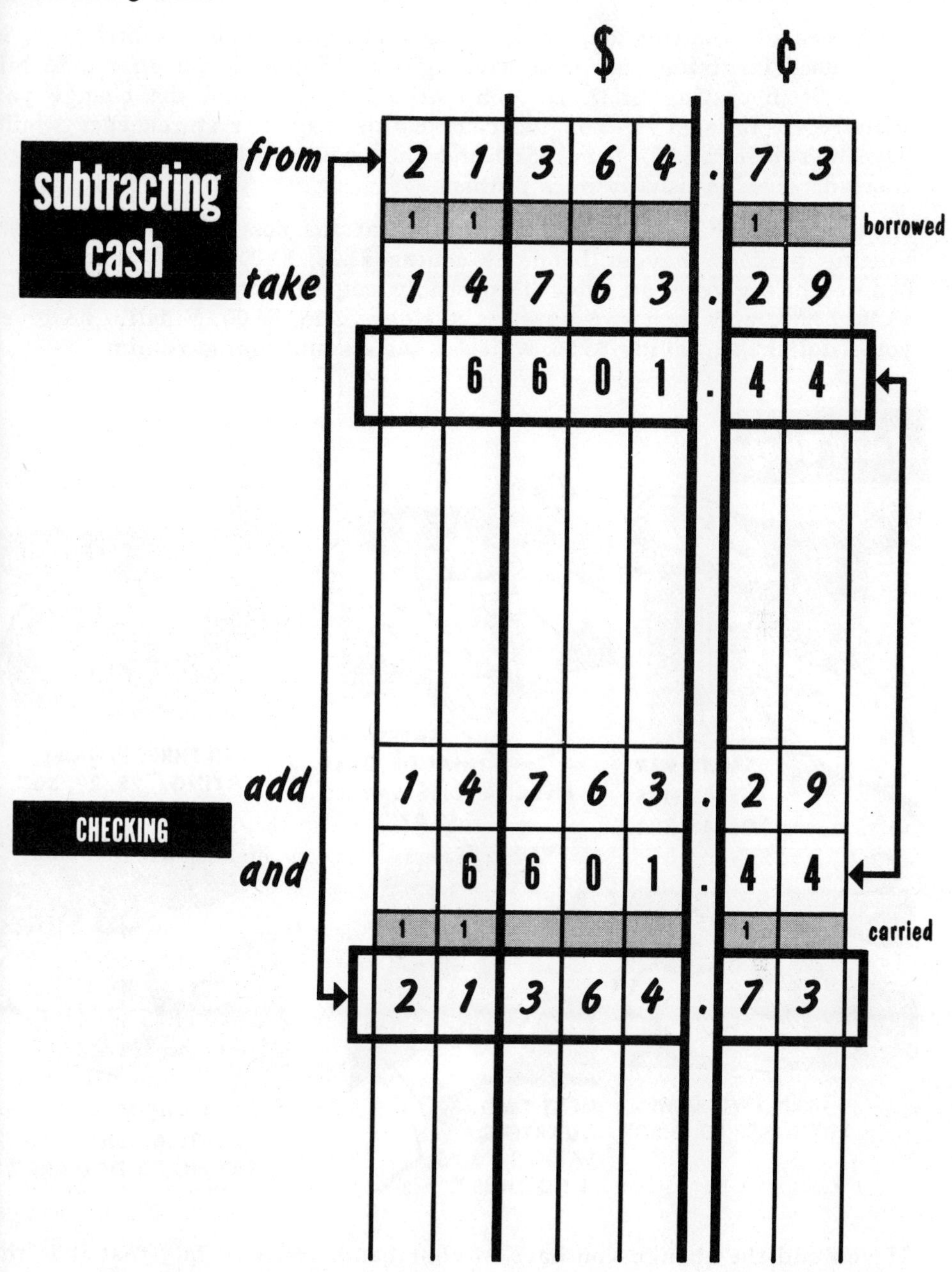

Cash is no more difficult to subtract than numbers meaning anything else. The only difference is the hundred-cents-to-the-dollar part. We start at the cents end and work back, just as with numbers. And in just the same way the subtraction can be checked by addition.

Making Change

This idea of counting on, or of using addition to check subtraction, is often used in giving change to save figuring. Suppose you offer a $5 bill for an item costing $3.27. By subtraction you can find the change you should get. It is $1.73. To give change this way, the storekeeper would have to subtract $3.27 from $5.00 and then count out your $1.73 change. Instead, what he usually does is this:

He takes the change and starts counting at the cost of the item: $3.27. Putting pennies in your hand, he counts $3.28, $3.29, $3.30—that's three pennies he's given you. Now he probably counts you two dimes, saying $3.40, $3.50; and then two quarters saying: $3.75, $4.00. Finally, he gives you a dollar bill, saying $5.00, which is the amount you gave him.

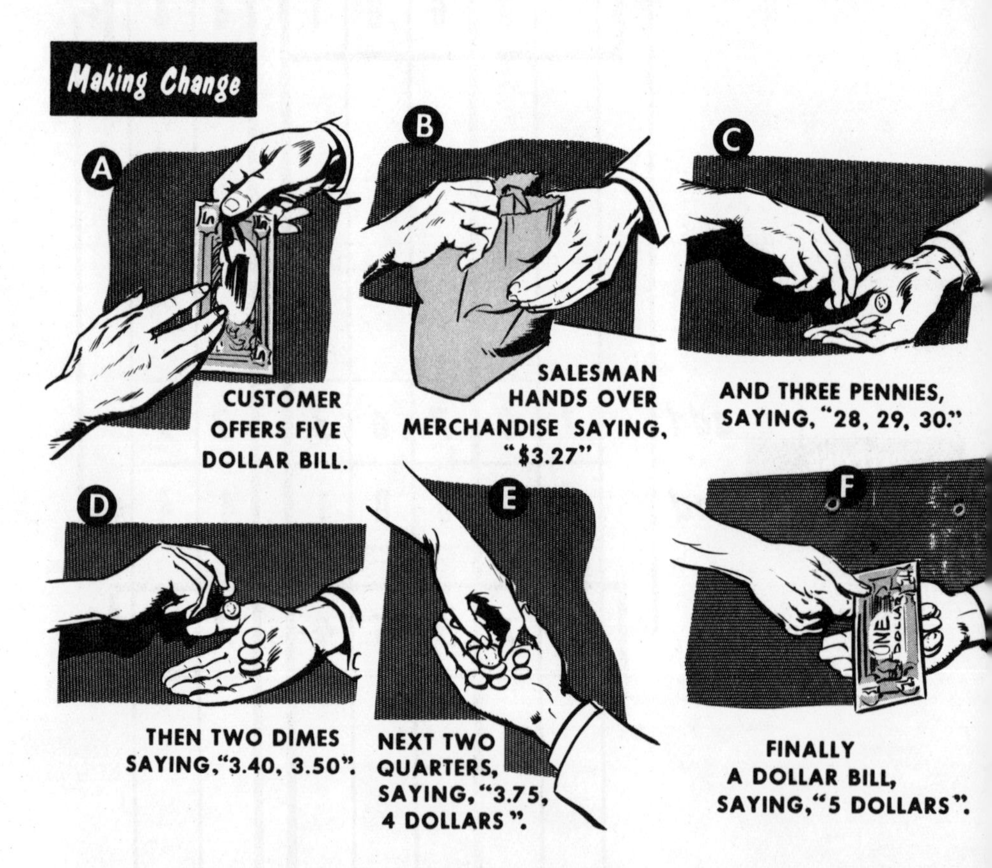

If you add the change you have in your hand, you will find that it is the right amount: $1.73. But he did not use that amount at all in his figuring. Instead of subtracting and then adding as a check, he did the equivalent of the addition check, without first making the subtraction. At the end, the amount you have in your hand is the amount you would have figured had you gone to the trouble of subtracting.

Subtracting Weights

There are many occasions when we have to subtract with weights. Suppose a mother wants to weigh her baby, who is too big to go on the baby scales. The baby won't hold still enough to measure his weight on a regular scale. So the mother weighs herself holding the baby in her arms and then weighs herself again without the baby. The difference, obtained by subtraction, is the weight of the baby.

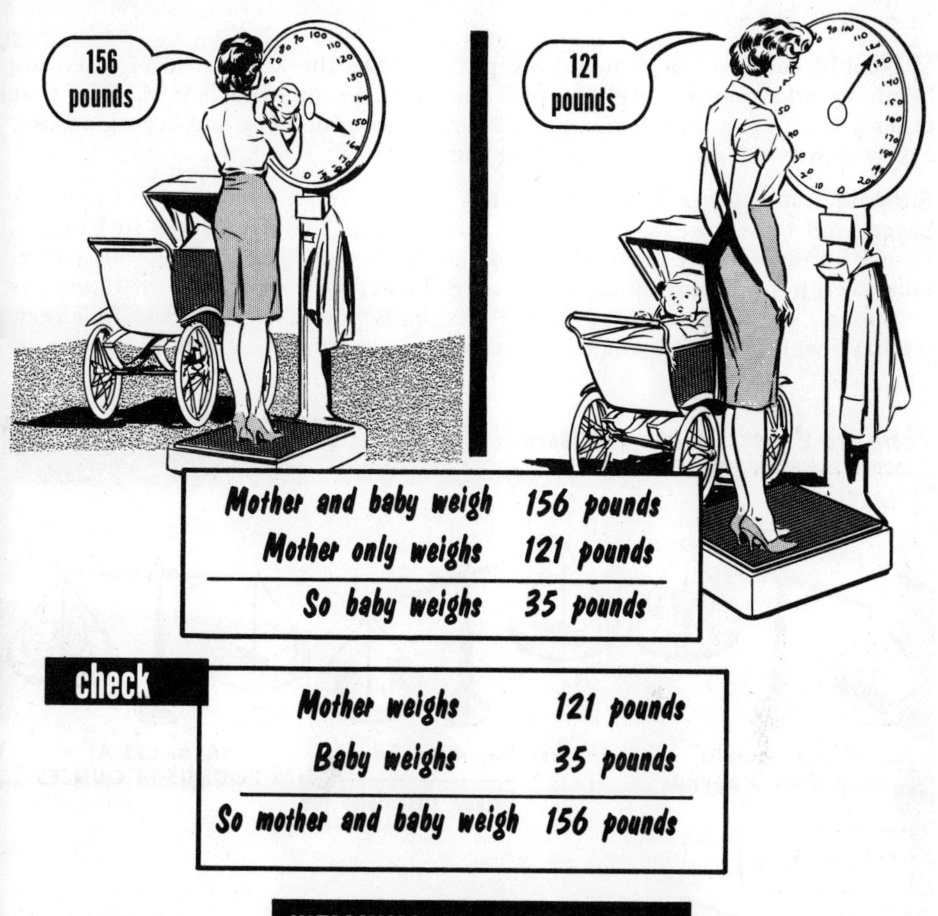

WEIGHING BY SUBTRACTION

Suppose mother and baby together weigh 156 pounds. Mother without the baby weighs 121 pounds. Now we subtract: the result is 35 pounds, which is what the baby must weigh. Check it by adding 121, the weight of the mother, to 35, the weight figured for the baby, and the total is 156 pounds, which the scale showed for the weight of mother and baby. The result checks.

Use of a Balance

Suppose that we again have a parcel to mail and it must be weighed on a set of old-fashioned scales with two pans that balance. We place the parcel in the left-hand pan, and place weights amounting to 3 pounds in the right-hand pan. The scale tips quickly to the left. We replace the 3 pounds in the right-hand pan with the 4-pound weight, and the scale tips to the right, but not nearly so fast, and we assume that the true weight of the parcel is closer to 4 pounds than to 3. Now we can proceed in one of two ways.

We could remove the 4-pound weight, replace the 2 and the 1, and then begin to add ounce weights until the scale becomes balanced. But that takes a lot longer than leaving the 3-pound weight there and trying adding a few ounce weights to the parcel pan.

Suppose that we get a balance with 4 pounds in the weight pan, and the parcel and a 2-ounce weight in the parcel pan. The scales are in balance, so we know that we have 4 pounds in both pans. Therefore, the parcel must weigh 4 pounds minus 2 ounces. Subtracting 2 ounces from 16 ounces (1 pound), we find that the parcel weighs 3 pounds 14 ounces. In effect, we have weighed it by counting on from 3 pounds 14 ounces to 4 pounds.

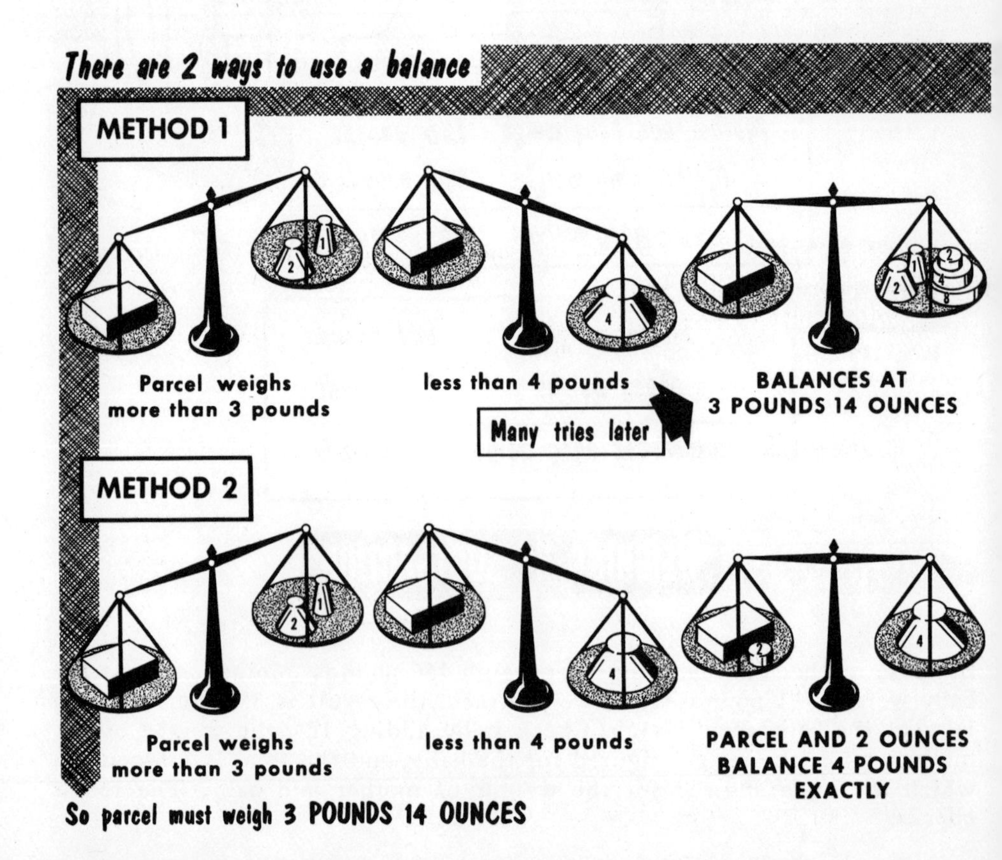

Subtracting Lengths

Often subtraction is the only way to find the length of something. Suppose the distance from one side of a hill to the other is 1 mile, or 1,760 yards. On one side, a cutting is made to allow the road to proceed into the hillside with level grade for 250 yards. On the other side another cutting is made for 350 yards. For the remaining distance, the hill is so high that a tunnel must be made. How long will the tunnel be?

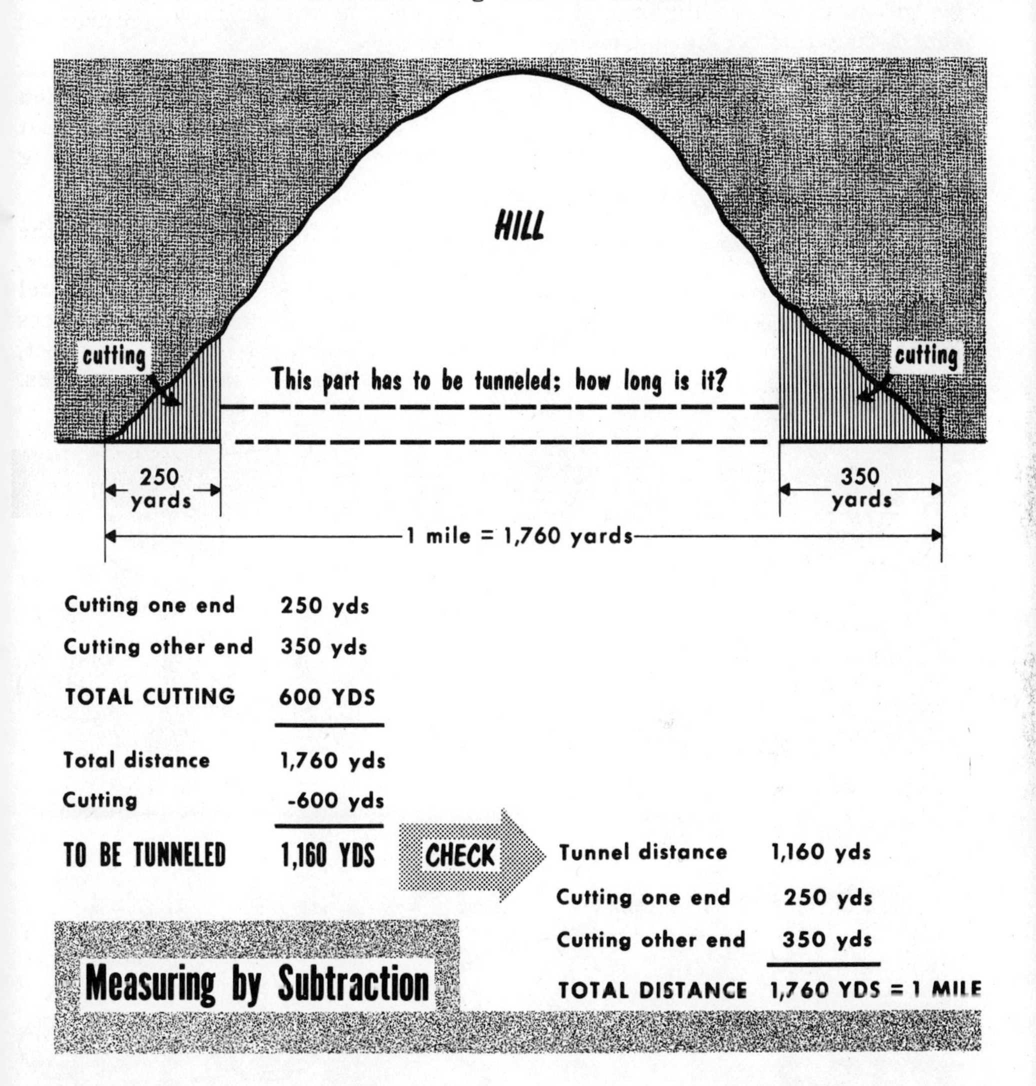

After the tunnel is built, of course, you could measure it directly. But someone has to build the tunnel. He needs to find out how long it must be before he starts. Of the mile of 1,760 yards, two cuttings have used up 250 and 350 yards, making a total of 600 yards. Subtracting 600 from 1,760 reveals that the tunnel must be 1,160 yards long.

Subtracting Liquid and Dry Measures

In just the same way, we may want to subtract measures. Suppose we start with a tankful of gas to go a specific distance; the tank holds 20 gallons. We drive the car where we have to go and want to know how much gas has been used.

We cannot measure the gas used, because we no longer have it. But if we measure the remainder and find 11 gallons in the tank, we know by subtraction that we must have used 9 gallons.

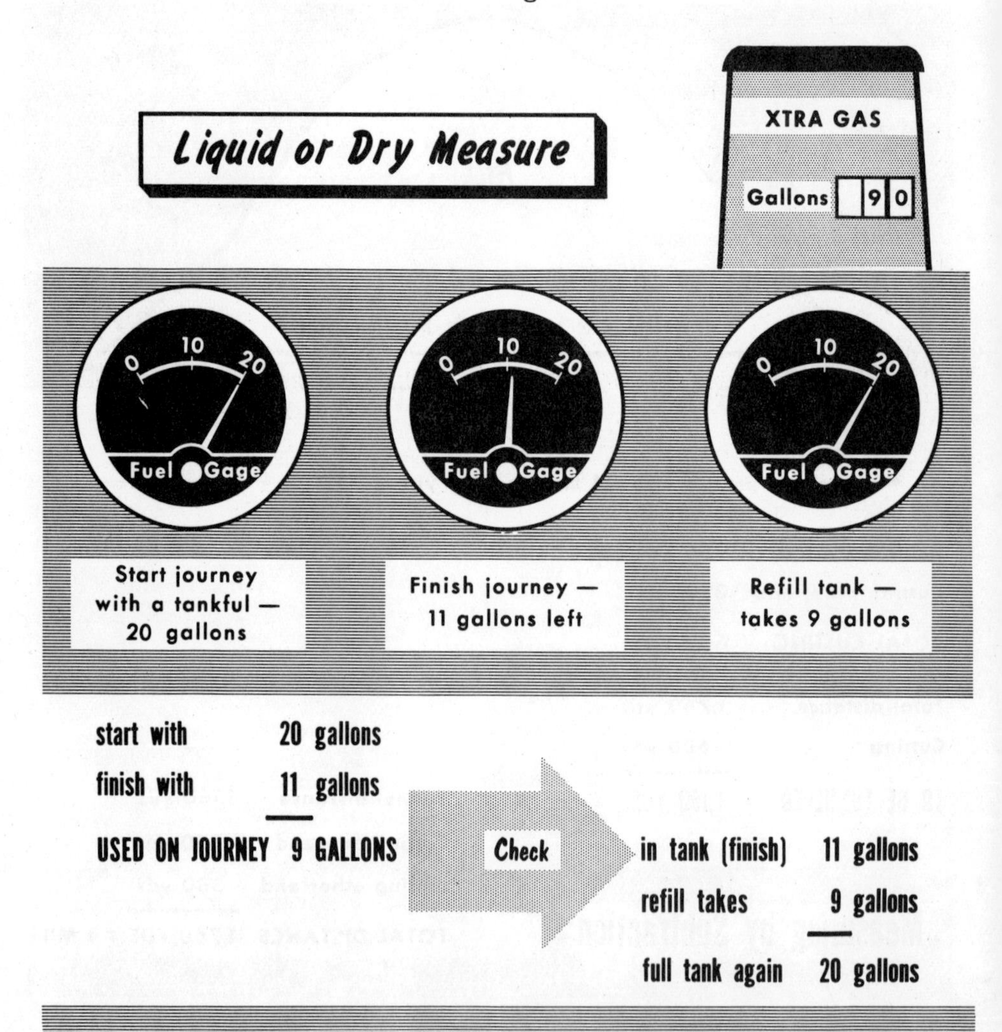

We can check this too, by filling up the tank again, and measuring how much we put in (the gas pump will do this automatically). In this case we should find it to be 9 gallons.

1. Make the following subtractions, and check your results by addition:

(a)	(b)	(c)	(d)	(e)	(f)
69	123	543	762	509	263
−46	−81	−37	−371	−410	−74

(g)	(h)	(i)	(j)	(k)
4,321	6,532	11,507	31,675	92,560
−1,234	−2,356	−8,618	−13,765	−29,651

2. The list price for a certain refrigerator is $359.95; a local discount store advertises a saving of $110 on this item. How much should you pay at that store? Check your result by addition.

3. A lady made several purchases of items priced at $2.95, $4.95, $3.98, $10.98, and $12.98. After adding up the bill, the shopkeeper said he would knock off the cents, making it even dollars. But the lady was smart: she suggested that he knock the cents off each item, instead of the total bill, to which the shopkeeper agreed as a credit to her shrewdness. How much more did she save by this suggestion? Check your answer in any way possible.

4. A child wants to weigh her pet cat. As the cat will not stay on the scales long enough to read its weight, she holds the cat, weighs herself with the cat, and then weighs herself without the cat. With the cat she weighs 93 pounds; without it she weighs 85 pounds. How much does the cat weigh?

5. In making a certain mixture, the recipe calls for 1 pound 12 ounces of rice. The pound weights are all available, but some of the ounce weights have been lost; only the 1- and 4-ounce weights remain. How can I weigh out this quantity? Prove it by showing the scale balances.

6. On a certain superhighway, town B is between towns A and C. The mileage chart only shows selected distances between points. It shows the distance from A to B as 147 miles and the distance from A to C as 293 miles. I have to travel from B to C, the distance for which is not listed. How far is it?

7. A freight company bases part of its charges on weight and part on distance. For distance, the charge is based on direct distance, even though the company's handling may necessitate carrying it further. In one instance, a package addressed to town B had to travel from A to C, which is 1,200 miles, and back to B, on the direct route between A and C, which is 250 miles. What distance is the charge based on?

8. A man has a parcel of land with a 1-mile frontage. He has sold pieces of it with 300-yard, 450-yard, 210-yard, and 500-yard frontages. How much frontage does the remaining parcel have?

Multiplication — Short Cut for Repeated Addition

Suppose we go into a store and buy seven articles for $1 each. The total cost will be $7. That's easy, because it is a matter of counting ones, and it makes no difference whether we count articles or dollars. But suppose the articles cost $3 apiece. To find the total, we have to count 3 seven times.

It Takes Less Time To MULTIPLY Than to Add

1	2	3	→	three	ONE
4	5	6	→	and three are six	TWO
7	8	9	→	and three are nine	THREE
10	11	12	→	and three are twelve	FOUR
13	14	15	→	and three are fifteen	FIVE
16	17	18	→	and three are eighteen	SIX
19	20	21	→	and three are twenty-one.	SEVEN

Seven threes added together are twenty-one
or
Seven times three are twenty-one
7 × 3 = 21

This is the next step in calculating: *multiplication* takes a short cut by our remembering what so many counts of any particular number come to. Instead of counting 3 seven times over and finding that the count ends up at 21, we remember, from having done it before, that 7 threes are 21. We write this 7×3, using the multiplication sign ($\times$) to show that we are to *multiply*, rather than to add or subtract.

At one time, children learning arithmetic would spend hours learning printed multiplication tables, often without knowing what it was all about. If you were lucky enough to remember that 7 threes are 21, it was because you had a good memory. But you would probably not be able to tell anyone *why* 7 threes are 21.

Multiplication — Use of Tables

Rather than making such an effort out of learning multiplication tables without knowing why, we shall construct our own tables: that way, we'll know *what* they mean, and that they are *right*. It will also save us the trouble of deliberately memorizing each combination, because when we want to know what 5 nines are, we have only to look at the table. After using the tables for a while, we will begin to remember them, without having made a special effort to do so.

To make the tables, start by counting, 2 at a time, and put every *second* number in the second column, under "2 times." Next count 3 at a time, and put every *third* number in the next column, under "3 times." Proceed in this way, counting in the various numbers at a time, up to 9. Now we have a table. When we want to know what 5 nines are, we look down the column headed "5 times" to the ninth line, the first column of which reads "9 are," and the number in this line and column is 45. So 5 nines are 45.

Patterns in Numbers

If we counted carefully enough, our multiplication table should be right. But the very arrangement into a table helps us check that it is correct. First notice that we shaded both the columns and lines corresponding with *even* numbers, which are 2, 4, 6, 8, and 10, and numbers above 10 with 2, 4, 6, 8, or 0 in the ones place. The other numbers are *odd* numbers, and the ones figure for an odd number is always 1, 3, 5, 7, or 9. Now look at the table: all the numbers in shaded squares are even numbers; all the numbers in white squares are odd numbers. This is a consistent pattern and the first useful check that there is no mistake in your table.

MULTIPLICATION TABLE

➡ ⬇	2 times	3 times	4 times	5 times	6 times	7 times	8 times	9 times
2 are	4	6	8	10	12	14	16	18
3 are	6	9	12	15	18	21	24	27
4 are	8	12	16	20	24	28	32	36
5 are	10	15	20	25	30	35	40	45
6 are	12	18	24	30	36	42	48	54
7 are	14	21	28	35	42	49	56	63
8 are	16	24	32	40	48	56	64	72
9 are	18	27	36	45	54	63	72	81

Patterns in Numbers (contd.)

Notice the column and line opposite 5; these are shown in Part (A). All the numbers have a ones figure of either 0 or 5; this is another useful check—at least for these numbers. Notice too (B) that any multiplication can be found in two places, except where the number is multiplied by itself. Thus when you read 3 times 7 and when you read 7 times 3, the answer, 21, will appear in both places; but when you read 3 times 3, or 7 times 7, the answer only appears once.

In the 9's column (C), the ones figure counts *down* one and the tens figure counts *up* one at each step; further, in every one of these numbers, if you add the two figures together, the answer is 9.

You may notice other special patterns (D) among numbers moving diagonally between squares, for instance. If you take the numbers moving down from left to right — 4, 9, 16, 25, 36, 49, 64, 81 — and then look at them diagonally from the other way, you see that the next number is always 1 less. And there are many more patterns.

are \ times	2	3	4	5	6	7	8	9
2				10				
3				15				
4				20				
5	10	15	20	25	30	35	40	45
6				30				
7				35				
8				40				
9				45				

(A) CHECKING THE FIVES

are \ times	2	3	4	5	6	7	8	9
2								
3						21		
4								
5								
6								
7		21						
8								
9								

(B) CHECKING BY SYMMETRY

are \ times	2	3	4	5	6	7	8	9
2								18
3								27
4								36
5								45
6								54
7								63
8								72
9	18	27	36	45	54	63	72	81

(C) CHECKING THE NINES

are \ times	2	3	4	5	6	7	8	9
2	4		8					
3		9		15				
4	8		16		24			
5		15		25		35		
6			24		36		48	
7				35		49		63
8					48		64	
9						63		81

(D) CHECKING BY DIAGONALS

Some PATTERNS in numbers make useful CHECKS

Multiplying by Tens

We finished the multiplication table at 9 in each direction, because multiplying a number by 10 merely shifts the same figure into a different "place." Multiplying 5 by 10 makes 50: the 5 has moved from the ones to the tens place. Multiplying 50 by 10 makes 500; the 5 moves from the tens to the hundreds place.

Multipyling 50 by 30, for example, extends this a stage further: 30 is 3 times 10; so we can take this by stages. If we multiply 50 by 10, the answer is 500. Now if we multiply it by 3, the answer must be 3 times 500. 3 times 5 is 15. As 500 is 100 times 5, 3 times 500 must be 100 times 15, or 1,500.

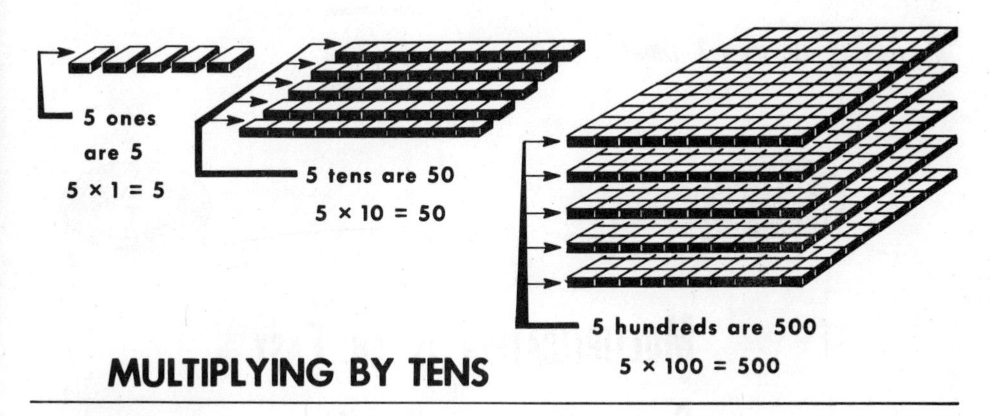

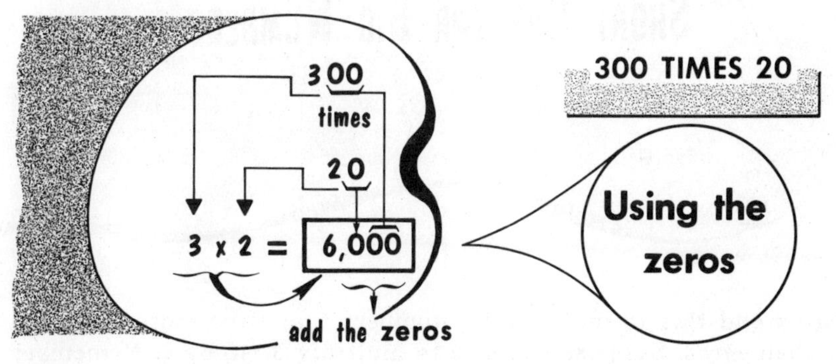

When there are zeros, as in 30 and 50, to tell us that the 3 and 5 are in the tens place, we use this fact to tell us that the *product* of multiplying 30 and 50 together has two zeros, so the 1 and 5 of 1,500 are in the thousands and hundreds place. But in 15, the 1 and 5 are in the tens and ones place. So the zeros help us keep track of place with the other figures. If we multiply 300 by 20, the answer is 6,000. We multiply the figures 3 and 2 to get 6. Then there are three zeros altogether in the original numbers, so the answer has three zeros, indicating that the figure 6 is in the thousands place.

Multiplying Bigger Numbers

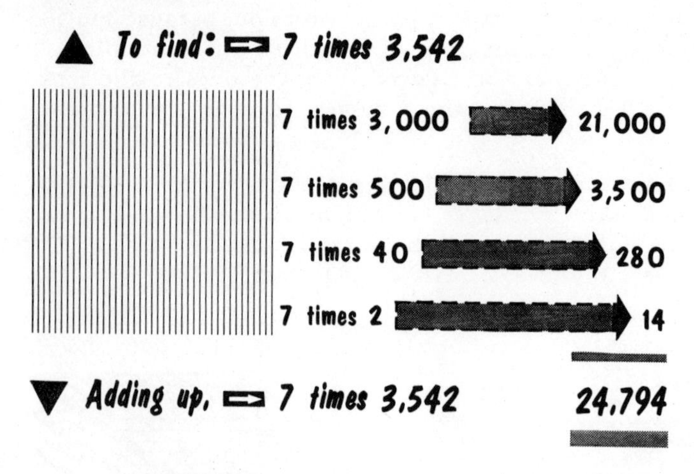

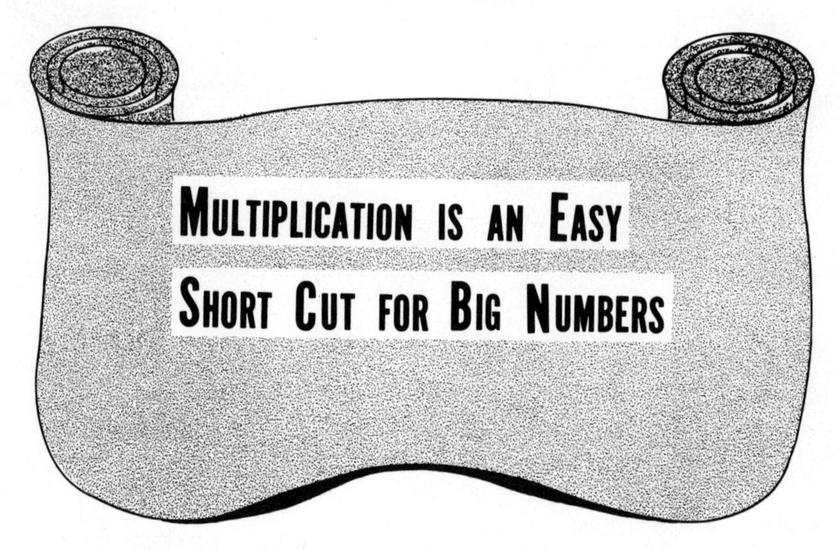

Now we can extend this to multiplying numbers that have more than one figure other than zeros. Suppose we have to multiply 3,542 by 7. Remember that multiplication is really a short cut for addition. So 7 times 3,542 is really the same as 7 times 3,000, added to 7 times 500, added to 7 times 40, added to 7 times 2.

Making each of these multiplications, we have 21,000, 3,500, 280, and 14. Now we add, just as in the first section of this book. Starting with the ones: there is only the last one, 4, which we write. Next the tens: 8 and 1 are 9, which we write in the tens place. Now the hundreds: 5 and 2 are 7, which we write in the hundreds place. Then the thousands: 1 and 3 are 4. Finally, the *ten thousands:* there is just one figure, 2. So 7 times 3,542 is 24,794.

Multiplying Bigger Numbers by Bigger Numbers

There is one more step, before we show how to take another short cut, in writing down multiplication. This is where both numbers have more than one figure. Suppose we have to multiply 3,542 by 27: this is the same as 3,000 and 500 and 40 and 2, each to be multiplied by both 20 and 7. Every figure in one number has to be multiplied by every figure in the other, and the product put in its proper place. The product of the two complete numbers will be all the individual products added together.

First multiply all of 3,542 by 20: 3,000 times 20 is 60,000; 500 times 20 is 10,000; 40 times 20 is 800; 2 times 20 is 40. Now multiply all of 3,542 by 7: 3,000 times 7 is 21,000; 500 times 7 is 3,500; 40 times 7 is 280; and 2 times 7 is 14. Now we have to add: 60,000, 10,000, 800, 40, 21,000, 3,500, 280, and 14. This adds up to 95,634.

We did the multiplying systematically, to make sure no parts were left out. Because we had 4 figures in the first number and 2 in the second, we ended up with 4 times 2, or eight numbers to be added together. This is a way to check that we have all the parts. But it does not check that they are the right parts. For example, we could have multiplied 5 by 4, which is taking two figures from the first number and none from the second. If this had been one of our eight products, the answer must be wrong. So it's a good idea to have a more systematic method.

To find: 27 times 3,542

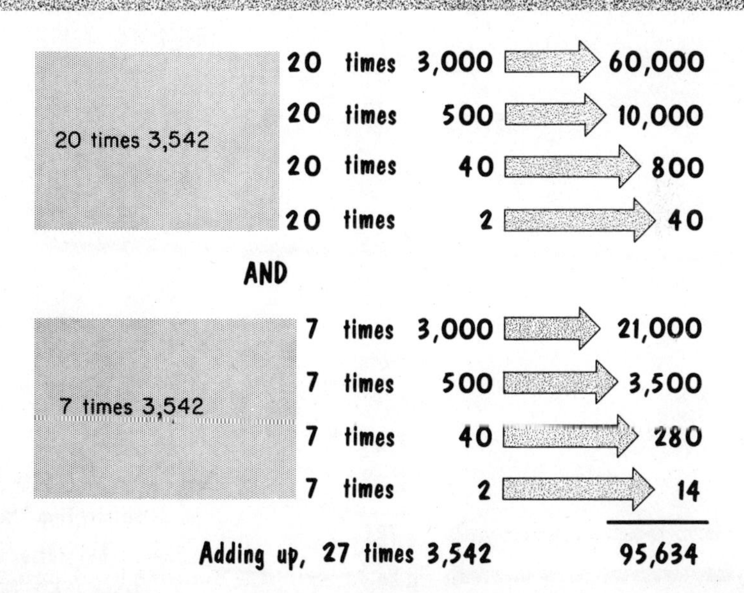

AND FOR EVEN BIGGER NUMBERS

Carrying in Multiplication

In addition, we used carrying as a method of saving on the amount that has to be written down. We can do the same in multiplication. It helps us to be systematic too. When the *multiplier* has only one figure, this method enables us to write down the product right away. Take 3,542 multiplied by 7:

First the *ones*: 7 times 2 is 14; write 4 and carry 1. The *tens*: 7 times 4 is 28; now add 1 carried; this is 29; write 9 and carry 2. The *hundreds*: 7 times 5 is 35; now add 2 carried; this is 37; write 7 and carry 3. The *thousands*: 7 times 3 is 21; now add 3 carried; this is 24; as there are no ten thousands, write 24: 24,794.

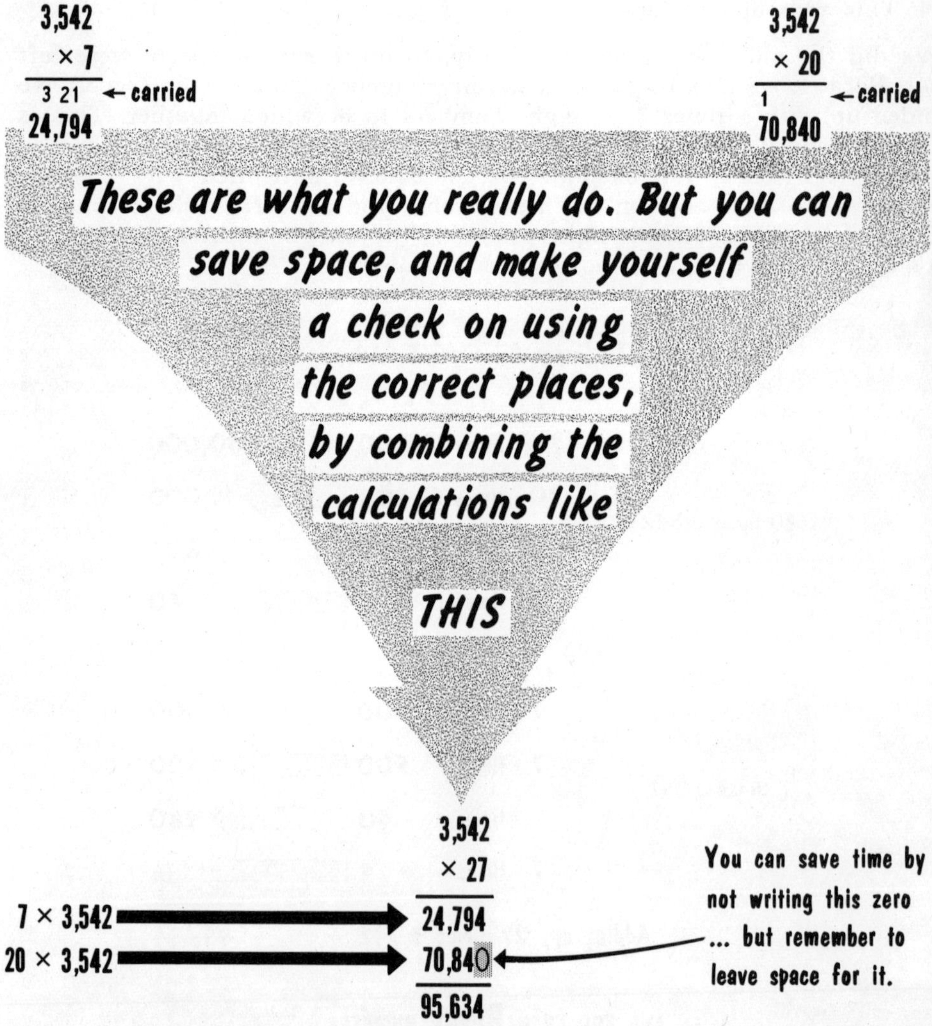

```
 3,542                                   3,542
   × 7                                    × 20
 ------                                  ------
  3 21  ← carried                        1       ← carried
24,794                                   70,840
```

These are what you really do. But you can save space, and make yourself a check on using the correct places, by combining the calculations like

THIS

```
                 3,542
                  × 27
                ------
 7 × 3,542 ───→ 24,794
20 × 3,542 ───→ 70,840 ←── You can save time by not writing this zero
                ------      ... but remember to leave space for it.
                95,634
```

Carrying in Multiplication (contd.)

Now we can extend this to the tens in the multiplier. Multiplying the ones by the tens figure of the multiplier puts the answer in the tens place. So we start with the *tens* place: 2 times 2 is 4; write 4 in the tens place, under the 9 from the previous product. The *hundreds*: 2 times 4 is 8; write 8 in the hundreds place. The *thousands*: 2 times 5 is 10; write 0 in the thousands place and carry 1. The *ten thousands*: 2 times 3 is 6; now add 1 carried; this is 7; write 7 in the ten thousands place, under the 2.

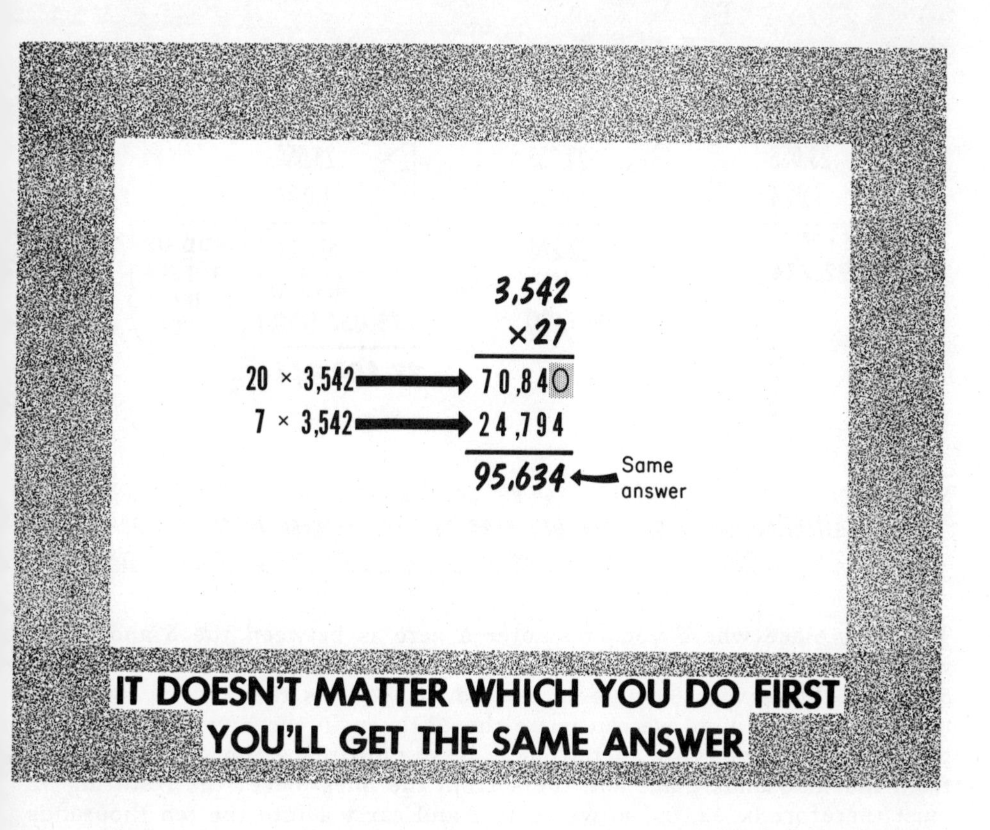

Now add up these two lines, representing 7 times 3,542 and 20 times 3,542: 24,794 and 70,840. This comes to 95,634, as before. Notice that we have an organized way of writing it down, with less writing, and we can check at any point that we are writing a figure in its correct place.

Writing It The Other Way

In the work above we write down the first number multiplied by the ones figure of the multiplier first. It doesn't matter which one you do first. We could equally well have started with the tens first. But if you have three or more figures in the multiplier, you should work systematically from one end to the other. So these are two abbreviated ways of writing down what is called *long multiplication*.

Skipping Zeros

What takes a little more care is when a number has one or more zeros *in the middle places.* Until you are sure what you are doing, the best thing is to check the place each figure should go in, when you have any doubt, by the rule we gave on page 1-39. Let us work through multiplying 23,056 by 1,024.

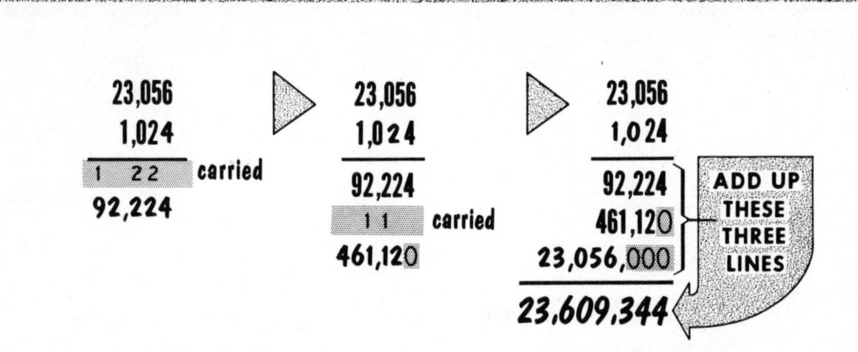

In multiplication too, zeros are used to keep figures in their "places."

The first place where you encounter a zero is between the 5 and the 3 when multiplying through by 4. When you multiply the 5, which means 50, by 4, this gives 200 plus 20 carried, or 220. As there is no figure in the hundreds column, we can write the 22 down in the hundreds and tens places, without carrying that front 2. Next multiply 4 times 3, with the 3 from the thousands place and the 4 from the ones place; the resulting 12 must therefore be 12,000, so we write 2 and carry 1 into the ten thousands place.

In the next line we have the same thing: 2 times 5 is 10, with 1 carried making 11, which we write in the thousands and hundred places, because there is a zero in the hundreds place of the first number, to be multiplied by the 2 for that place.

Now we have a zero in the multiplier too. So we have to be sure that 1 times 6 goes in the right place. As the 1 represents 1,000 and the 6 is ones, the 6 goes in the thousands place. Multiplying the next figure, 5 by 1 does not produce any carrier, so the 0 comes down in the hundred thousands place. Next the 1,000 times 23,000 gives 23 that means 23 millions. Finally add up in the usual way.

Either Number Can Be the Multiplier

Reversing the sequence is not too strong a method of checking multiplication: you merely write down the same sets of figures in different sequences and add them up. If any of the figures is wrong, there is a strong probability that you will make the same mistake both times. But if you use the other number as multiplier, you write down quite different sets of figures, which should add up to the same answer. This provides a better check.

We have worked out the multiplications discussed on pages 1-42 and 1-44 by this method, and it will be seen they get the same answer in each case.

One way is usually much shorter than the other. So naturally, when you are confident of not making mistakes, it is best to use the shorter way.

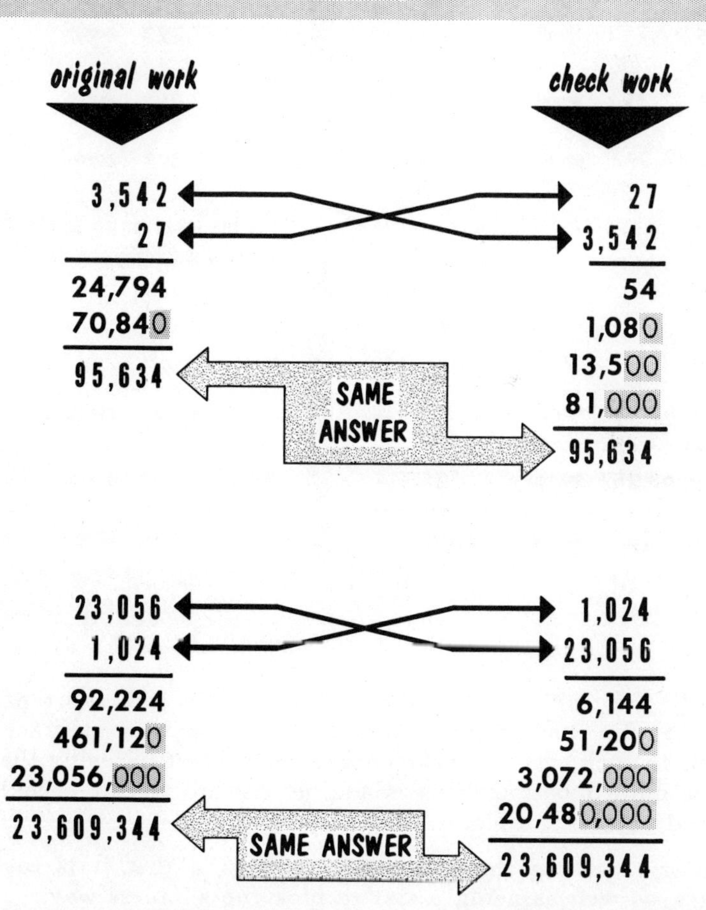

Using Subtraction in Multiplication

Sometimes the multiplication can be made easier by using subtraction instead of addition. For example, if you have to multiply by 29, it is simpler to multiply by 30 and subtract 1 times the number, which is itself.

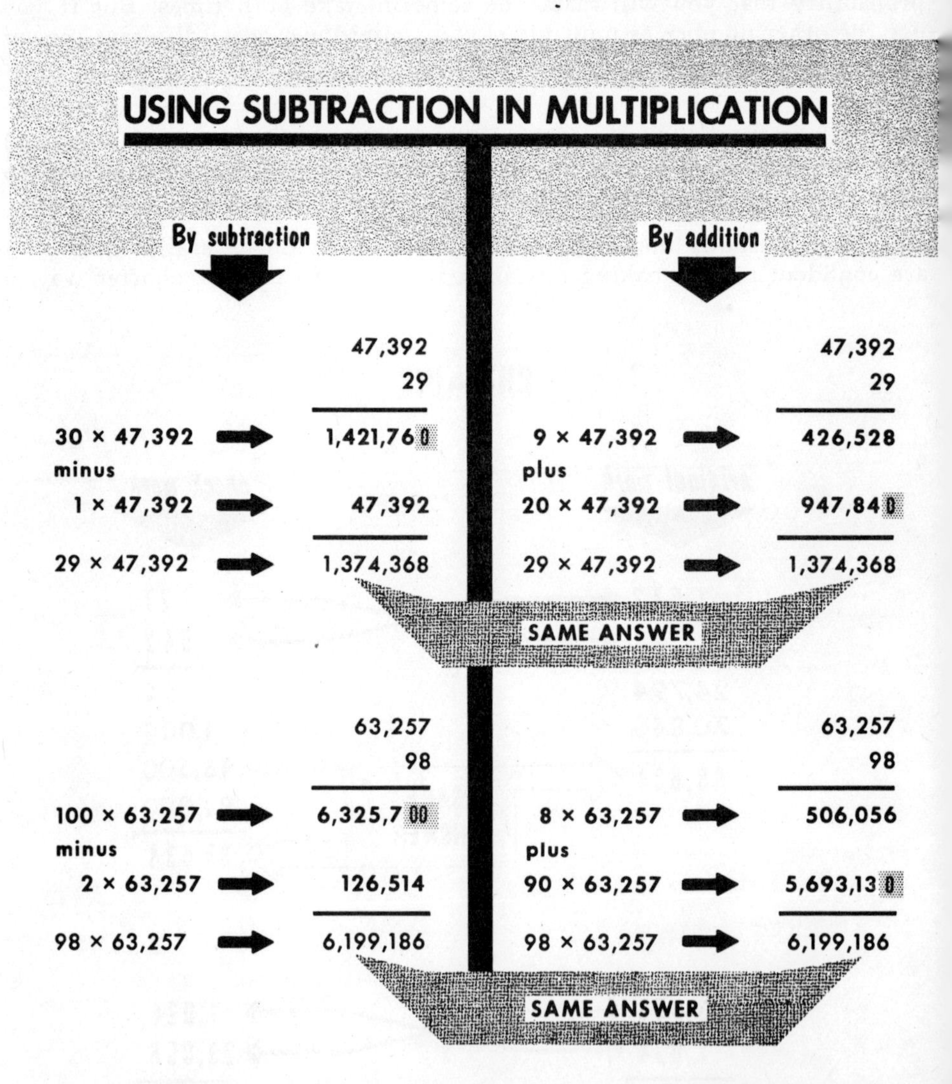

Similarly, if you have to multiply by 98, this is 2 short of a hundred. Multiplying by 100 is merely adding two zeros. Now subtract 2 times the number. In each case, we have checked the result by using the more usual additive multiplication. This is another useful way of checking your results and of saving time.

If you try working these through, you'll find that it is easier to avoid mistakes, as well as being easier to pick the simplest way.

Multiplying by Factors

Here is another way that can sometimes be used for checking. Some multipliers happen to be the product of two numbers multiplied together, themselves. For example, 35 is the product of 5 times 7. Thus we say that 5 and 7 are *factors* of 35. If we have to multiply a number by 35, we have two completely different ways: the long multiplication method multiplies it first by 5, then by 30, and adds the results.

To do the same multiplication by factors, we multiply first by 5, then multiply that answer by 7. Again the result should check.

If the two answers do not agree, you have two ways to work and double check, until you find which way you made your mistake.

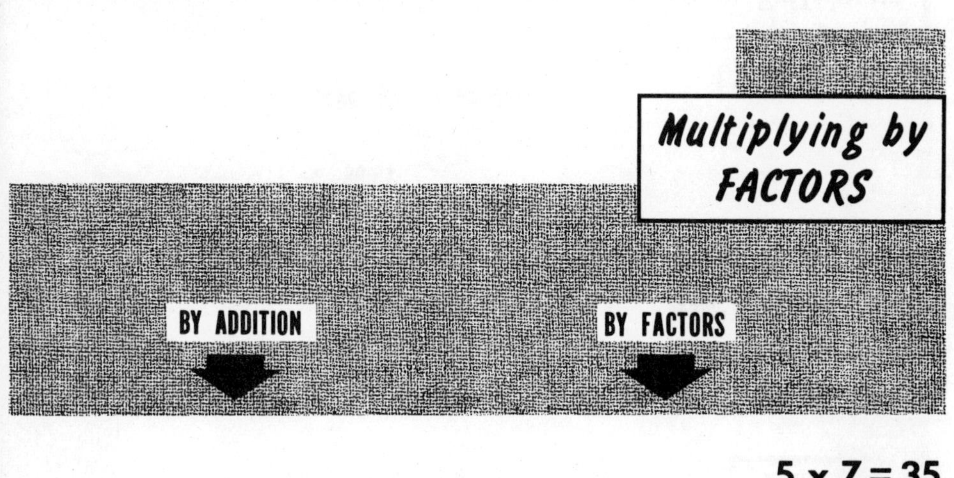

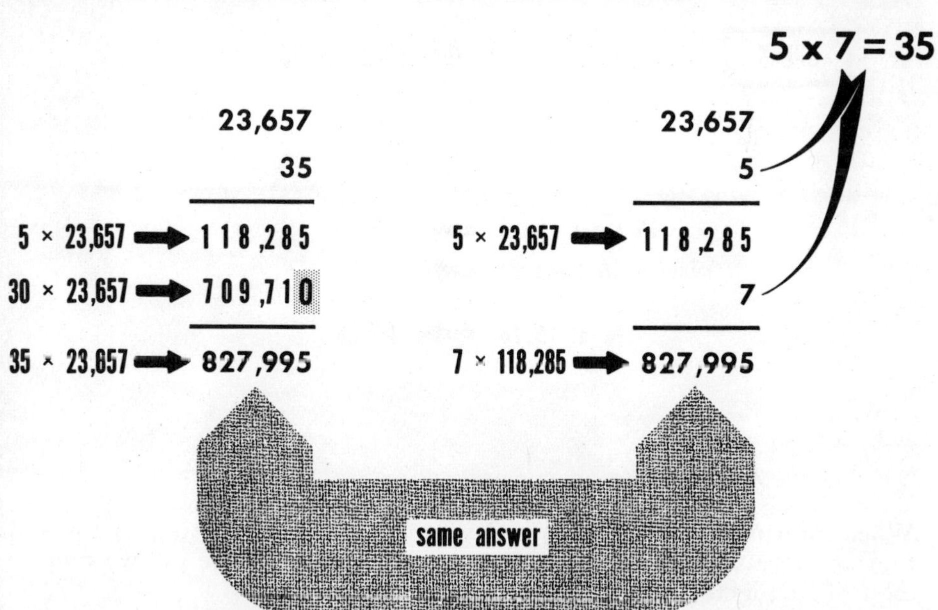

Multiplying Cash

Multiplying cash, or any other commodity, is no more difficult than multiplying numbers. It is still a short cut for repeated addition. This means that when you multiply cash, or any other commodity, only *one* of the numbers can represent cash or the commodity. The other number tells the *number of times* the cash or commodity is to be multiplied.

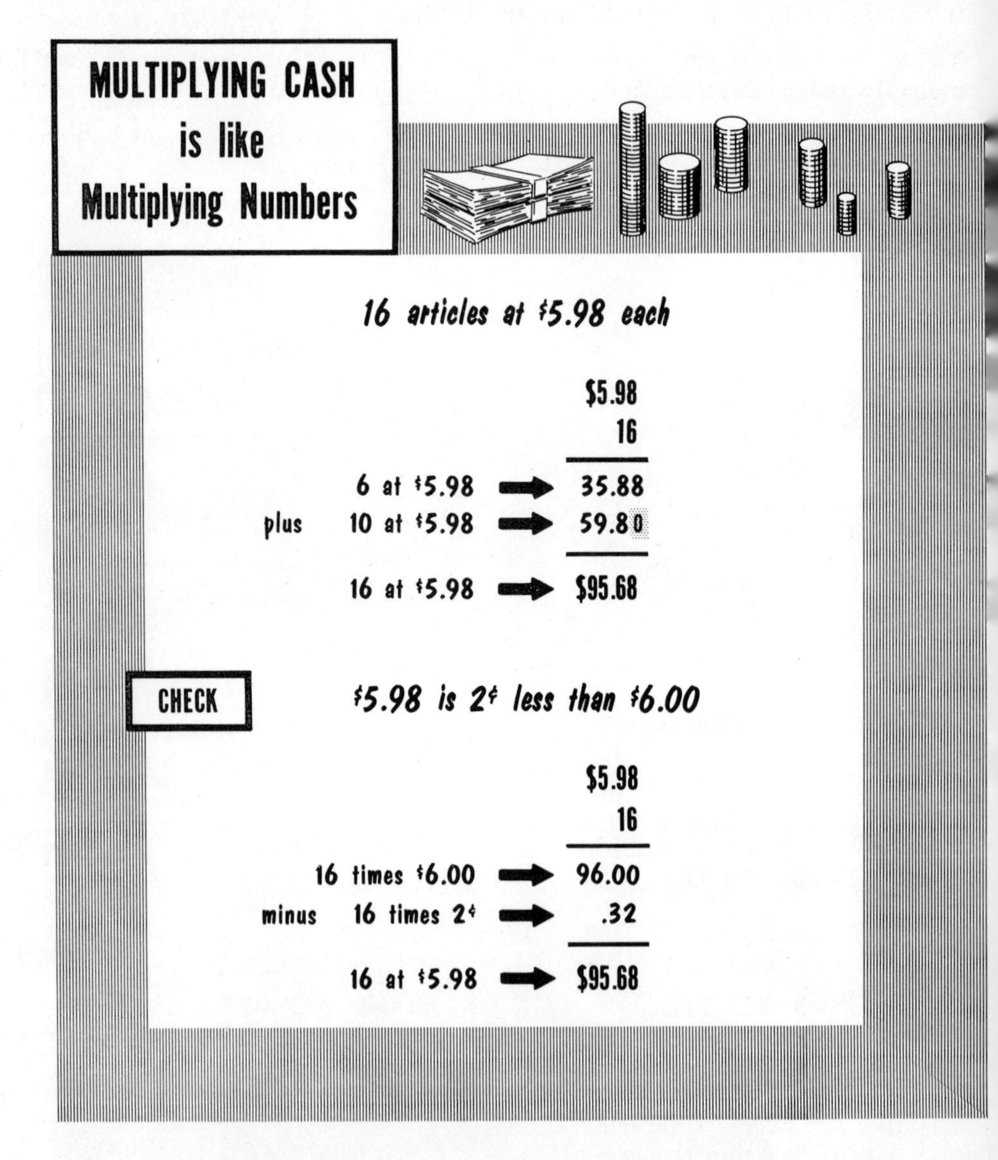

When multiplying cash, we use the same method of writing as for addition or subtraction with cash, remembering that only one of two numbers multiplied together can be cash.

Multiplying with Weights

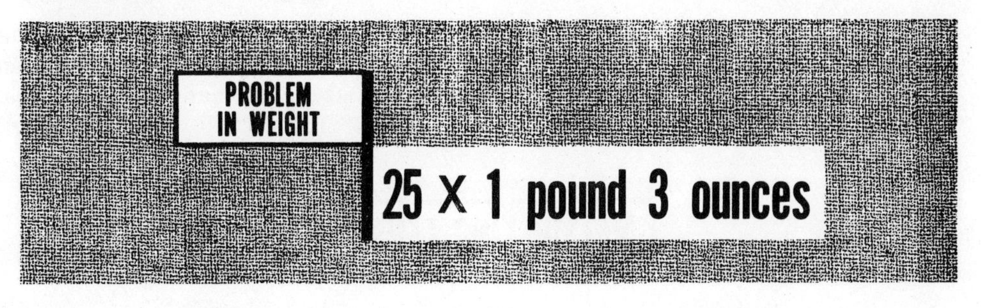

25 times	**3 ounces is**	**75 ounces**
		—16
		or 1 pound 59 ounces
		—16
		or 2 pounds 43 ounces
		—16
		or 3 pounds 27 ounces
		—16
		or 4 pounds 11 ounces
25 times 1 pound is		**25 pounds**

25 times 1 pound 3 ounces is 29 Pounds 11 Ounces

This, too, follows the same principle through, except that the units used for weights do not follow the tens or decimal system.

Suppose we have to multiply 1 pound 3 ounces by 25. First, multiplying 3 ounces by 25 gives 75 ounces. This is several complete pounds, with some ounces left over. To find how many pounds there are and how many ounces left over, we can subtract 16 ounces for each pound from the total 75 ounces. We find that we can subtract 16 four times from 75, leaving 11 ounces—this is 4 pounds 11 ounces. Now multiplying 25 by 1 pound gives 25 pounds. So the whole multiplication of 1 pound 3 ounces by 25 gives 29 pounds 11 ounces (25 pounds + 4 pounds + 11 ounces).

Multiplying Lengths

Multiplying lengths is quite similar, except that the English system uses 12 inches to the foot, 3 feet to the yard, etc., instead of the decimal or metric system. Where necessary, conversion has to be made from inches to feet or from feet to yards.

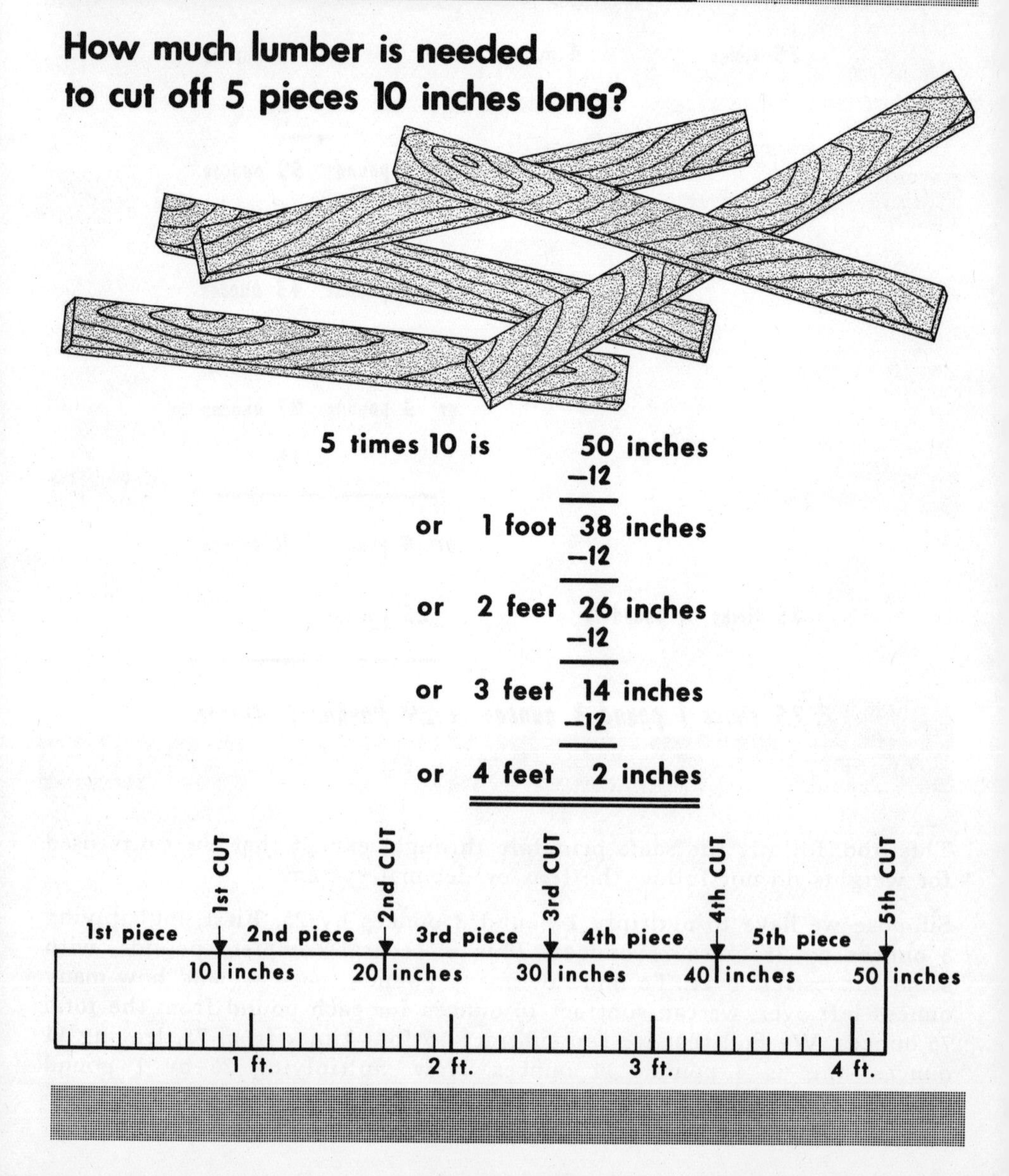

Multiplying Measures

If we multiply a measure by a fairly large number, it is usually convenient to change the unit of measure in which we express it.

Suppose we multiply 3 pints by 250. This is quite easily found to be 750 pints. But quantities this big are usually given in gallons, not in pints. Remembering that there are 8 pints to each gallon, we can proceed to count off in eights. This is a long process. From 750, 8 can be subtracted 93 times and then there are 6 pints left over. The 6 pints can also be called 3 quarts. But in this case it would more likely be written $93\frac{3}{4}$ gallons.

Changing units in this way by counting out is laborious, which is why *division* was invented—as another short cut.

One motor crankcase takes 3 pints of oil

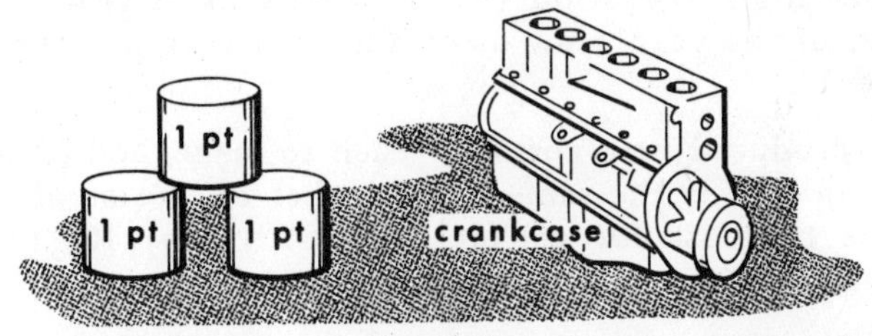

How much is needed for 250 motors?

250 time 3 pints is		750 pints
or 1 gallon	−8	742 pints
or 2 gallons	−8	734 pints
or 3 gallons	−8	726 pints
or 4 gallons	−8	718 pints

AFTER SUBTRACTING 8 FROM PINTS AND ADDING 1 TO GALLONS 93 TIMES (IF WE DIDN'T MAKE A MISTAKE)...

or 93 gallons 6 pints
or 3 quarts
or $\frac{3}{4}$ gallon

$93\frac{3}{4}$ gallons

There MUST be an easier way!

1. Multiply the following pairs of numbers together as shown; check your results by using the upper number as multiplier in each case.

(a) 357 × 246 (b) 243 × 891 (c) 24 × 36 (d) 37 × 74 (e) 193 × 764 (f) 187 × 263

2. Multiply the following pairs by using *subtraction* to make the working simpler; check your results by the more usual addition method.

(a) 2,573 × 19 (b) 7,693 × 28 (c) 4,927 × 18 (d) 5,396 × 59 (e) 7,109 × 89

3. Multiply the following pairs of numbers by using *factors* of the second number; check your results by long multiplication.

(a) 1,763 × 45 (b) 7,456 × 32 (c) 8,384 × 21 (d) 9,123 × 63 (e) 1,024 × 28

4. An airline runs 4 flights a day between two cities, every day of the week except Sunday, when it runs 2. How many flights a week is this?

5. The same flight (question 4) is also only made twice on the 12 public holidays of the year. How many flights a year will there be (based on 52 weeks)?

6. A mass-produced item costs 25¢ each to make, and $2 to package. The packaging cost is the same for a packet of one or of many thousand. What is the cost for packets of: (a) 1; (b) 10; (c) 25; (d) 100; (e) 250; (f) 1,000; (g) 5,000; and (h) 10,000?

7. If you ignore the manufacturing cost, how much is saved by packaging the items of question 6 in packets of 250 instead of 100? (Assume a total quantity of 500.)

8. On a commuter train journey, single tickets sell for 75¢. However, you can buy a ten-trip ticket for $6.75. How much does this save, over the single-ticket rate?

9. On the same journey, a monthly ticket can be bought for $22.50. If a commuter makes an average of 22 round trips a month, how much will he save by buying a monthly ticket?

10. For an employment contract, an employer offered an agreement starting at $100 a month, with a raise of $10 a month every year, for 5 years. At the end of 6 years, the contract expired. The employees bargained for a starting figure of $115 a month, with a raise of $3.50 a month every 6 months. Which rate gave the higher pay by the *beginning* of the sixth year? At which rate resulted greatest total earnings per employee for 6 years? By how much?

11. A certain part used by manufacturers is priced according to how many are bought at once. The price quoted is *per hundred pieces* in each case, but the manufacturer must take the quantity stated to get a particular rate. The rates are $7.50 for 100, $6.75 for 500, $6.25 for 1,000,

$5.75 for 5,000, and $5.50 for quantities over 10,000. The rate for any quantity ordered is taken from the next lower number quoted. What is the difference in total cost for quantities of 4,500 and for 5,000?

12. An often-used method of counting small parts is to weigh them. Suppose that 100 of a particular part weigh $2\frac{1}{2}$ ounces, and we need 3,000 of them. What weight will that be? (*Hint:* change the $\frac{1}{2}$ ounces to drams.)

13. A certain bucket holds 4 gallons of water. Using this bucket, it takes 350 fillings to fill a tank to capacity. What is the capacity of the tank?

14. A freight train has 182 cars. Each is loaded to its maximum which, including the weight of the car, is 38 tons. What is the total weight that the locomotive has to haul?

15. A car runs 260 miles on a tankful of gas. The owner has rigged an an ingenious alarm that lets him know when it needs refilling. He goes on a journey that takes 27 fillings and finishes ready for another. How long is the journey?

16. One railroad bases its rates on 2¢ a mile; another, serving the same two cities, bases its rates on 3¢ a mile. The distance by the first railroad is 450 miles. The second railroad takes a shorter route, cutting the distance to 320 miles. Which company offers the cheaper fare? By how much?

17. One airline offers rates based on 5¢ a mile for first-class facilities, and the distance between two cities is 2,400 miles. Another airline offers rates based on 3¢ a mile for coach facilities, but takes a longer route covering 3,200 miles between these particular cities. Which fare is cheaper and by how much?

18. The first airline in question 17 offers a family plan, in which each passenger of a family, after the first, pays a rate based on 3¢ a mile. Which way will be cheaper for a family (a) of 2, (b) of 3, and by how much?

19. A health specialist recommends that every mouthful of food should be chewed 50 times before swallowing. Careful experimenting shows that 1 ounce of a particular food can be eaten in 7 mouthfuls. A helping of this food consists of 3 ounces. How many times will a person have to chew to eat this helping, according to our health specialist?

20. An intricate pattern on an earthenware plate is repeated 9 times around the edge of the plate. Each pattern has 7 flowers in this repetition. How many flowers are there altogether around the edge?

Division Is Counting Out

Division is a short cut for counting out. Counting out can be done in a variety of ways, according to the purpose. Suppose 28 items have to be divided, or counted out, among four people. We write this 28 ÷ 4, using the division sign (÷).

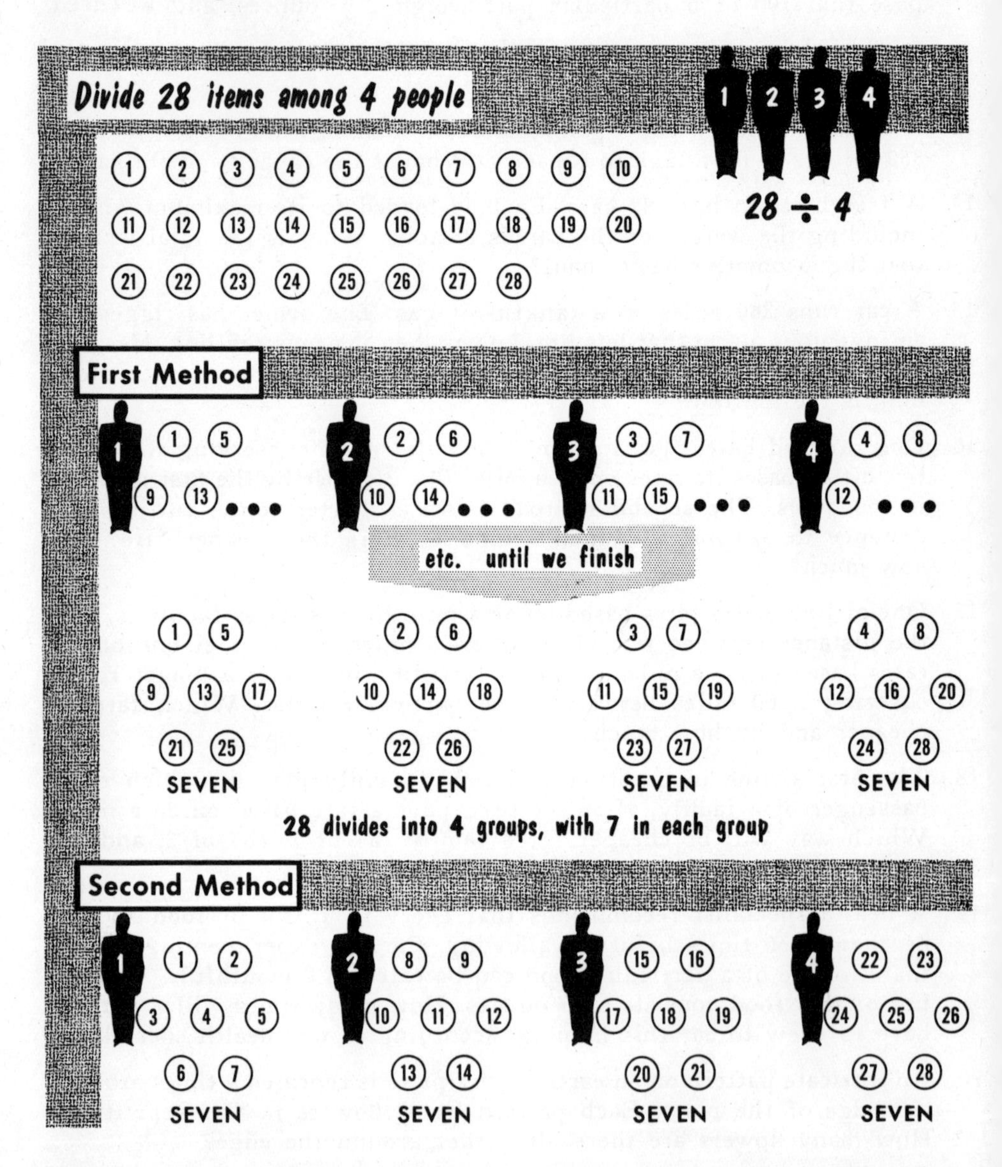

One way is to count one to each of the four, then a second one, and so on, till all 28 are used up. But if you know how many each gets, it is quicker to count out 7 each, right off. Division enables you to arrive at this quicker way of doing it.

Division Is Multiplication in Reverse

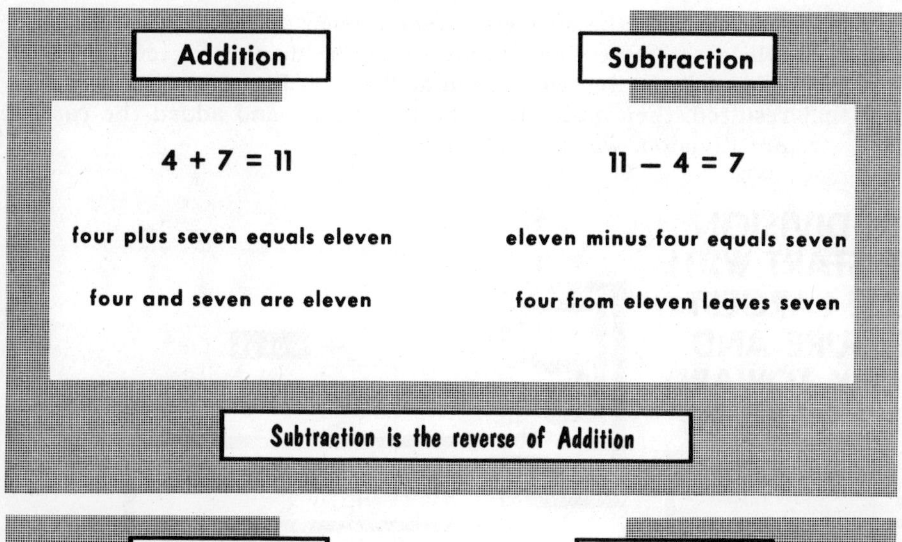

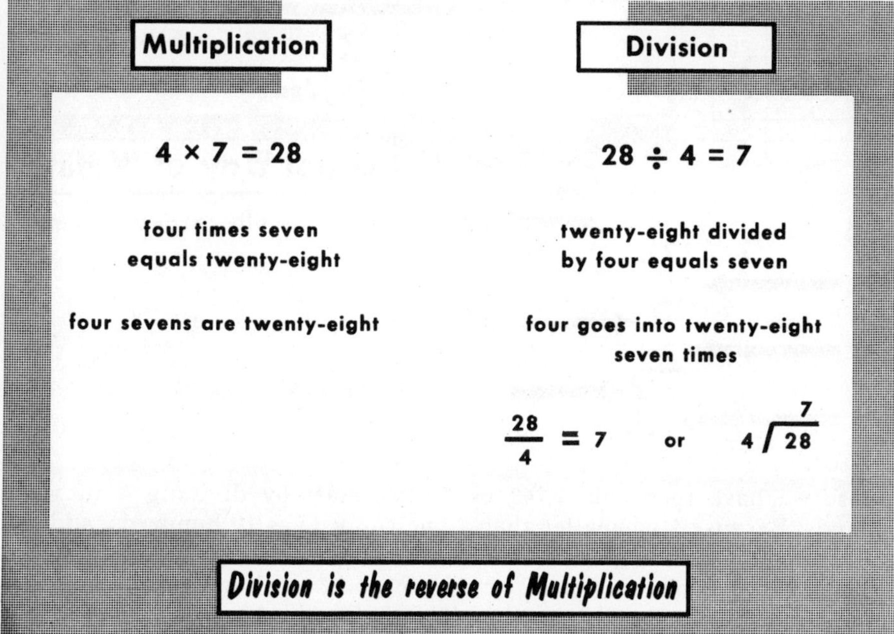

Just as subtraction proved to be addition in reverse, so division proves to be multiplication in reverse. With addition, when we add 4 and 7, the total is 11. Reversing it, if we subtract 4 from 11, we have 7 left.

Similarly, multiplying 4 by 7 gives 28. And if we divide 28 by 4, we get 7. This is usually expressed by saying "4 goes in 28, 7 times."

Dividing into Longer Numbers

It is easy when we pick the answers directly from the multiplication table we made a while ago. But what do we do if the number is too big to be in the table? In multiplying, we started at the ones figure, carried any tens figure that resulted, then multiplied the tens figure and added the carried figure, etc. For division, we simply *reverse* it.

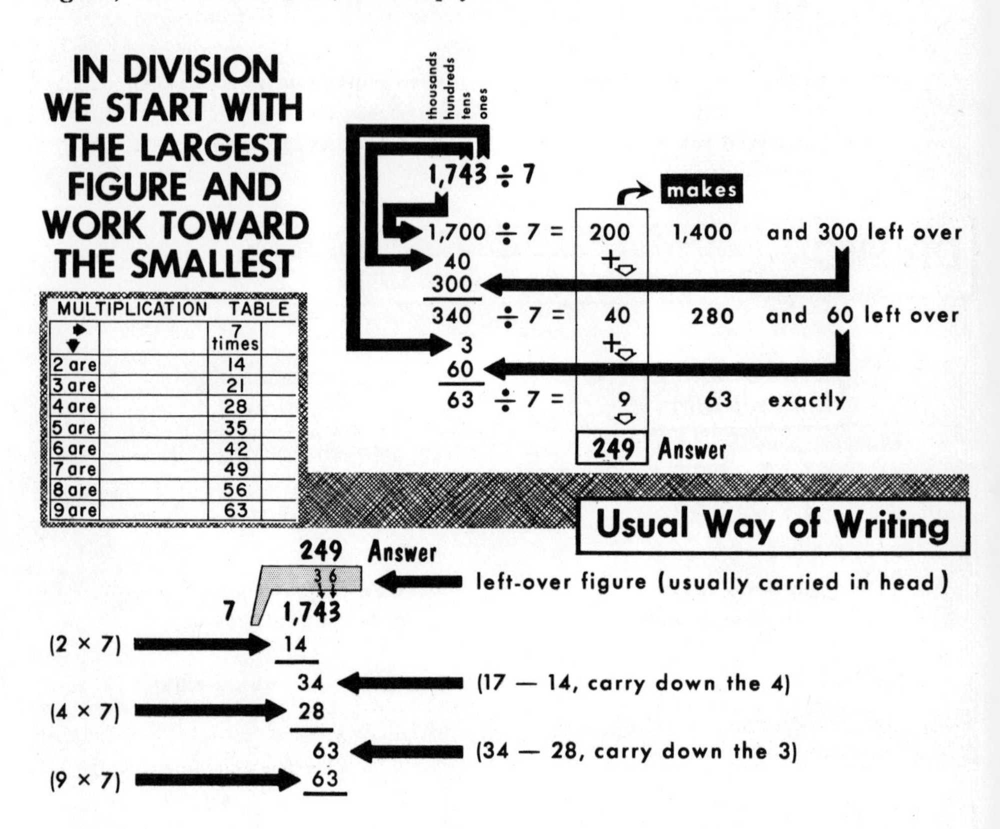

Suppose we have to divide 1,743 by 7. We start by dividing 7 into the *thousands*. Because 1 is smaller than 7, we count is as 10 hundreds, add the 7 hundreds from the original number and divide 7 into 17 hundreds. From our multiplication table, in the 7's row, for the 2's column we have 14 and for the 3's, we have 21. The number 17 is between 14 and 21. This means that 7 divides into 17 hundred 2 times and leaves us 3 (14 subtracted from 17) hundreds, which we can count as 30 tens. We then add the 30 tens to the 4 tens in our original number to get 34 tens and divide 7 into 34 tens. From our table we see that 7 times 4 is 28 and 7 times 5 is 35. As 35 is too big, we write 7 as dividing into 34 tens 4 times, leaving 6 (28 subtracted from 34) tens to add to the ones. Adding the 6 tens to the 3 ones in the original number gives us 63. Thus 7 divides into 63 exactly 9 times, because we see from the table that 7 times 9 is 63. Now we have the complete answer for 1,743 ÷ 7. It is 249.

Multiplication Checks Division

Just as subtraction, which is the reverse of addition, can be checked by *it*, so division, being the reverse of multiplication, can be checked by it. Taking the same example, multiplying 249 by 7 gives 1,743. As this is the number we started by dividing into, we have checked our division.

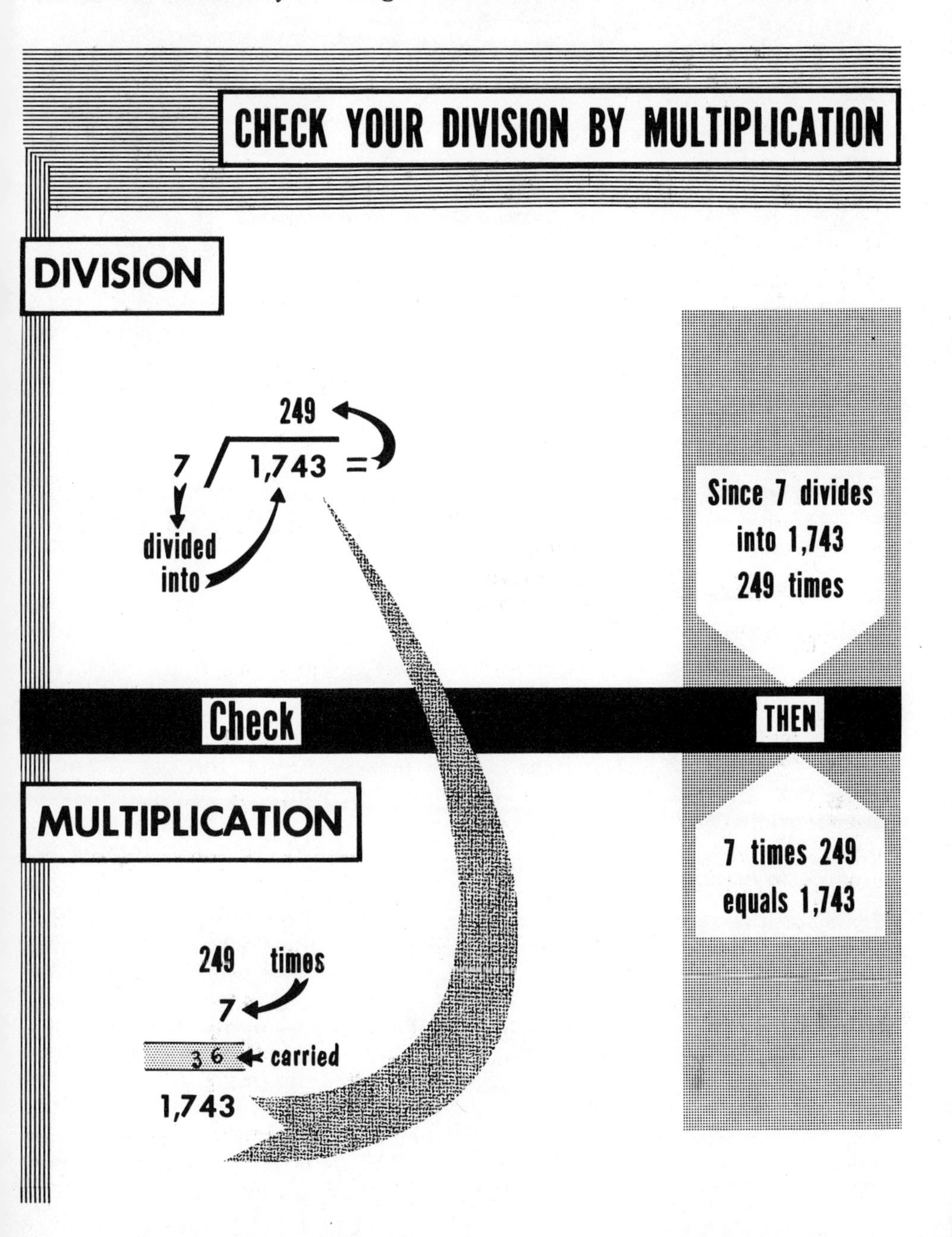

Dividing by Bigger Numbers

Like multiplication, division is easy when each step can be taken directly from the multiplication table. But how would you divide 14,996 by 23?

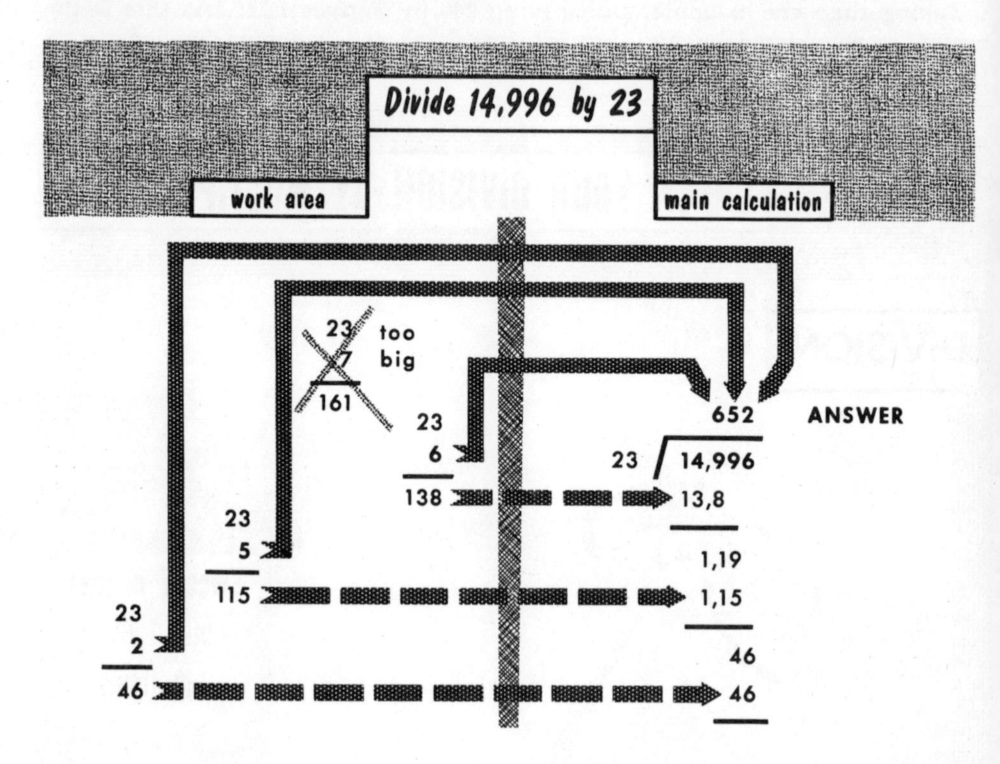

We follow the same method, but it takes a little more working out. We start at the "front end' just the same. 23 obviously does not divide into 14 thousand, because it's too big. But it will divide into 149 hundred. As a first "try" we divide just the tens into the tens—2 into 14; this goes 7 times, so we multiply out 7 times 23. This gives 161, which is bigger than 149, because we had 2 to carry from ones to tens. So we try 6 times 23: multiplying this out gives 138. which can be subtracted from 149, leaving 11 hundred to be used as 110 tens.

Next, for the tens figure, we divide 23 into 119, by bringing down the 9 figure in the tens from our original number. Taking the tens figure again, divide 2 into 11; it goes 5 times, with 1 over, so we try 5 times 23; this gives 115. Subtracting this from 119 leaves 4, which counts as tens for division into the ones. Bringing down the original ones figure, 6, we divide 23 into 46. The tens part, 2 into 4, goes twice; we try 2 times 23 and find it exactly 46. So dividing 23 into 14,996 gives 652.

It is an advantage to write down each little multiplication you do in the margin of your work. If you happen to need the same figure again, it's already multiplied out, and you don't have to try it all over again.

Multiplication as a Check Again

With long division, which is what the operation on the previous page is called, there is much more chance of making a mistake. So it's a good idea, until you are really confident of these calculations, to check them by multiplication. In this case, multiplying 652 by 23 gives 14,996, proving that our division must have been right.

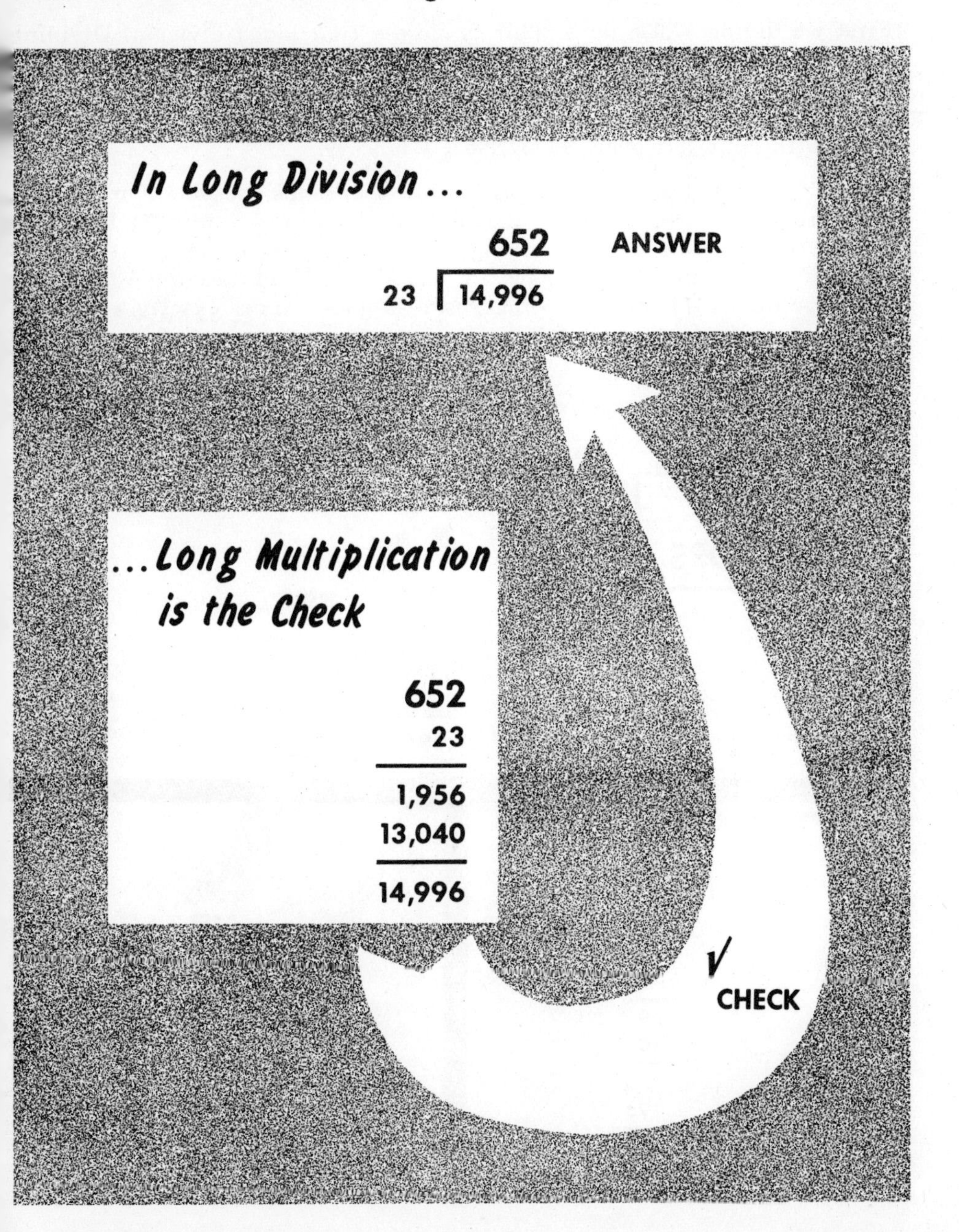

Division by Factors

Suppose our problem required us to divide 37,996 by 28. We could do this in just the same way. But there is also another way. In multiplication, some numbers could be multiplied by using factors. This can also be done in division. In this case, 28 is 4 times 7, so we can do the division by dividing successively by the factors, 4 and 7.

First we divide 37,996 by 4. This is simple (not long) division. Dividing 4 into 37 thousands gives 9 times 4 is 36, with 1 left over. Dividing 4 into 19 hundreds gives 4 times 4 is 16, with 3 left over. Dividing 4 into 39 tens gives 9 times 4 is 36, with 3 left over. Dividing 4 into 36 gives 9 times 4 is 36, with none left over. So, 37,996 ÷ 4 is 9,499.

Now we divide 9,499 by 7. Dividing 7 into 9 thousands goes one time, leaving 2 thousands over to count as 20 hundreds. Dividing 7 into 24 hundreds goes 3 times giving 21 and leaving 3 hundreds over to be counted as 30 tens. Dividing 7 into 39 tens goes 5 times giving 35 and leaving 4 tens over to be counted as 40 ones. Dividing 7 into 49 goes 7 times exactly with none left over. So the answer is 1,357.

Therefore, 37,996 ÷ 28 is 1,357. We can check this by multiplying back, 28 by 1,357, or 1,357 successively by 4 and 7, or by the long division method.

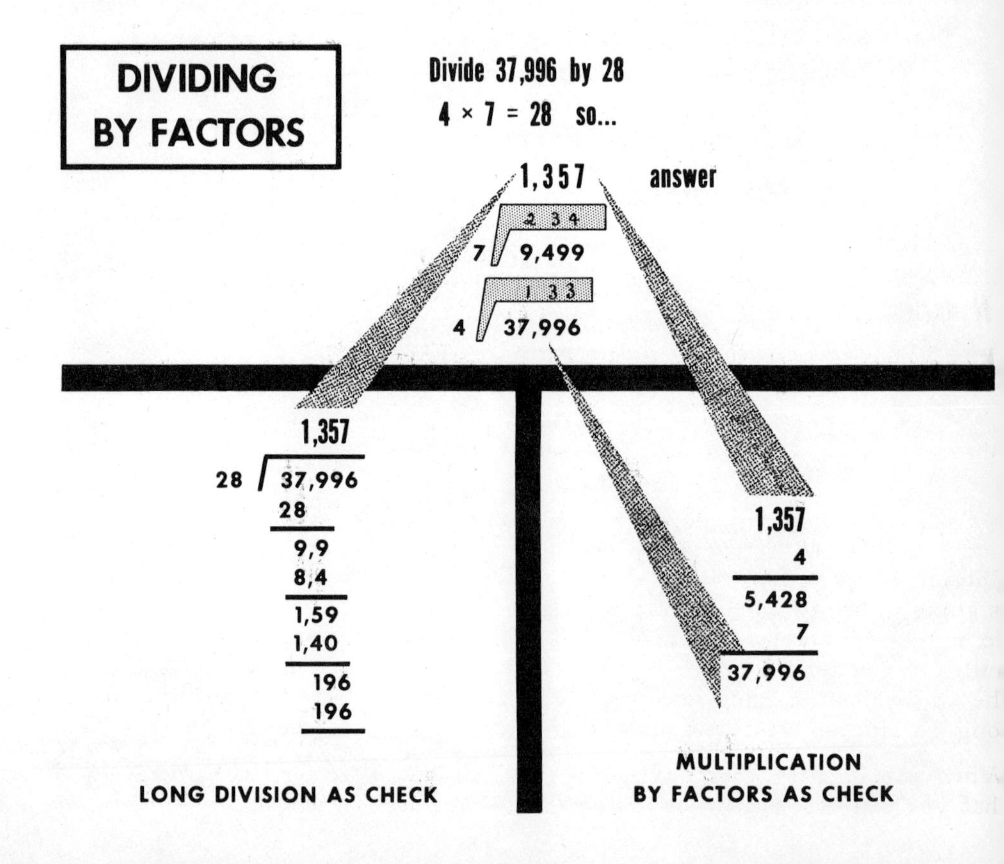

Which Method Is Best

As you can see from the opposite page, we get the same answer for the division of 37,996 by 28, whether we use factors to divide or whether we use long division.

TIMES / ARE	2	3	4	5	6	7	8	9
2	4	6	8	10	12	14	16	18
3	6	9	12	15	18	21	24	27
4	8	12	16	20	24	28	32	36
5	10	15	20	25	30	35	40	45
6	12	18	24	30	36	42	48	54
7	14	21	28	35	42	49	56	63
8	16	24	32	40	48	56	64	72
9	18	27	36	45	54	63	72	81

Therefore, it's a matter of personal preference in selecting the method one is going to use to do a given calculation, *if* both are possible. All numbers do not have factors: for instance, there are no two numbers which, if multiplied together, amount to 29. Only the numbers which appear on the multiplication table have factors small enough to allow anything but long division, so we do not always have the choice of methods.

When you do have the choice, it is well to have practiced both ways so that you can use whichever method seems easiest for you.

When There Is a Remainder

In the examples we have used so far, the numbers conveniently divided one into the other *exactly*. They were deliberately chosen to do so. But most often this does not happen. If we have two numbers not specially arranged to do this, they probably will not come out exactly.

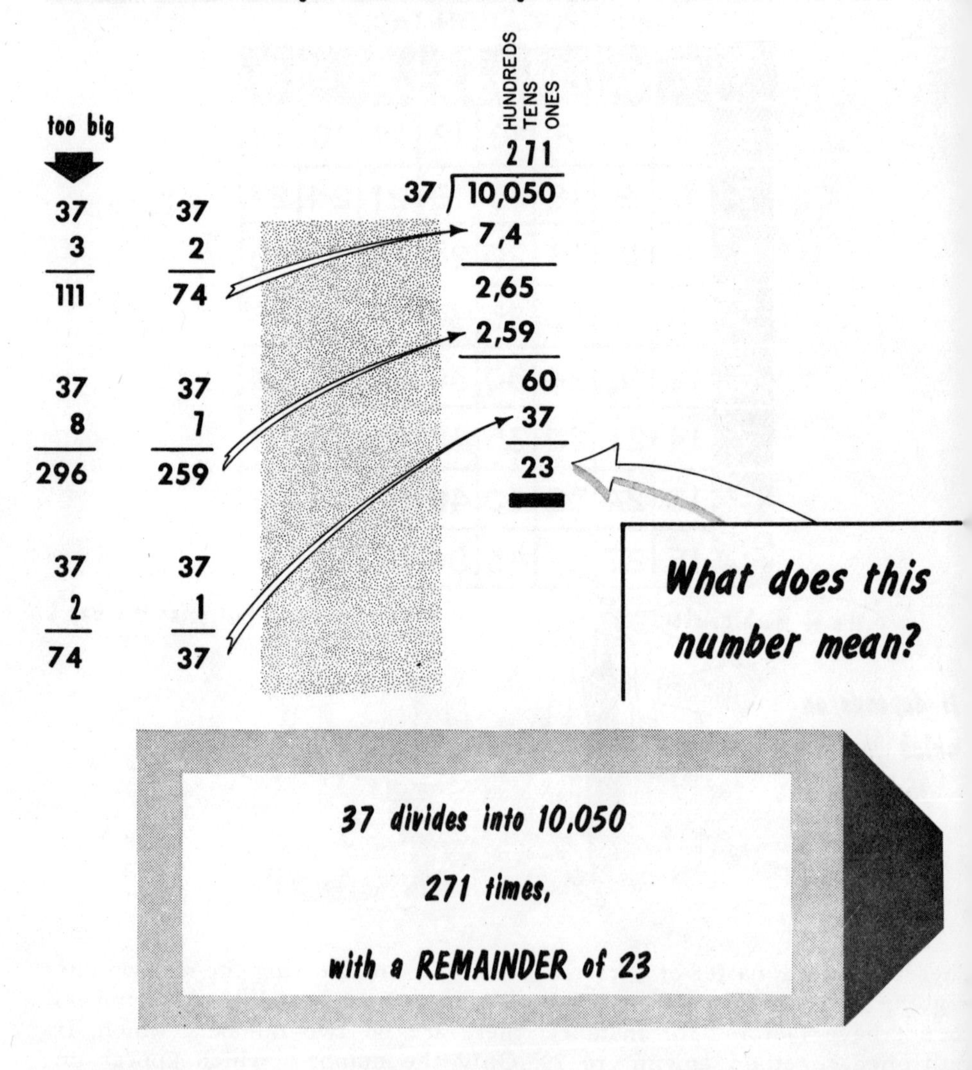

For example, suppose we divide 10,050 by 37. The answer includes figures from hundreds down to ones. But after we have subtracted 37 from the ones figure (which is 60 here), there is 23 left over. For the moment, we call it a remainder.

What Does the Remainder Mean

Remember that division is counting out. Suppose we have to divide 25 by 6. We count out 25 into 6 groups. When we get to 24, we have four in each group, exactly. The 25 is one over. If we give it to any one group, the groups will not have an equal share of the original 25: one will have 5 and the other five will have 4. So we have to keep the odd one as a remainder.

Divide 25 by 6

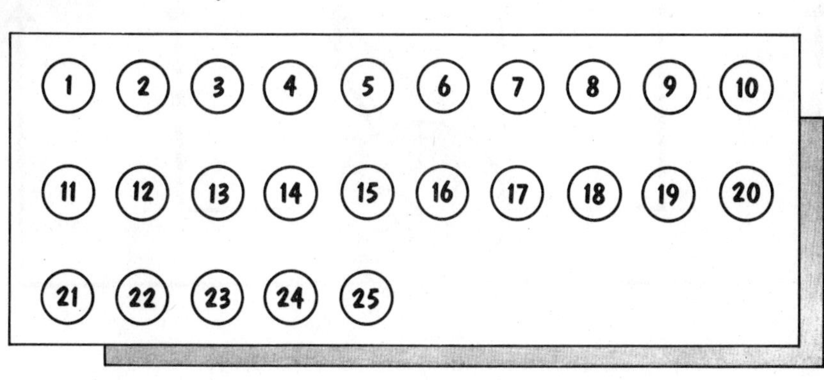

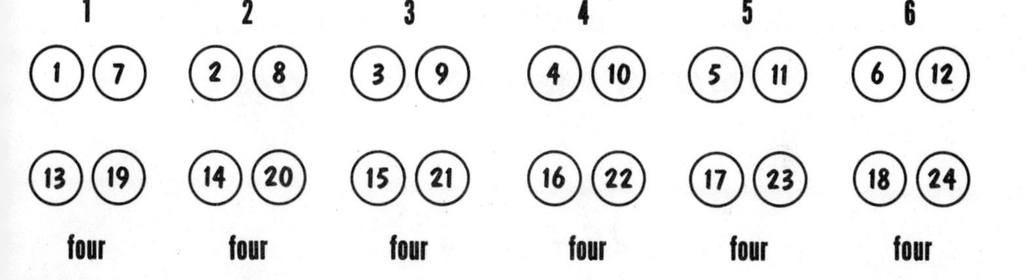

Using 24 makes 4 each in 6 groups.

WHAT ABOUT THE ODD ONE 25 ?

The Remainder as a Fraction

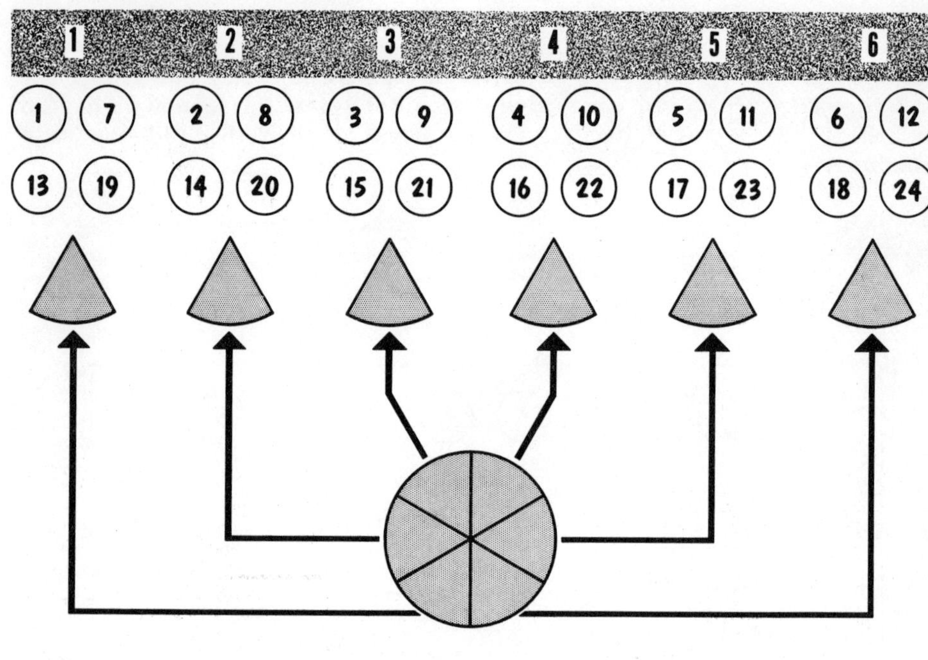

Divide Number (25) into six equal parts.

Each part is one-sixth of the whole.
The fraction one-sixth is written $\frac{1}{6}$

$$25 \div 6 = 4\frac{1}{6}$$

The only way we can complete the division of 25 into 6 parts is to *divide* the odd one left over into 6 equal pieces. Each piece is then one-sixth ($\frac{1}{6}$) of the whole. We have completed the division of 25 into 6 parts; each part is $4\frac{1}{6}$—four and one-sixth. Those parts that enable the division to be completed are called *fractions*. Whenever anything is divided into a number of equal parts, each part, called a fraction, is identified by a horizontal line, with a number (called the *numerator*) over it and the number of equal parts used (called the *denominator*) under it.

Fractions That Are Multiple Parts

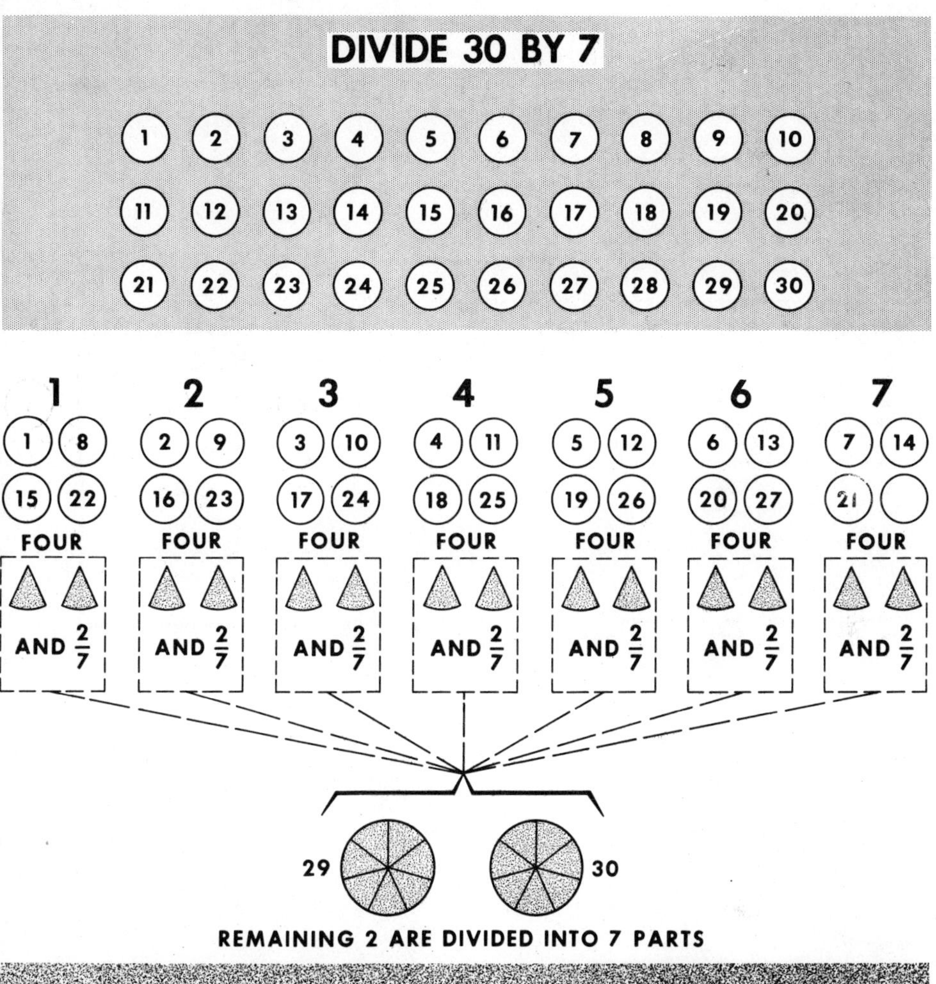

$$30 \div 7 = 4\frac{2}{7}$$

The example on the previous page had a remainder of only 1 to be divided into parts; often the remainder is a number more than 1, but never more than the dividing number (called "divisor" in older textbooks).

Try dividing 30 by 7. Four times seven gives 28, leaving a remainder of 2. If we divide each of these remaining 2 into seven parts, we shall have 14 equal parts. So each group gets two-sevenths.

This we show in fractional form by writing 2 (called the numerator) above the horizontal line and 7 (called denominator) below it. So 30 divided by seven is four and two-sevenths, written $4\frac{2}{7}$.

Multiplying and Dividing Fractions

On the previous page, dividing 2 by 7 resulted in the fraction $\frac{2}{7}$. This represents 2 of the fraction $\frac{1}{7}$. *To multiply a fraction by any whole number, we multiply its numerator (top number) by that number.* If we further multiply the fraction $\frac{2}{7}$ by 3, we have $\frac{6}{7}$, because 3 times 2 is 6.

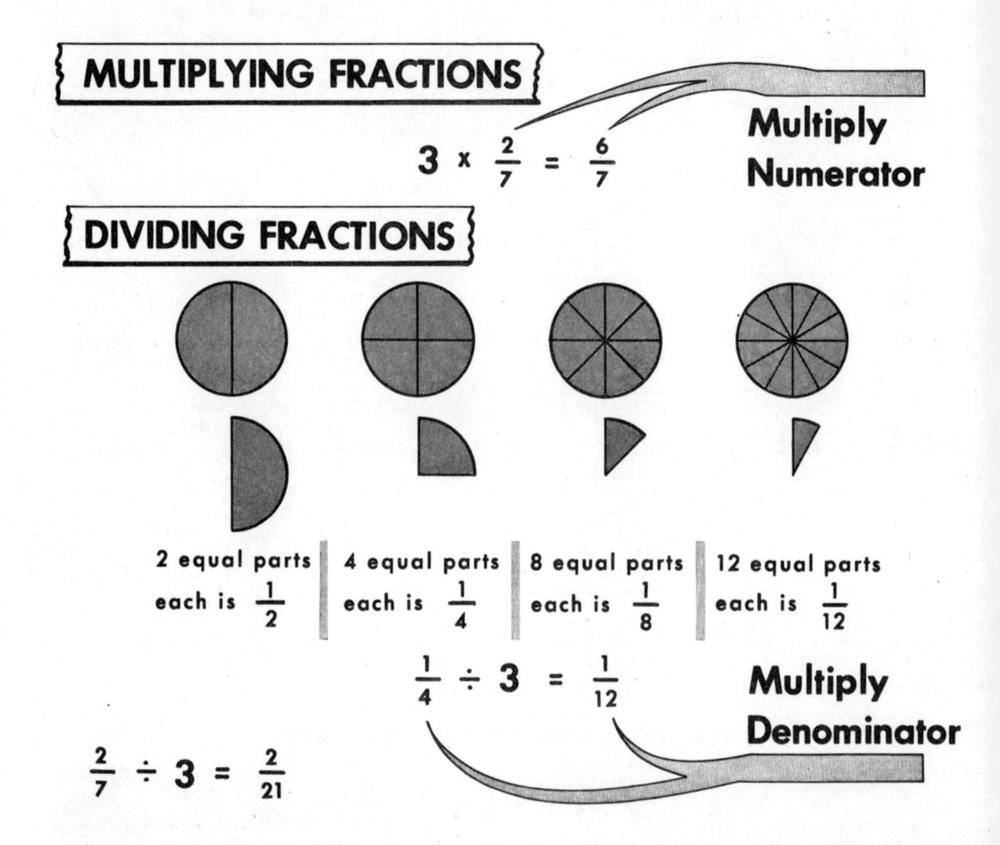

Division is equally simple when we understand the fraction system (numerators and denominators) for writing parts. If we divide $\frac{1}{2}$ by 2, each part is then a quarter, $\frac{1}{4}$. If we further divide this by 2, each part is then an eighth, $\frac{1}{8}$. This is so, because by dividing each original half by 2, and then each quarter by 2, we should have eight equal parts.

If we divide $\frac{1}{4}$ by 3, we should have 3 times 4, or 12, equal parts: so each part is $\frac{1}{12}$. Further, if we divide $\frac{2}{7}$ by 3, we should have $\frac{2}{21}$.

The rule is plain: *to divide a fraction by any whole number, we multiply its denominator by that number.*

Remainders in Long and Successive Division

Now we can see more precisely what remainders mean in division. To illustrate, we shall take a problem that can be done two ways: divide 23,514 by 28.

Doing this by long division, we have a remainder of 22, which represents a fraction of $\frac{22}{28}$. So the answer (called the "quotient" in many textbooks) is 839 $\frac{22}{28}$.

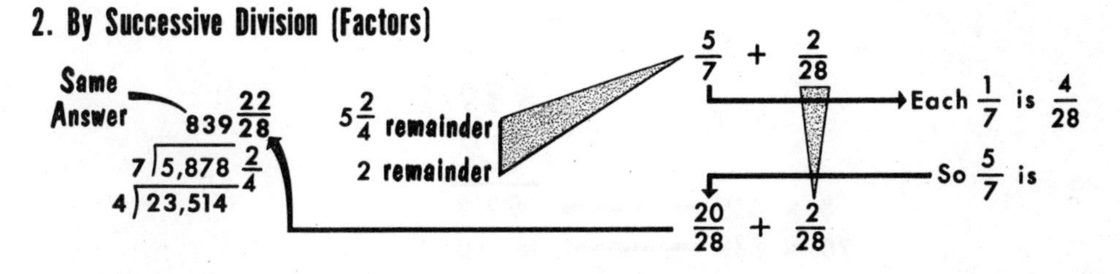

Doing it by successive division (another name for division by factors), the first division by 4 leaves a remainder of 2. At this stage it means $\frac{2}{4}$. Now dividing through by 7, we have a remainder of $5\frac{2}{4}$; 7 divided into $5{,}878\frac{2}{4}$ goes 839 times, with $5\frac{2}{4}$ remainder. This has to be divided by 7, or expressed as a fraction in sevenths. The 5 is no problem: that is just five sevenths (written $\frac{5}{7}$). The $\frac{2}{4}$ divided by 7 is $\frac{2}{28}$. So the total remainder represents $\frac{5}{7} + \frac{2}{28}$.

To make this one fraction, we have to use the same size parts—to make the denominator the same. This is called the "common" denominator. Each seventh can be subdivided into four twenty-eighths. So five sevenths is actually the same as 5 times $\frac{4}{28}$ or 20 twenty-eighths. Now we can add the 20 and 2, both being $\frac{1}{28}$ parts, and get $\frac{22}{28}$, which is the same as we got by the long division method.

Multiplying Mixed Numbers to Check Division

The use of multiplication to check division can be extended to numbers with remainders. We can multiply $839\frac{22}{28}$ by 28 to check the division on the previous page. Multiplying 839 by 28 by long method is quite easy. We are then left with $\frac{22}{28}$ to multiply by 28.

As each of the 22 one-twenty-eighths is an equal one-twenty-eighth part of one, 28 of them will make up 1. So 28 times 22 of them will make up 22. Now we add in the 22, along with the other lines of the long multiplication.

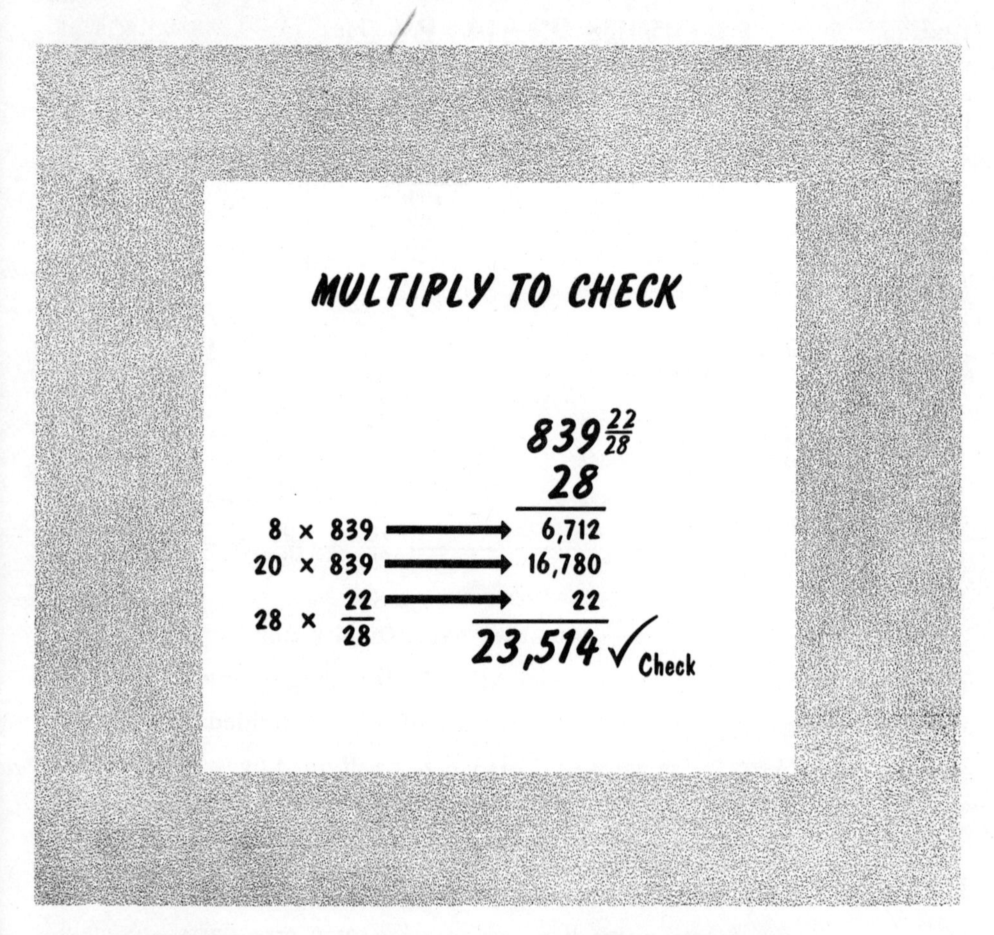

The total comes to 23,514, which was the number we started with, serving as a check on our working. If we had used long division, we might just possibly make the same mistake twice, once in division and once in multiplication, and not detect our error. But if we used successive division and check by long multiplication, we are much less likely to make two mistakes such that both could pass undetected by finishing up with the same number.

Division of Other Things

As well as dividing numbers, we may divide money, weight, or measures of various kinds. We may have some money, say $2,800, to be distributed equally among some people, say 175 of them, as a bonus. This calls for division.

Or we may have a load of 2 tons of material to be divided equally among 1,280 packages. This calls for conversion from tons to pounds. Then the fraction needs converting from pounds to ounces. The answer is 3 pounds 2 ounces. As a check, 3 pounds 2 ounces is multiplied by 1,280. As we arrive at 4,000 pounds again, our working is checked.

Another job may be to divide a mile stretch of land into lots all the same width, 88 of them. We convert the mile to yards (1,760) or feet (5,280) and divide by 88. The answer is 60 feet (or 20 yards). To check, we multiply this result by 88 and prove we have a total that is a mile's worth of yards or feet.

Division of Money

Divide $2,800 by 175

```
          $16.00
175 ) 2,800.00
      1,75
      -----
      1,050
      1,050
```

```
  175      175
    7        6
-----    -----
1,225    1,050
```

Division of Weight

Divide 2 tons by 1,280

2 tons is 4,000 pounds

```
              160
            3 -----   3 pounds
              1,280   2 ounces
1,280 ) 4,000
        3,840
        -----
          160

            2
1,280 ) 2,560
        2,560
```

```
1,280
    3
-----
3,840
```

$\frac{160}{1,280}$ pounds is $\frac{160}{1,280} \times 16$ ounces

or $\frac{2,560}{1,280}$ ounces

Division of Measures

Divide 1 mile by 88

1 mile is 1,760 yards or 5,280 feet

```
      60 feet
88 ) 5,280
     528
```

```
 88     88
  7      6
---    ---
616    528
```

1. Make the following divisions:

   (a) 343 ÷ 7 (b) 729 ÷ 9 (c) 4,928 ÷ 8 (d) 3,265 ÷ 5
   (e) 6,243 ÷ 3 (f) 7,862 ÷ 2 (g) 3,936 ÷ 4 (h) 3,924 ÷ 6

   Check your answers by multiplication.

2. Make the following divisions:

   (a) 3,081 ÷ 13 (b) 16,324 ÷ 11 (c) 6,443 ÷ 17
   (d) 8,341 ÷ 19 (e) 28,382 ÷ 23 (f) 125,309 ÷ 29

   Check your answers by multiplication.

3. Make the following divisions by successive (division by factors) and long division; if your answers do not agree, check them with long multiplication:

   (a) 3,690 ÷ 15 (b) 15,813 ÷ 21 (c) 73,625 ÷ 25
   (d) 10,136 ÷ 28 (e) 26,355 ÷ 35

4. Make the following divisions and write the remainder if any, as a fraction:

   (a) 3,459 ÷ 7 (b) 23,431 ÷ 8 (c) 13,263 ÷ 9 (d) 14,373 ÷ 3
   (e) 29,336 ÷ 6 (f) 8,239 ÷ 17 (g) 34,343 ÷ 28 (h) 92,929 ÷ 29

   Check your answers by another method or by multiplication.

5. A profit of $14,000,000 has to be shared among the holders of 2,800,000 shares of stock. What is the profit per share?

6. The total operating cost for an airline flight between two cities is estimated as $8,415. What fare should each passenger be charged so that a flight with 55 passengers just meets operating expenses?

7. A part needs a special tool that costs $5,000. With this tool, the parts can be made by machine for 25 cents each. But the estimated cost of parts must include the cost of the tool. If the tool cost is to be paid for out of the first 10,000 parts made, what will be their total cost each?

8. A freight car carries a load, including its own weight, of 58 tons (1 ton is 2,000 pounds). The car runs on 8 wheels, and its suspension is designed so the load is distributed equally among the wheels. How much weight does each wheel support?

9. A man makes 1,200 of a certain part in 8 hours. Based on this check, how much time should a time study allow for making each part?

10. A package of small parts weighs 1,565 pounds. The empty package weighs $2\frac{1}{2}$ pounds. If there are 10,000 parts in the package, how much does each weigh? (The easiest way to tackle this one is to convert the whole weight to ounces.)

11. A package of parts weighs 2,960 pounds full and 5 pounds empty. One

of the parts weighs 3 ounces. How many parts are there in the full package?

12. A narrow strip of land 1 mile long, is to be divided into lots. If 66 lots are to be equal in size, what is their width?

13. On a test run, a car goes 462 miles on 22 gallons of gas. Assuming that the consumption is uniform throughout the run, how far does the car go on each gallon?

14. A particular compound is usually made up in quantities of 160 gallons. It consists of 75 gallons of ingredient 1, 50 gallons of ingredient 2, 25 gallons of ingredient 3, and 10 gallons of ingredient 4. But a quantity of only 1 gallon is required. What amounts of each ingredient should be used?

15. An order is being made out for parts to make 27 items of a certain product. The total figure obtained for one part was 685. This figure is suspected to be wrong, but the original list giving the number of parts for a single item of the product is no longer available. How can you tell whether the figure 685 could be correct? If it is not, suggest what it should be, assuming an error in only one figure, and state how many per unit the figure was based on.

16. In question 7, how many parts would have to be made to bring the cost down to 35 cents each?

Different Fractions with the Same Value

Have you noticed that different fractions can mean the same quantity? It depends on what parts, or denominators, you use. For example 1 quarter can be divided into two-eighths, three-twelfths, four-sixteenths, etc. It's still a quarter. So each of these fractions means the same quantity, or has the same value.

Obviously, the simplest way to write a quarter is $\frac{1}{4}$. You would only write it as $\frac{2}{8}$, $\frac{3}{12}$, $\frac{4}{16}$, etc., for some special reason—to match another fraction's denominator, for example. You might at first think the simplest form of a fraction would be to use 1 for the numerator. But take $\frac{2}{5}$. You cannot reduce this to a form with 1 for the numerator, because, although 2 divides by 2, 5 doesn't, without involving a fraction. You could write it is $\frac{1}{2\frac{1}{2}}$; but that isn't as simple as $\frac{2}{5}$.

So the rule for the simplest form is that no number shall be exactly divisible into both the numerator and denominator. If it is, then you can divide it into both and make a simpler form. For example, $\frac{22}{28}$; both denominator and numerator will divide by 2 (because they are even numbers), so the fraction can be written $\frac{11}{14}$, which is the simplest form.

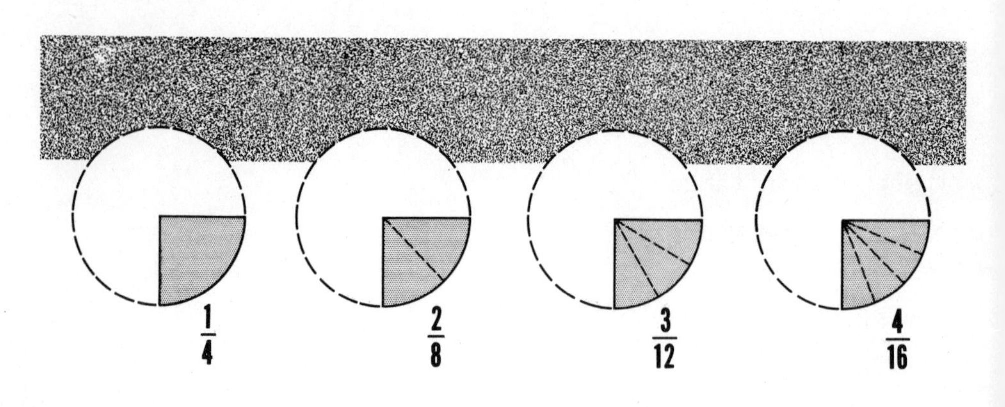

$$\frac{22 \div 2}{28 \div 2} = \frac{11}{14} \qquad \frac{18 \div 6}{42 \div 6} = \frac{3}{7} \qquad \frac{10 \div 5}{25 \div 5} = \frac{2}{5}$$

Fractions with the Same Value

Factors Help Find the Simplest Form — Cancellation

Always Find the Factors in a Fraction

$$\frac{160}{1,280} = \frac{16}{128} = \frac{8}{64} = \frac{1}{8}$$ Simplest Form

$$\frac{455}{462} = \frac{5 \times 91}{2 \times 231} = \frac{5 \times 7 \times 13}{2 \times 3 \times 7 \times 11}$$

by canceling 7's $$\frac{5 \times \not{7} \times 13}{2 \times 3 \times \not{7} \times 11} = \frac{5 \times 13}{2 \times 3 \times 11} = \frac{65}{66}$$

When you get to fractions with really big numbers for both numerator and denominator, it may not be immediately obvious whether you have the simplest form or not. A simple way to find out is to find factors for both numbers. Factors are the numbers that, multiplied together, give the original number. Take the fraction $\frac{160}{1,280}$.

First, we can see immediately that both numerator and denominator divide by 10, simplifying it to $\frac{16}{128}$. Then we could divide both 16 and 128 by 2, reducing it to $\frac{8}{64}$. We might then spot that 8 divides exactly into 64, reducing it to the simplest form, $\frac{1}{8}$.

For another example take $\frac{455}{462}$. At first glance this looks difficult. But try taking different numbers out of the numerator and denominator, as factors: The numerator obviously divides by 5, making $455 = 5 \times 91$; next 7 divides into 91 thirteen times. So $455 = 5 \times 7 \times 13$. The denominator divides by 2, making $462 = 2 \times 231$. Try 231 divided by 3: yes that goes, too, making $462 = 2 \times 3 \times 77$. Now divide 77 by 7, making $462 = 2 \times 3 \times 7 \times 11$. Write the whole fraction in factors and strike out any that appear in both—in this case 7. So the simplest form is

$$\frac{5 \times 13}{2 \times 3 \times 11} = \frac{65}{66}$$

Spotting the Factors

Of course you can try every number for a factor until you find one that goes, then start over with what's left, until you get the first number broken down into its factors. But there are some easy ways to spot certain factors, without going through all the motions of dividing out.

We already know that any even number divides by 2. We can take this principle a stage further: that way, if a number divides by 4 or 8, we won't have to divide by 2, two or three times; if a big number is divisible by 4, its last two figures will divide by 4; if its last three figures divide by 8, the whole number will.

The reason for this is easy: 100 divides by 4: 25 times. So any number of hundreds divides by 4 too. This means if the number less than 100—the last two figures—divides by 4, the whole number must.

For 3, a quick way to check is to add up the figures: for example, 138: $1 + 3 + 8$ makes 12, which does divide by 3; so the whole number 138 does too. For 9, there's a similar trick: take 135: $1 + 3 + 5 = 9$; so 135 divides by 9. Or 738: $7 + 3 + 8 = 18$, which divides by 9; so 738 does. We saw why in the multiplication table—the numbers in the nines column add up to 9.

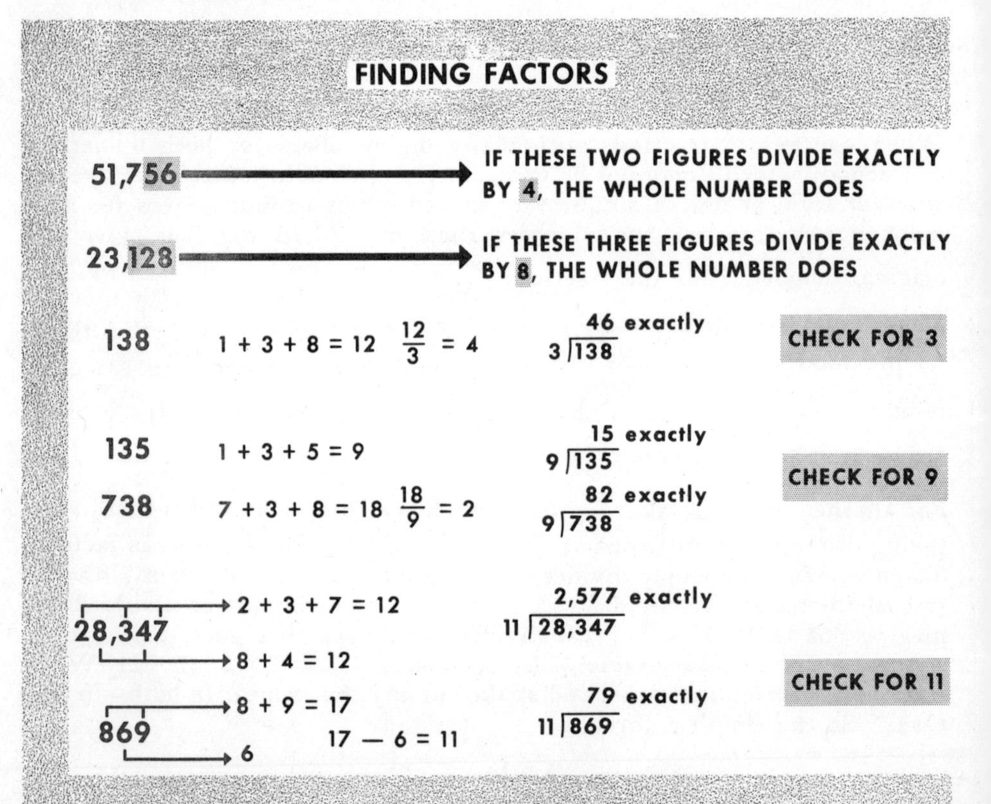

Spotting the Factors (contd.)

For 5, as we saw in the multiplication table too, the last figure is always 5 or 0. Incidentally, there's an extension of this too. If the last two figures are 00, 25, 50, or 75, the whole number divides by 25, which is 5×5.

Finally, there is a simple rule for finding if a big number will divide by 11: add up all the odd and even position figures; if the two sums are the same number, or two figures differ by 11, the original number will divide by 11: for example: 28,347 and 869. In 28,347: $2 + 3 + 7 = 12$; also $8 + 4 = 12$; so 28,347 divided by 11 = 2,577. In 869, $8 + 9 = 17$; which is 11 more than the only number in the other group, 6; so 869 divided by 11 = 79.

Rules for Finding Other Factors

That covers simple numbers—2, 3, 4, 5, 8, 9, 11, and 25. If 2 and 3 both "go," obviously the number divides by 6. There is no easy way to find if 7 is a factor. If 4 and 3 "go," 12 must, and so on.

But if we have already found 4 and 3, the fact that both "go" is not important. The important numbers are the ones we come to first, without their being made up of smaller factors. These are called *prime numbers.* They are 2, 3, 5, 7, 11, 13, 17, 19, 23, 29, and so on. Other numbers, less than 30, are not prime numbers, because they will factorize into smaller numbers.

So, after trying for the numbers with simple rules: 2, 3, 5, 11, (and including 4, 8, 9, and 25 if they are relatively obvious), the next thing is to try the various prime numbers—7, 13, 17, 19, etc.

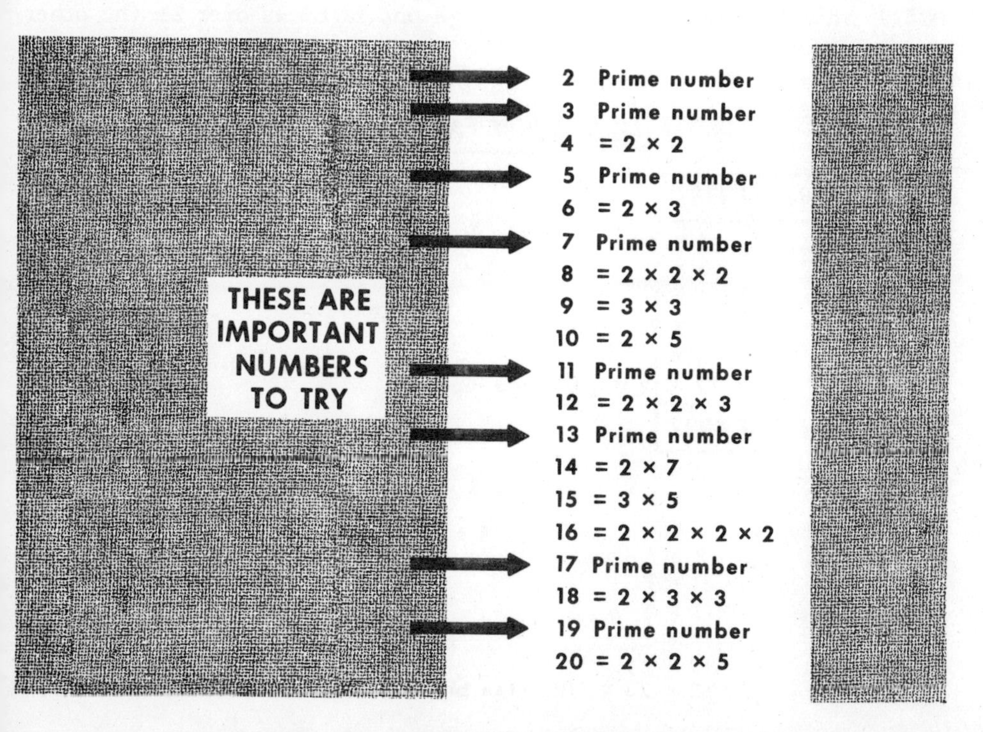

How Far to Try

Of course we could go on picking out the prime numbers all the way up to the number we are testing, but this is a waste of time: if there are factors to a number, there must be at least two—one number multiplied by one other; the multiplication table shows that any two numbers multiplied together give an answer (some textbooks call the answer to multiplication the "product") that is always less than the larger number mulitplied by itself.

This means that, when we get to a number that, multiplied by itself, gives a product (called a "square" for reasons we shall see a little further on in this book) bigger than our original number, and if we have not found a factor, there cannot be one. Put the other way, had there been any factors at all, we would have found them before we had come to a number whose square is bigger than our original number.

Suppose our original number is 139. Tests for 2, 3, and 5 show none of these is a factor. Trial division by 7 shows that it is not. The test for 11 shows it is not. Then, we multiply 12 by 12 and find that the square is 144, which is more than our original number. As we have not found any factors so far, we know that 139 is a prime number without trying any further.

Now suppose our original number is 493. Tests for 2, 3, 5, 7, 11, and 13 all fail to find a factor. But 17 does divide exactly, 29 times. If 17 had not been successful, we could have stopped at 23 because the square of 23 is 529, which is more than 493. Although one factor is over 23, the other one has to be less.

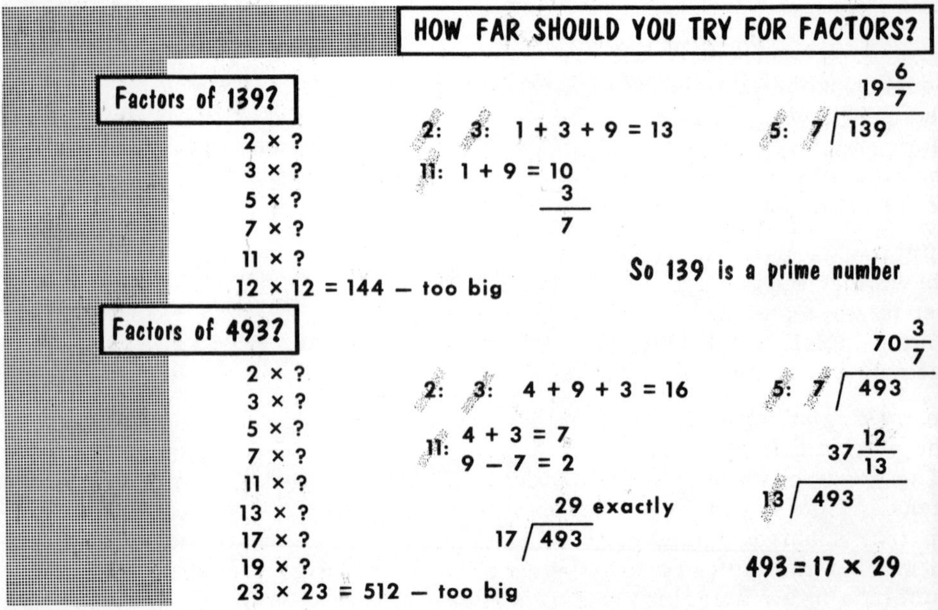

HOW FAR SHOULD YOU TRY FOR FACTORS?

Factors of 139?

2 × ?
3 × ?
5 × ?
7 × ?
11 × ?
12 × 12 = 144 — too big

2: 3: 1 + 3 + 9 = 13

11: 1 + 9 = 10

$\frac{3}{7}$

5: $7\overline{)139}$ = $19\frac{6}{7}$

So 139 is a prime number

Factors of 493?

2 × ?
3 × ?
5 × ?
7 × ?
11 × ?
13 × ?
17 × ?
19 × ?
23 × 23 = 512 — too big

2: 3: 4 + 9 + 3 = 16

5: $7\overline{)493}$ = $70\frac{3}{7}$

11: 4 + 3 = 7
9 − 7 = 2

$13\overline{)493}$ = $37\frac{12}{13}$

$17\overline{)493}$ = 29 exactly

493 = 17 × 29

Squares and Prime Numbers

TABLE OF SQUARES, 1—100

NO.	SQ.	NO.	SQ.	NO.	SQ.	NO.	SQ.	NO.	SQ.
1	1	21	441	41	1,681	61	3,721	81	6,561
2	4	22	484	42	1,764	62	3,844	82	6,724
3	9	23	529	43	1,849	63	3,969	83	6,889
4	16	24	576	44	1,936	64	4,096	84	7,056
5	25	25	625	45	2,025	65	4,225	85	7,225
6	36	26	676	46	2,116	66	4,356	86	7,396
7	49	27	729	47	2,209	67	4,489	87	7,569
8	64	28	784	48	2,304	68	4,624	88	7,744
9	81	29	841	49	2,401	69	4,761	89	7,921
10	100	30	900	50	2,500	70	4,900	90	8,100
11	121	31	961	51	2,601	71	5,041	91	8,281
12	144	32	1,024	52	2,704	72	5,184	92	8,464
13	169	33	1,089	53	2,809	73	5,329	93	8,649
14	196	34	1,156	54	2,916	74	5,476	94	8,836
15	225	35	1,225	55	3,025	75	5,625	95	9,025
16	256	36	1,296	56	3,136	76	5,776	96	9,216
17	289	37	1,369	57	3,249	77	5,929	97	9,409
18	324	38	1,444	58	3,364	78	6,084	98	9,604
19	361	39	1,521	59	3,481	79	6,241	99	9,801
20	400	40	1,600	60	3,600	80	6,400	100	10,000

PRIME NUMBERS, 1—100

2
3
5
7
11
13
17
19
23
29
31
37
41
43
47
53
59
61
67
71
73
79
83
89
97

Squares, which are the results of multiplying a number times itself, are useful in finding factors. Take, for instance, $10 \times 10 = 100$ and $9 \times 11 = 99$. Notice that 99 is less than 100, and 9 is less than 10. If a number is less than a certain square and it has factors, at least *one of these factors must be less than the number that was squared.* To illustrate:

Suppose we want the factors for the number 8,249. The table of squares shows that the square of 91 is 8,281. So we need to try the prime number list up to 89, which is the last one before 91. In doing so, we find that 73 is a factor, which gives the other as 113. If we had reached 89 with no factors found, the original number (8,249) would have been a prime.

In making a table like this, it is again useful to look for patterns in the numbers. Notice, for example, how the middle column (squares from 41 to 59) steps up by 1 in the hundreds column, while the last two columns (tens and ones) run from 9 squared down to 1, then 0, the 1 squared back up to 9 squared. These patterns serve as checks on your multiplication in making the table. From 90 to 99 there is a similar sequence, with the hundreds figure stepping up 2 at a time.

Adding Fractions

As we saw earlier (page 1-67), we can only add fractions by making them have the same denominators—in other words, making sure we are adding numbers of the same basic fraction. Then we just add the number (or numerator) of each represented.

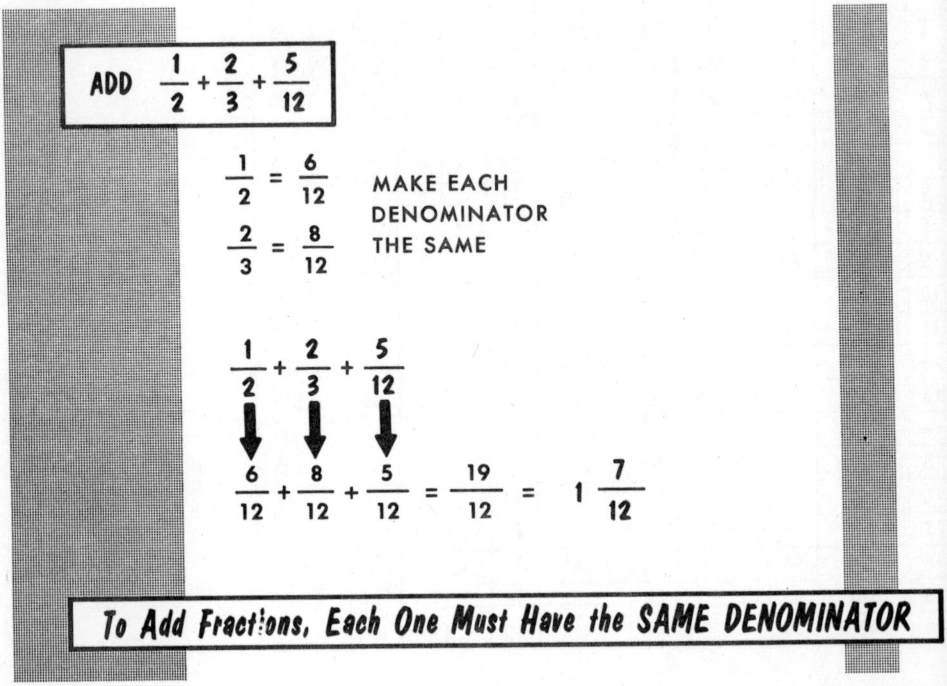

ADD $\frac{1}{2} + \frac{2}{3} + \frac{5}{12}$

$\frac{1}{2} = \frac{6}{12}$

$\frac{2}{3} = \frac{8}{12}$

MAKE EACH DENOMINATOR THE SAME

$$\frac{1}{2} + \frac{2}{3} + \frac{5}{12}$$

$$\frac{6}{12} + \frac{8}{12} + \frac{5}{12} = \frac{19}{12} = 1\frac{7}{12}$$

To Add Fractions, Each One Must Have the SAME DENOMINATOR

Suppose we have to add three fractions: $\frac{1}{2}$, $\frac{2}{3}$, and $\frac{5}{12}$: the smallest part used is $\frac{1}{12}$ and each of the others can be subdivided into twelfths. So we convert them all to this. $\frac{1}{2}$ subdivides into $\frac{6}{12}$; $\frac{1}{3}$ subdivides into $\frac{4}{12}$, so $\frac{2}{3}$ will be $\frac{8}{12}$. Now we can add $\frac{6}{12}$, $\frac{8}{12}$, and $\frac{5}{12}$, which gives $\frac{19}{12}$.

When the numerator is bigger than the denominator, it means the quantity is bigger than 1. Although it is written as a fraction, it is more than a "part," which is what *fraction* really means; some of the older books call a fraction having the numerateor bigger than the denominator an "improper fraction," for this reason. To convert it into a "proper fraction," the part bigger than 1 has to be expressed in complete numbers, leaving a part less than 1, which is then a "proper fraction."

$\frac{19}{12}$ can be divided into two parts: $\frac{12}{12}$ added to $\frac{7}{12}$; $\frac{12}{12}$ is twelve one-twelfth parts, or one whole number; so the quantity can now be written $1\frac{7}{12}$. This is sometimes called a "mixed number."

Adding Fractions When a Working Denominator Has To Be Found

In that example, we deliberately chose a case where one of the fractions used parts that each of the other would subdivide into. But this is not always so convenient. We may have to *find* a part that each of the fractions to be added will subdivide into. We will call this a "working denominator." Many books call it the "lowest common denominator."

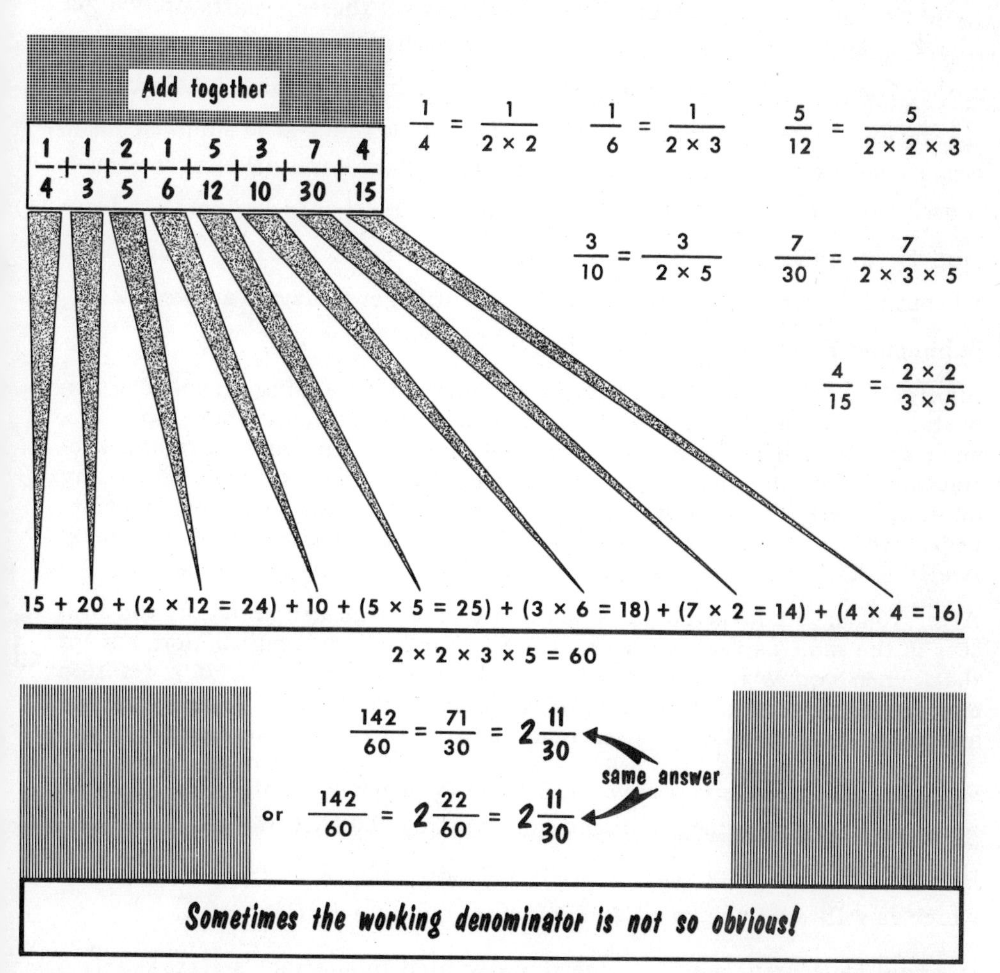

Suppose we have to add $\frac{1}{4} + \frac{1}{3} + \frac{2}{5} + \frac{1}{6} + \frac{5}{12} + \frac{3}{10} + \frac{7}{30} + \frac{4}{15}$. The way is to find the factors of each denominator: 4 is 2×2; 3 and 5 are prime numbers. 6 is 2×3; 12 is $2 \times 2 \times 3$; 10 is 2×5; 30 is $2 \times 3 \times 5$; 15 is 3×5. We have to make sure the working denominator contains enough factors to include all these combinations. Starting with the first and adding factors as we find them needed, our working denominator must be $2 \times 2 \times 3 \times 5$. This satisfies all of them, so we multiply it out and find that our working denominator is 60. Now we convert each fraction to this denominator.

Adding Fractions When a Working Denominator Has To Be Found (contd.)

Subdividing $\frac{1}{4}$ into $\frac{1}{60}$ gives 15 parts; $\frac{1}{3}$ gives 20 parts; $\frac{1}{5}$ gives 12 parts, so $\frac{2}{5}$ gives 24 parts; $\frac{1}{6}$ gives 10 parts; $\frac{1}{12}$ gives 5 parts, so $\frac{5}{12}$ gives 25 parts; $\frac{1}{10}$ gives 6 parts, so $\frac{3}{10}$ gives 18 parts; $\frac{1}{30}$ gives 2 parts, so $\frac{7}{30}$ gives 14 parts; $\frac{1}{15}$ gives 4 parts, so $\frac{4}{15}$ gives 16 parts. Adding all these $\frac{1}{60}$ parts up, we get $15 + 20 + 24 + 10 + 25 + 18 + 14 + 16 = 142$ parts. This represents the improper fraction $\frac{142}{60}$, which can be made proper by extracting 2 "wholes" of $\frac{60}{60}$, making it $2\frac{22}{60}$. Now the fraction part can be reduced to simplest form, because both numerator and denominator have 2 as a factor. The answer now is $2\frac{11}{30}$. We could have reduced the improper fraction to its simplest form first, by dividing numerator and denominator by 2, giving $\frac{71}{30}$, and then subtracted $\frac{30}{30}$ twice to make it proper. We still get the same answer—$2\frac{11}{30}$.

Subtracting Fractions

Subtracting fractions follows the same method as adding them. The important thing is that the numbers in the numerator, or above the line, must use the same denominator, or number below the line. Then the subtraction of the numbers in the numerator is just like subtraction of any other numbers. All that we are saying is that, just as you can't subtract pears from apples, you cannot subtract so many fifths from so many twelfths. The fractions must be "so many" of the same denominator.

After you have converted the fractions to the same denominator, the process is the same as that we learned before for ordinary subtraction, except that, when you write the answer, you keep it in the form of a fraction and write it over the denominator, *unless* the numerator of the one you are subtracting from is smaller than the one to be subtracted.

For example, suppose you have to subtract $\frac{2}{5}$ from $\frac{5}{12}$: first convert these to a common (the same) denominator, which is 60 in this case. The fractions are now $\frac{24}{60}$ and $\frac{25}{60}$, respectively. Subtracting 24 from 25 leaves 1, which is still over the same denominator, giving a fraction of $\frac{1}{60}$.

It would have been just the same if we wanted to subtract $3\frac{2}{5}$ from $7\frac{5}{12}$. Subtracting the fraction part gives us $\frac{1}{60}$ as just now; subtracting the whole number part, 3 from 7, leaves 4. So the answer is $4\frac{1}{60}$.

It is not always this easy, however. Often when you have mixed numbers to subtract, you find that, after you have converted the denominators to the same number, you have a number which must be subtracted from a smaller number. This is where *borrowing* comes in again. So the next problem we must solve is this: how do you take $4\frac{1}{2}$ from $6\frac{1}{4}$?

Subtracting Fractions (contd.)

Suppose that our problem in this case is to subtract $3\frac{3}{5}$ from $7\frac{5}{12}$. When we convert the fractions to the same denominator, $\frac{3}{5}$ is $\frac{36}{60}$ and $\frac{5}{12}$ is $\frac{25}{60}$. Obviously you cannot take 36 from 25, because it is bigger. So we have to borrow one from the whole number (7), just as we might borrow from tens if the ones figures had the same trouble.

When we borrow 1 from the ones figure, we divide it into the number of pieces stated by the denominator—in this case 60. So we now have to subtract $3\frac{36}{60}$ from $6\frac{60+25}{60}$ or $6\frac{85}{60}$. Now it's as easy as it was before: 36 from 85 leaves 49; 3 from 6 leaves 3. So $3\frac{36}{60}$ from $6\frac{85}{60}$ leaves $3\frac{49}{60}$ which is the same as $3\frac{3}{5}$ from $7\frac{5}{12}$.

Subtract $\frac{2}{5}$ from $\frac{5}{12}$

① Common denominator = 60

② $\frac{2}{5} = \frac{2 \times 12}{5 \times 12} = \frac{24}{60}$ and $\frac{5}{12} = \frac{5 \times 5}{12 \times 5} = \frac{25}{60}$

③ $\frac{25}{60} - \frac{24}{60} = \frac{1}{60}$ or $\frac{5}{12} - \frac{2}{5} = \frac{1}{60}$

Subtract $3\frac{2}{5}$ from $7\frac{5}{12}$

① Common denominator = 60

② $\frac{5}{12} = \frac{5 \times 5}{12 \times 5} = \frac{25}{60}$ $\quad \frac{2}{5} = \frac{2 \times 12}{5 \times 12} = \frac{24}{60}$ $\quad \frac{25}{60} - \frac{24}{60} = \frac{1}{60}$

③ $7 - 3 = 4$

④ $7\frac{5}{12} - 3\frac{2}{5} = 4\frac{1}{60}$

Subtract $3\frac{3}{5}$ from $7\frac{5}{12}$

① Common denominator = 60

② $\frac{3}{5} = \frac{3 \times 12}{5 \times 12} = \frac{36}{60}$ and $\frac{5}{12} = \frac{5 \times 5}{12 \times 5} = \frac{25}{60}$

③ Because $\frac{36}{60}$ is bigger than $\frac{25}{60}$, change $7\frac{25}{60}$ to $6 + 1\frac{25}{60} = 6\frac{60+25}{60} = 6\frac{85}{60}$

④ $6\frac{85}{60} - 3\frac{36}{60} = 3\frac{49}{60}$ or $7\frac{5}{12} - 3\frac{3}{5} = 3\frac{49}{60}$

Multiplying Fractions

MULTIPLYING a FRACTION by a WHOLE NUMBER

MULTIPLY $\frac{1}{30} \times 5$

Method i $\frac{1}{30} \times 5 = \frac{5}{30} = \frac{\not{5}}{2 \times 3 \times \not{5}} = \frac{1}{2 \times 3} = \frac{1}{6}$

Method ii $\frac{1}{30} \times 5 = \frac{1}{30 \div 5} = \frac{1}{6}$ same answer

MULTIPLY $\frac{1}{30} \times 6$

Method i $\frac{1}{30} \times 6 = \frac{6}{30} = \frac{\not{2} \times \not{3}}{\not{2} \times \not{3} \times 5} = \frac{1}{5}$

Method ii $\frac{1}{30} \times 6 = \frac{1}{30 \div 6} = \frac{1}{5}$ same answer

MULTIPLY $\frac{1}{10} \times 4$

$\frac{1}{10} \times 4 = \frac{4}{10} = \frac{\not{2} \times 2}{\not{2} \times 5} = \frac{2}{5}$

As we found earlier, to multiply a fraction, you only multiply the numerator, leaving the denominator the same. But this often enables a simplification to be made. Suppose we multiply $\frac{1}{30}$ by 5: this is $\frac{5}{30}$; which simplifies to $\frac{1}{6}$. This is because five fractions of $\frac{1}{30}$ make up a fraction of $\frac{1}{6}$. Had we multiplied $\frac{1}{30}$ by 6, the result is $\frac{6}{30}$, which simplifies to $\frac{1}{5}$.

Where it is convenient, multiplying fractions can be performed by *dividing* the denominator by the number the fraction has to multiplied by.

When you cannot divide entirely, the fraction may be still be simplified. Suppose a fraction of $\frac{1}{10}$ has to be multiplied by 4: 4 does not divide into 10; so multiplying the numerator by 4, we have $\frac{4}{10}$; which simplifies to $\frac{2}{5}$.

Multiplying Fractions by Fractions

We've learned how to multiply and divide fractions by whole numbers, but sometimes a problem involves multiplying a fraction by a fraction. You may have noticed that multiplying by a fraction is the same as dividing by a number. Suppose you have to divide \$10 into four parts. You could call this dividing \$10 by 4, or multiplying \$10 by $\frac{1}{4}$. It means the same thing.

So if you have to multiply \$10 by $2\frac{1}{4}$, the 2 part you can do by multiplying and the $\frac{1}{4}$ part by dividing. It's really no more difficult if you have fractions in both parts of what you multiply.

For example, suppose you need $2\frac{1}{4}$ times $1\frac{5}{8}$ inches: just like long multiplication, you have to make sure each part of one number is multiplied by each part of the other: 2 times 1 are 2; 2 times $\frac{5}{8}$ are $\frac{10}{8}$, which simplifies to $\frac{5}{4}$ or $1\frac{1}{4}$; $\frac{1}{4}$ times 1 is $\frac{1}{4}$; and $\frac{1}{4}$ times $\frac{5}{8}$ (which is taking 1 fourth part, or dividing by 4) is $\frac{5}{32}$. Adding up, we convert all the fractions to denominator 32: $2 + 1\frac{8}{32} + \frac{8}{32} + \frac{5}{32} = 3\frac{21}{32}$.

That's the long way. The more usual way, and often an easier one less liable to mistakes, is to convert each quantity to an improper fraction, then multiply numerators and denominators, and finally return to the "proper" form: $2\frac{1}{4}$ is $\frac{9}{4}$; $1\frac{5}{8}$ is $\frac{13}{8}$; multiplying $\frac{9}{4} \times \frac{13}{8} = \frac{117}{32} = 3\frac{21}{32}$. Same answer. So it's convenient to use both methods as a check.

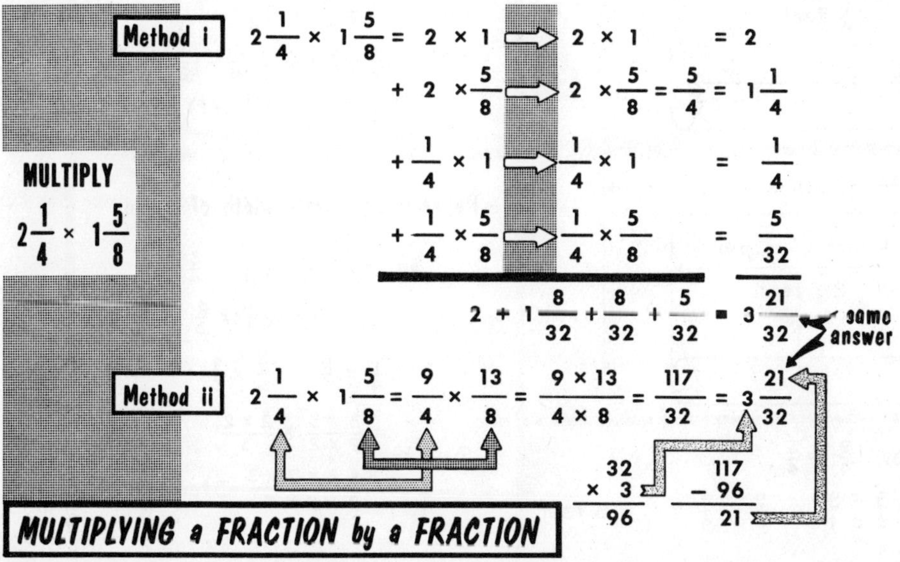

MULTIPLY $2\frac{1}{4} \times 1\frac{5}{8}$

Method i

$$2\frac{1}{4} \times 1\frac{5}{8} = 2 \times 1 \rightarrow 2 \times 1 = 2$$
$$+\ 2 \times \frac{5}{8} \rightarrow 2 \times \frac{5}{8} = \frac{5}{4} = 1\frac{1}{4}$$
$$+\ \frac{1}{4} \times 1 \rightarrow \frac{1}{4} \times 1 = \frac{1}{4}$$
$$+\ \frac{1}{4} \times \frac{5}{8} \rightarrow \frac{1}{4} \times \frac{5}{8} = \frac{5}{32}$$
$$2 + 1\frac{8}{32} + \frac{8}{32} + \frac{5}{32} = 3\frac{21}{32}$$

same answer

Method ii

$$2\frac{1}{4} \times 1\frac{5}{8} = \frac{9}{4} \times \frac{13}{8} = \frac{9 \times 13}{4 \times 8} = \frac{117}{32} = 3\frac{21}{32}$$

$$32 \times 3 = 96 \qquad 117 - 96 = 21$$

MULTIPLYING a FRACTION by a FRACTION

Dividing Fractions

On the previous page, we saw that multiplying by $\frac{1}{4}$ and dividing by 4 are really two ways of saying the same thing. Although it may be less obvious, we can reverse this: multiplying by 4 is the same as dividing by $\frac{1}{4}$. An example may help clarify this.

Suppose that a piece of wallpaper $2\frac{1}{4}$ feet wide needs $\frac{3}{4}$ of its width to fill a certain space: then the required width is $\frac{3}{4} \times 2\frac{1}{4}$ feet $= 1\frac{11}{16}$ feet, which we find by using the method given on the previous page.

But now suppose the piece of wallpaper only fills $\frac{3}{4}$ of the space. (To understand this, let us take a simpler case first: if it took 3 pieces of paper to fill a given space, which is another way of saying that each piece of paper fills $\frac{1}{3}$ of the space, we simply multiply the width of the paper by 3, which is the same as dividing by $\frac{1}{3}$.) For the case in which the wallpaper fills $\frac{3}{4}$ of the space, we need to divide by $\frac{3}{4}$ to find our answer. This is the same as multiplying by $\frac{4}{3}$.

In short, then, dividing by a fraction is the same as multiplying by the same fraction turned upside down—changing it to what is called its *reciprocal.*

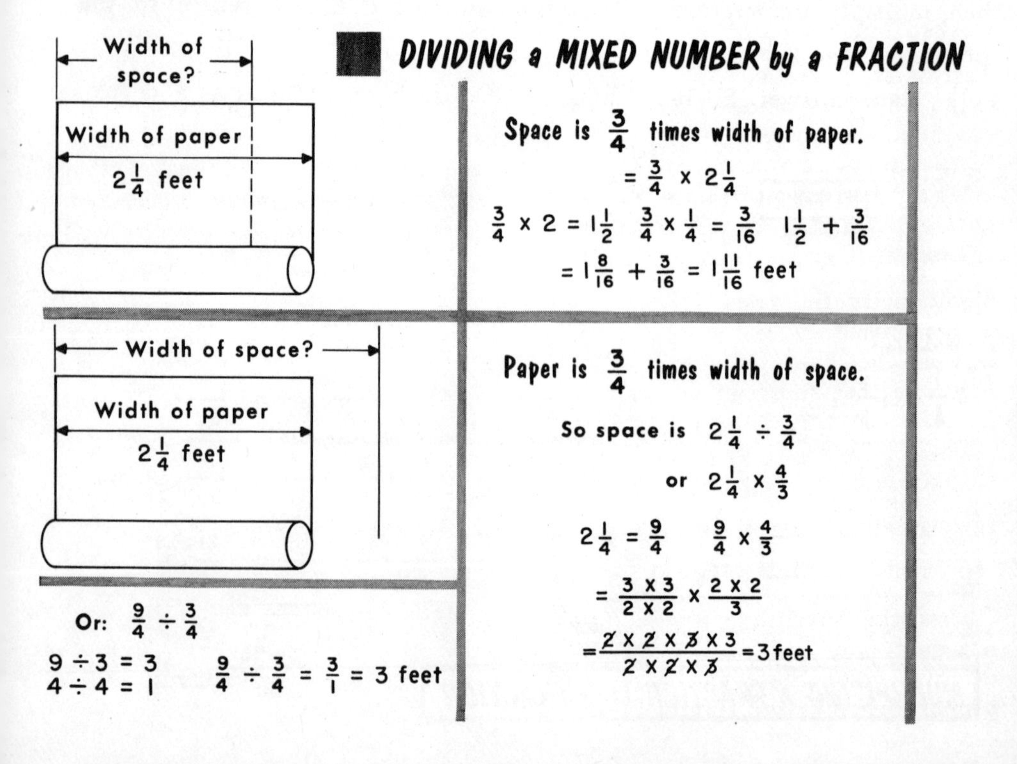

Decimals

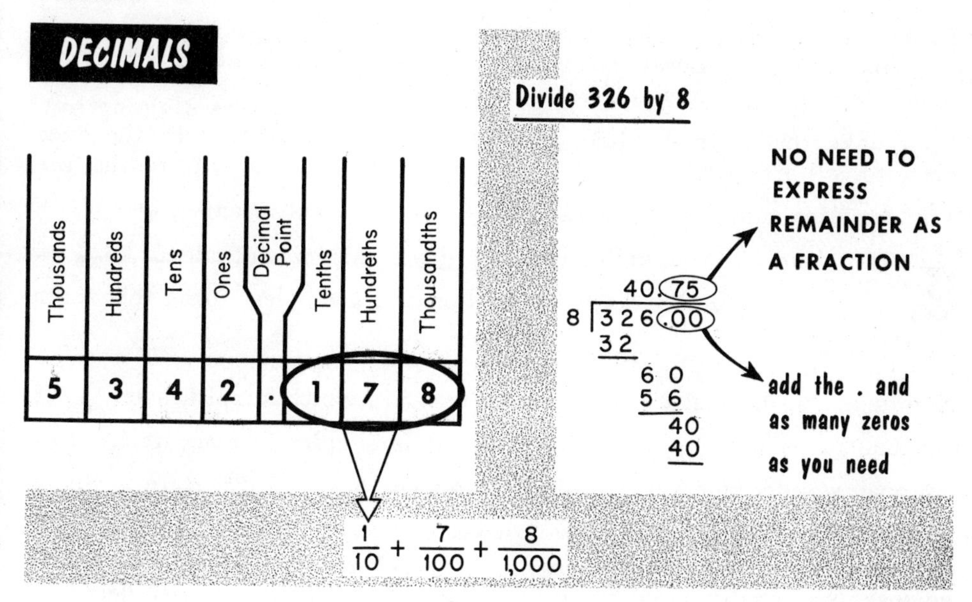

Fractions are one way of handling parts in counting; but—as you may already see—they can become cumbersome to handle. You always need two lines of figures to write a fraction. This is why another way was worked out, called *decimals*.

Just as in fractions where we make parts by writing the number identifying the part below a horizontal line, we use the decimal method to extend counting to quantities smaller than one complete unit, by adding more figures to the *right* of the ones figure. Figures to the left of the ones figure represent tens, hundreds, thousands, etc. So, in the decimal system, figures to the right of the ones figure represent tenths, hundredths, thousandths, etc.

To identify the ones figure, a decimal point (in America a period, in Europe a dot above the base line ·) is placed to its right, to separate the last number (as you move right) representing whole numbers from the first one that represents a part.

The decimal system has the advantage that, instead of having many different part units: $\frac{1}{2}$, $\frac{1}{3}$, $\frac{1}{4}$, $\frac{1}{5}$, $\frac{1}{6}$, $\frac{1}{7}$, $\frac{1}{8}$, $\frac{1}{9}$, $\frac{1}{10}$, etc., it uses relatively few "standard" parts, with corresponding places: the first figure, or "point," epresents $\frac{1}{10}$, the next $\frac{1}{100}$, the next $\frac{1}{1,000}$, etc.

. has the advantage, in doing division—simple or long—that you do not just stop bringing down numbers at the ones figure, but place a decimal point there and carry on. There is no puzzling out what the proper denominator should be.

Correspondency between Decimals and Fractions

Because on different occasions we may use either fractions or decimals as a means of writing down parts, we shall need to know how they correspond, and how to convert from one to another.

First, take the decimal 0.125: (the zero is usually written in the ones place to call attention to the decimal point). The 1 represents tenths, the 2, hundredths, and the 5, thousandths. So the decimal means $\frac{1}{10} + \frac{2}{100} + \frac{5}{1,000}$. This can be brought to the same denominateor and added: $\frac{100}{1,000} + \frac{20}{1,000} + \frac{5}{1,000} = \frac{125}{1,000}$. By normal reduction to its simplest form, this turns out to be $\frac{1}{8}$.

Now take the decimal 0.8: this represents $\frac{8}{10}$, which simplifies to $\frac{4}{5}$. If you had to write $6\frac{4}{5}$, you can see that it is simpler to make it 6.8. But you may wonder whether it is simpler to write $5\frac{1}{8}$ as 5.125. Here is where it is definitely easier: suppose you have to add $6\frac{4}{5}$ and $5\frac{1}{8}$; by fractions you have to find a working denominator, and maybe take out the whole numbers, and finally simplify, in some cases, as we have seen. By decimals you set one figure under the other, lining up the decimal points and add, place by place, starting from the right: the total is quickly found to be 11.925. Had there been any whole numbers, these would have been "carried" as a matter of course, just the same as cents are carried to make dollars.

CONVERTING

$$0.125 = \frac{1}{10} + \frac{2}{100} + \frac{5}{1,000} = \frac{100+20+5=125}{1,000}$$

$$= \frac{\not5 \times \not5 \times \not5}{2 \times 2 \times 2 \times \not5 \times \not5 \times \not5} = \frac{1}{2 \times 2 \times 2} = \frac{1}{8}$$

$$0.8 = \frac{8}{10} = \frac{4}{5}$$

KNOWING HOW TO CONVERT FROM ONE TO THE OTHER MAKES SOME PROBLEMS EASIER

$6\frac{4}{5} = 6.8$

$5\frac{1}{8} = 5.125$

ADD $6\frac{4}{5} + 5\frac{1}{8}$ OR $6.8 + 5.125$

$$6\frac{32}{40} + 5\frac{5}{40} = 11\frac{37}{40}$$

$$\begin{array}{r} 6.8 \\ 5.125 \\ \hline 11.925 \end{array}$$

$$11.925 = 11 + \frac{9}{10} + \frac{2}{100} + \frac{5}{1,000}$$

$$= 11 + \frac{180}{200} + \frac{4}{200} + \frac{1}{200}$$

$$= 11\frac{185}{200}$$

$$= 11\frac{37}{40}$$

same answer

DECIMALS as FRACTIONS

Decimal Equivalents of Fractions — Reciprocals

On the opposite page, we found fraction equivalents for decimals. We also need to find the decimals equivalent to various fractions. As single fractions also happen to be the reciprocals of whole numbers (e.g., $\frac{1}{3}$ is the reciprocal of 3), the same process will find reciprocals.

CONVERTING FRACTIONS to DECIMALS

$\frac{1}{2}$: $\quad 2\overline{)1.0}$ = 0.5 $\quad$ so $\frac{1}{2} = 0.5$

$\frac{1}{4}$: $\quad 4\overline{)1.00}$ = 0.25 $\quad$ so $\frac{1}{4} = 0.25$

$\frac{1}{5}$: $\quad 5\overline{)1.0}$ = 0.2 $\quad$ so $\frac{1}{5} = 0.2$

$\frac{1}{8}$: $\quad 8\overline{)1.000}$ = 0.125 $\quad$ so $\frac{1}{8} = 0.125$

$\frac{1}{10}$: $\quad 10\overline{)1.0}$ = 0.1 $\quad$ so $\frac{1}{10} = 0.1$

The fractions $\frac{1}{2}$ or $\frac{1}{5}$ really mean 1 (a whole unit) divided by 2 or 5. So we merely do this the decimal way to find out the decimal equivalent, bringing down more "places" as we need them. We find that $\frac{1}{2}$ is 0.5; $\frac{1}{4}$ is 0.25; $\frac{1}{5}$ is 0.2; $\frac{1}{8}$ is 0.125; $\frac{1}{10}$ is 0.1, etc.

We can make a table of reciprocals. But we've only taken certain numbers; we missed $\frac{1}{3}$, $\frac{1}{6}$, $\frac{1}{7}$, and $\frac{1}{9}$. Why? Because the decimal equivalents of these numbers are not quite so simple as the ones we did.

Recurring Decimals

Now let us take the first one we missed — $\frac{1}{3}$. As we start dividing, we find that there is always 1 left over, so we bring down another zero (to allow us to use the next place), and divide again: the answer is 3 and again there is a remainder of 1.

If we attempted to write the decimal equivalent of $\frac{1}{3}$, it would be 0.33333333 . . ., and we would never stop writing 3's. To simplify this, when we get to a figure that keeps repeating itself indefinitely, we put a dot over the top of it, which indicates that it recurs indefinitely. Thus the decimal for $\frac{1}{3}$ is $0.\dot{3}$. This is read as "point three recurring."

Now we can fill in some of the gaps: $\frac{1}{3}$ is $0.\dot{3}$; $\frac{1}{6}$ is $0.1\dot{6}$; $\frac{1}{9}$ is $0.\dot{1}$. We can find some others in the same group, either directly or from those we have. For example, $\frac{1}{12}$ is half of $\frac{1}{6}$, so we can find it either by doing a long division by 12, or by dividing the equivalent for $\frac{1}{6}$ by 2, giving $0.08\dot{3}$. We can find $\frac{2}{9}$, $\frac{4}{9}$, $\frac{5}{9}$, etc., by multiplying by 2, 4, 5, etc., giving $0.\dot{2}$, $0.\dot{4}$, $0.\dot{5}$, etc.

If we want $\frac{5}{6}$, there are two ways, as well as dividing 6 into 5 to find it directly: 5 times $0.1\dot{6}$ comes to $0.8\dot{3}$; or $\frac{5}{6}$ is equal to $\frac{1}{2} + \frac{1}{3}$: so we add their equivalents: $0.5 + 0.\dot{3} = 0.8\dot{3}$. Note that in multiplying $0.1\dot{6}66$ by 5, the right-hand digit in the answer is 3, and not 0. The reason for this is that the 6's in $0.1\dot{6}66$ go on indefinitely, and when we multiply 5 times 6, we must add the 3 that is being carried from the previous 5 times 6 multiplication on the right.

$\frac{1}{3}$: $3\,\overline{)\,1.0000000}$ = 0.3333333... $\quad \frac{1}{3} = 0.\dot{3}$ point three recurring

$\frac{1}{6}$: $6\,\overline{)\,1.0000}$ = 0.1666... $\quad \frac{1}{6} = 0.1\dot{6}$

$\frac{1}{9}$: $9\,\overline{)\,1.00}$ = 0.111... $\quad \frac{1}{9} = 0.\dot{1}$

$\frac{1}{12}$: $2\,\overline{)\,0.1\dot{6}666666}$ = $0.08\dot{3}333...$ $\quad \frac{1}{12} = 0.08\dot{3}$

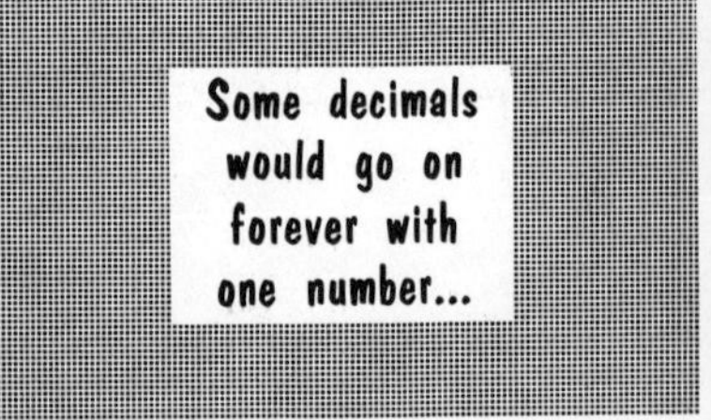

$\frac{5}{6}$: **1st Method**

$6\,\overline{)\,5.0000}$ = $0.8\dot{3}33$

$\frac{5}{6} = 0.8\dot{3}$

2nd Method

$5 \times \frac{1}{6}$

$0.1\dot{6}6666.....$
$\times\ 5$
3 carried
$0.8\dot{3}333....$

3rd Method $\frac{5}{6} = \frac{2}{6} + \frac{3}{6} = \frac{1}{3} + \frac{1}{2}$

$\frac{1}{3} = 0.\dot{3}33$

$\frac{1}{2} = 0.5$

$\frac{5}{6} = 0.8\dot{3}33$

Decimal Equivalent for One-Seventh

This—and some others—are more difficult than those we have just discussed, because more than one figure repeats. In finding the decimal equivalent of $\frac{1}{7}$, we find it to be 0.142857, and then it starts over and repeats the same six figures, indefinitely. To indicate this, we put a dot over the first figure that repeats and the last one before its does. So we write the decimal equivalent for $\frac{1}{7}$ as $0.\dot{1}4285\dot{7}$.

Now we find an interesting thing about this group: we can find the equivalents for $\frac{2}{7}$, $\frac{3}{7}$, and so on up to $\frac{6}{7}$; they are: $0.\dot{2}8571\dot{4}$, $0.\dot{4}2857\dot{1}$, $0.\dot{5}7142\dot{8}$, $0.\dot{7}1428\dot{5}$, and $0.\dot{8}5714\dot{2}$. Each is the same group of numbers, starting in a different place.

But when we multiply by 7, to get $\frac{7}{7}$, we get $0.\dot{9}9999\dot{9}$, which is really $0.\dot{9}$. Now we could notice also that multiplying $0.\dot{3}$ by 3 gives $0.\dot{9}$; also that multiplying $0.1\dot{6}$ by 6 gives $0.\dot{9}$, etc. Whenever we multiply a recurring decimal by a number that brings its corresponding *fraction* to unity (1), the *decimal* equivalent is $0.\dot{9}$. This is simply because $0.\dot{9}$ is really the same as 1.

However many times you write recurring decimals you could still go on and write them again, in theory, before you had a completely accurate equivalent. When you get to $0.\dot{9}$, if you can imagine adding $0.\dot{0}$ to mean an indefinite line of zeros, with 1 at the end (but there is never an end), you can see why $0.\dot{9}$ is really the same as 1. The amount by which $0.\dot{9}$ differs from 1 is that $0.\dot{0}$. And however many times you write zero, it's still zero, unless you have a number that means something at the beginning or end. In other words: $0.\dot{0} = 0$. But $0.\dot{9} + 0.\dot{0} = 1$; therefore $0.\dot{9} = 1$.

... and some keep going with groups of numbers

$\frac{1}{7}$: $7 \overline{)1.000000000000}$ = 0.142857142857 $\qquad \frac{1}{7} = 0.\dot{1}4285\dot{7}$

$\frac{2}{7}$: $7 \overline{)2.000000000000}$ = 0.285714285714 $\qquad \frac{2}{7} = 0.\dot{2}8571\dot{4}$

$$\text{or } 2 \times \frac{1}{7} = 2 \times 0.\dot{1}4285\dot{7} = 0.\dot{2}8571\dot{4}$$

$$\frac{7}{7} = 7 \times 0.\dot{1}4285\dot{7} = 0.\dot{9}9999\dot{9} = 0.\dot{9}$$

$$0.\dot{9} + 0.\dot{0} = 1 \quad \text{and} \quad 0.\dot{0} = 0$$

$$\text{so} \quad 0.\dot{9} = 1$$

Decimal Equivalents for Elevenths and Other Prime Numbers

Decimals recur in Pairs for Elevenths

$\frac{1}{11}$: $\quad 11\overline{)1.0000}$ = 0.0909 $\quad \frac{1}{11} = 0.\dot{0}\dot{9}$

$\frac{2}{11}$: $\quad 11\overline{)2.0000}$ = 0.1818 $\quad \frac{2}{11} = 0.\dot{1}\dot{8}$

OR $2 \times \frac{1}{11} = 2 \times 0.\dot{0}\dot{9} = 0.\dot{1}\dot{8}$

$\frac{3}{11} = 0.\dot{2}\dot{7} \quad \frac{4}{11} = 0.\dot{3}\dot{6} \quad \frac{5}{11} = 0.\dot{4}\dot{5} \quad \frac{6}{11} = 0.\dot{5}\dot{4}$

$\frac{7}{11} = 0.\dot{6}\dot{3} \quad \frac{8}{11} = 0.\dot{7}\dot{2} \quad \frac{9}{11} = 0.\dot{8}\dot{1} \quad \frac{10}{11} = 0.\dot{9}\dot{0}$

$\frac{11}{11} = 0.\dot{9}\dot{9} = 0.\dot{9} = 1$

$\frac{1}{13} = 0.\dot{0}7692\dot{3}$ — These numbers used for $\frac{1}{13}, \frac{3}{13}, \frac{4}{13}, \frac{9}{13}, \frac{10}{13}, \frac{12}{13}$

$\frac{2}{13} = 0.\dot{1}5384\dot{6}$ — These numbers used for $\frac{2}{13}, \frac{5}{13}, \frac{6}{13}, \frac{7}{13}, \frac{8}{13}, \frac{11}{13}$

$\frac{3}{13} = 0.\dot{2}3076\dot{9}$ (six numbers for thirteenths)

$\frac{1}{17} = 0.\dot{0}58823529411764\dot{7}$ (sixteen numbers for seventeenths)

and

$\frac{1}{19} = 0.\dot{0}5263157894736842\dot{1}$ (eighteen numbers for nineteenths)

One more group of recurring decimals almost completes the "numbers" picture—at least it covers the ones you're most likely to meet. When we find the decimal equivalents for $\frac{1}{11}$, $\frac{2}{11}$, $\frac{3}{11}$ etc., we get a decimal in which two figures recur alternately: the family are: $0.\dot{0}\dot{9}$, $0.\dot{1}\dot{8}$, $0.\dot{2}\dot{7}$, $0.\dot{3}\dot{6}$, $0.\dot{4}\dot{5}$, $0.\dot{5}\dot{4}$, $0.\dot{6}\dot{3}$, $0.\dot{7}\dot{2}$, $0.\dot{8}\dot{1}$, $0.\dot{9}\dot{0}$. Again, if we multiply any of them to get different numerators, they will check, and if we multiply $0.\dot{0}\dot{9}$ by 11, the result is $0.\dot{9}$, which is 1.

We could go on finding recurring decimals for $\frac{1}{13}$, $\frac{1}{17}$, $\frac{1}{19}$, and reciprocals of other prime numbers. It's an interesting game in numbers. Some of them produce smaller groups of numbers that repeat in different combinations, like the "11" family; some of them produce a very long group of numbers, like the "7" family. In the "7" family, there are six repeating numbers. In this kind, for higher prime numbers, there will be one less than the number, and multiplying by that prime will produce $0.\dot{9}$. These are numerical oddities that can be an interesting parlor game for mathematicians, but seldom find any *practical* use.

Converting Recurring Decimals to Fractions

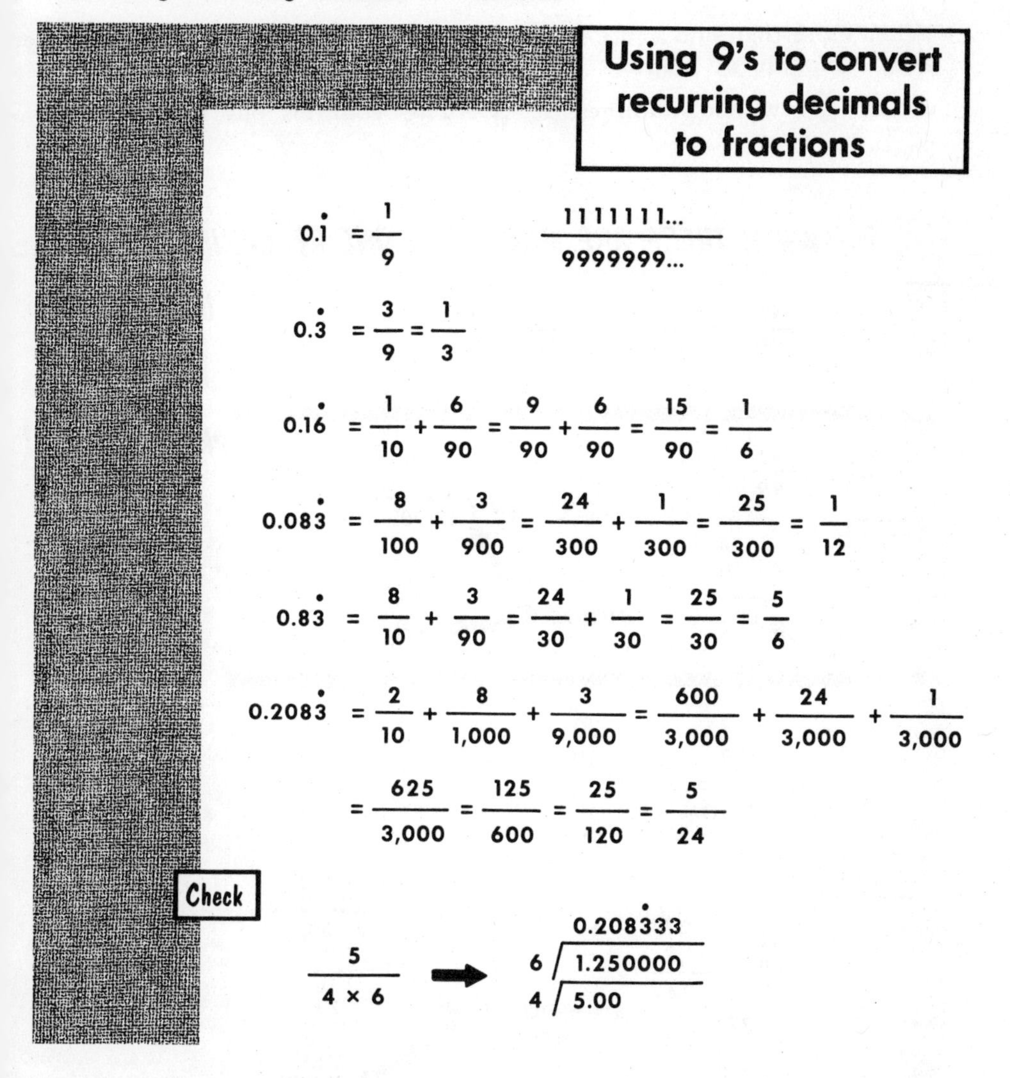

Although recurring decimals are not too difficult when you know what they mean, it is often easier to use fractions instead.

Parts that do not recur we put over their respective places, as before. A single recurring decimal is equivalent to that same number in the numerator with 9 in the denominator. If it's in the second decimal place, instead of the first, the denominator is 90, instead of 9, and so on.

For example, $0.\dot{3}$ is $\frac{3}{9}$, which simplifies to $\frac{1}{3}$; $0.1\dot{6}$ is $\frac{1}{10} + \frac{6}{90} = \frac{9}{90} + \frac{6}{90} = \frac{15}{90}$, which simplifies to $\frac{1}{6}$; similarly $0.08\dot{3}$ is $\frac{8}{100} + \frac{3}{900} = \frac{24}{300} + \frac{1}{300} = \frac{25}{300}$, which simplifies to $\frac{1}{12}$.

Converting Recurring Decimals to Fractions (contd.)

When more than one figure recurs in sequence, each one is effectively over a denominator of 9 *in its place.* Picking one from the 11 family: $0.\dot{4}\dot{5}$ means $\frac{45}{99}$, which simplifies to $\frac{5}{11}$. This confirms our figuring of two pages back.

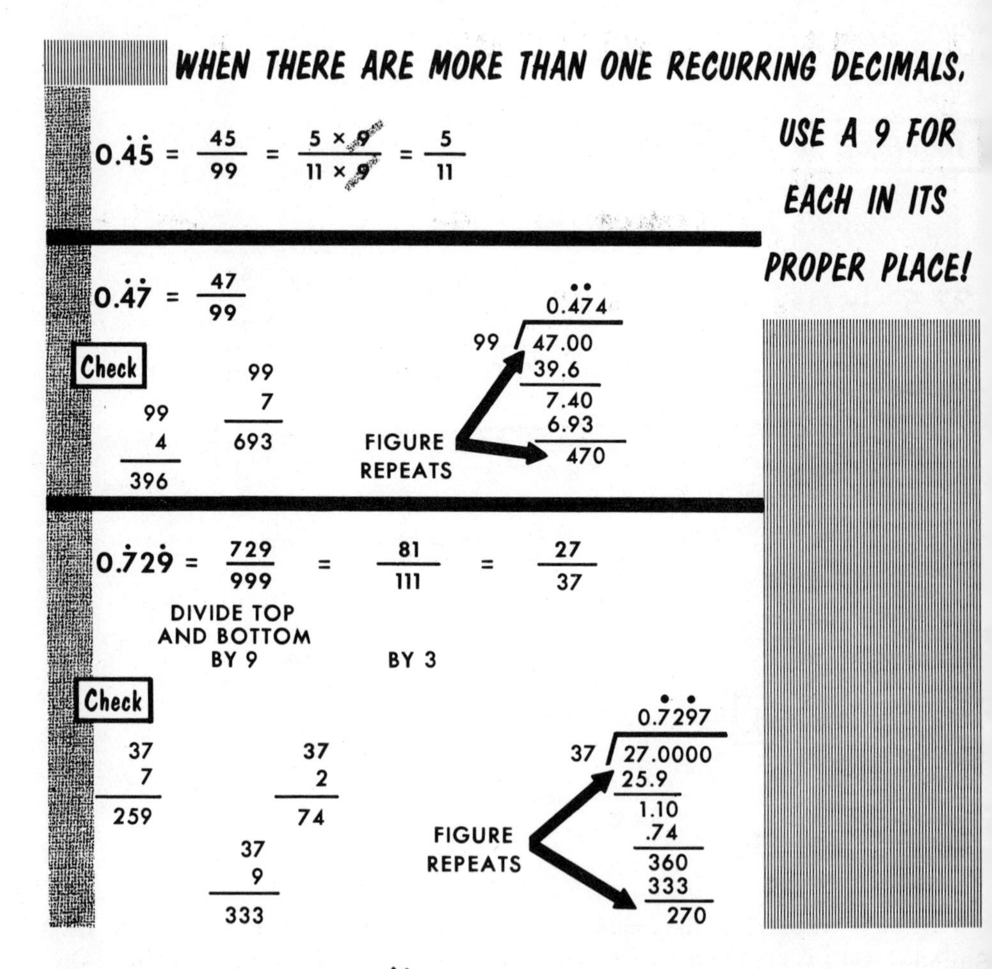

Suppose the decimal is $0.\dot{4}\dot{7}$, which doesn't happen to be one of the 11 family: this means $\frac{47}{99}$, which in this case is the simplest form as a fraction.

Now suppose it is $0.\dot{7}2\dot{9}$. Remember that the 2 dots mean that *all* the numbers recur; according to the rule we have worked out, this means $\frac{729}{999}$. This simplifies down to $\frac{27}{37}$. To check this, we can divide 37 into 27, using the decimal method. It gives us the recurring decimal we started with: $0.\dot{7}2\dot{9}$.

Dividing by Decimals

Occasionally there are cases of long division involving decimals in the numbers. You find where the answer place is by where the ones place of the dividing number would come. But what if there is no ones place in the dividing number, because it is smaller than 1?

Here we use the fact discovered in working with fractions—which is what a number less than 1 is, whether written as a decimal or otherwise—that dividing by a fraction is like multiplying by its reciprocal.

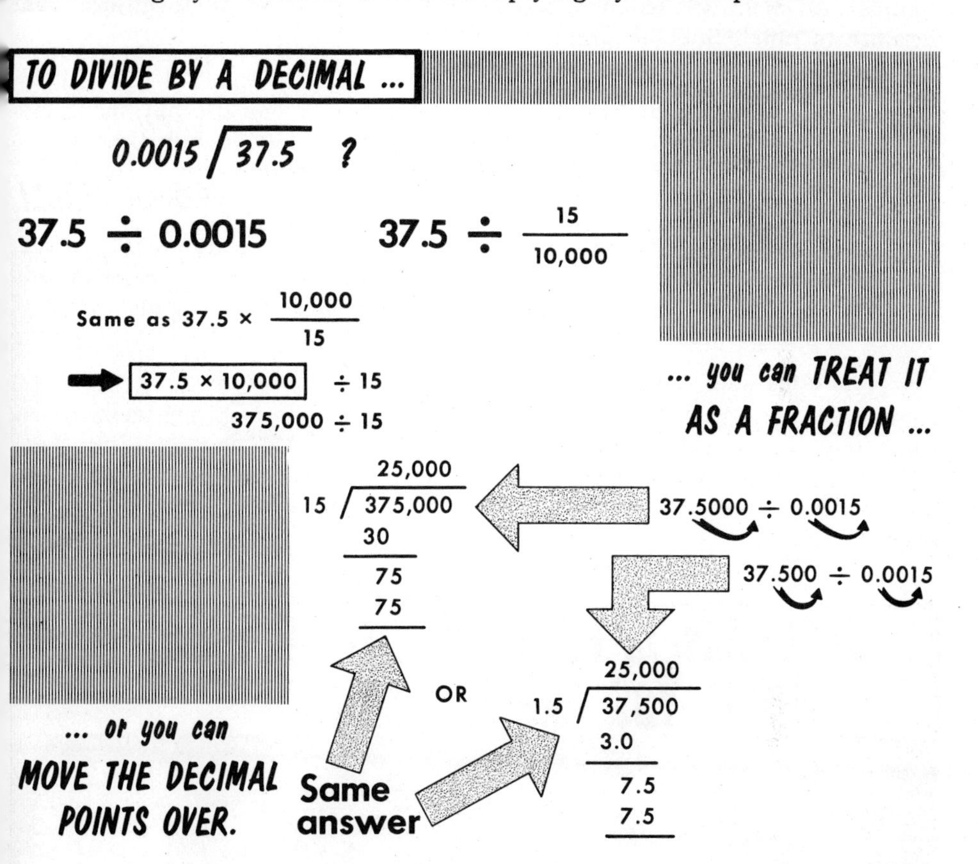

Suppose we have to divide 37.5 by 0.0015: this is really *dividing* 37.5 by $\frac{15}{10,000}$, which is the same as *multiplying* by $\frac{10,000}{15}$. So we multiply 37.5 by 10,000, making 375,000, and then divide by 15, giving 25,000.

Notice that the change from 37.5 to 375,000 and from 0.0015 to 15 both result in moving the decimal point 4 places to the right. This is the important thing: *you must move the decimal point in both numbers the same number of places.* You could move it three places in each, so you divide 37,500 by 1.5, and get the same answer, by putting the answer over the multiplied ones figure. Either way gives the right answer.

Significant Figures

We have gone far enough now to see that the more figures we use in a number, the more accurately we can express it. If you use a bathroom scale to weigh something, each mark probably represents two pounds. You can approximate the odd pounds when the needle stops in between marks. But you could never weigh something accurately to an ounce, much less to a dram. A letter balance, used for finding how much postage to put on mail, can measure to fractions of an ounce, and often up to 2 pounds. A chemical balance, used for mixing chemical formulas, can measure to much finer accuracy.

If you refer to "a 150-pound man," what do you mean? Exactly 150 pounds to the ounce? The bathroom scale could not assure you of that accuracy. More likely you have in mind that he's nearer to 150 pounds than he is to either 140 pounds or 160 pounds. In other words, only the 1 and 5 are really significant; he might weigh 151 pounds or 149 pounds.

If you gave his weight as 153 pounds, would you then mean exactly to the ounce? Most probably this would be a reading as close as the bathroom scale can give it. In this case, if you read the scales at 153, it means he is nearer to 153 pounds than to 152 or 154. To be precise, he is more than $152\frac{1}{2}$ pounds and less than $153\frac{1}{2}$ pounds. We are now using *three* significant figures, 1, 5, and 3. We are also expressing his weight ten times more accurately than the rough estimate of 150 pounds. The three figures, 153, represent three-figure accuracy of the quantity measured, however big or small, or whatever it is. So this is called "three significant figures."

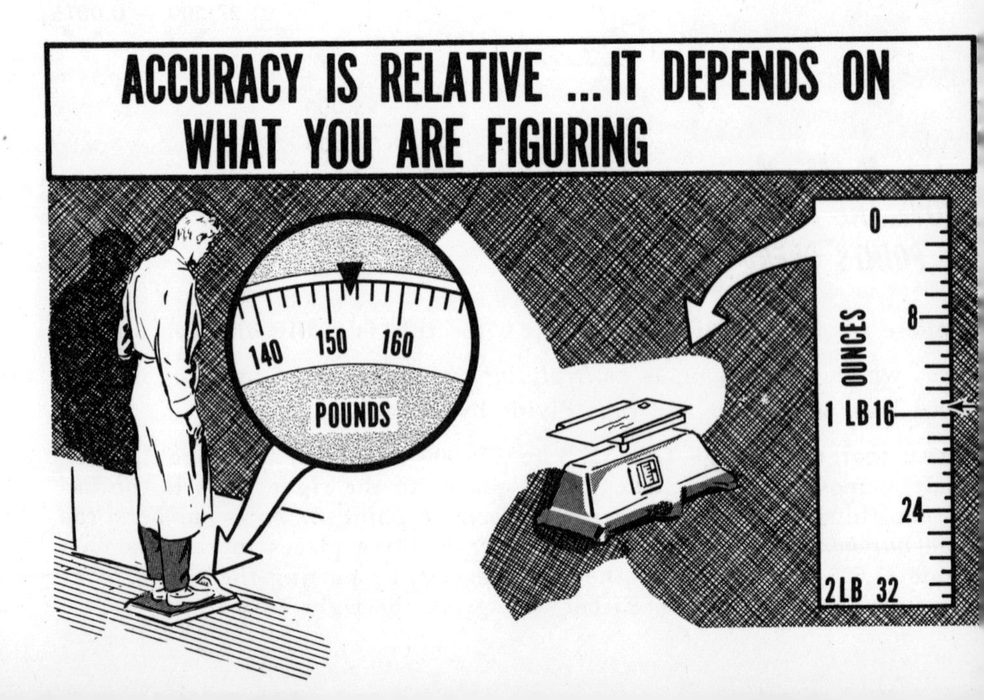

Approximate Long Division

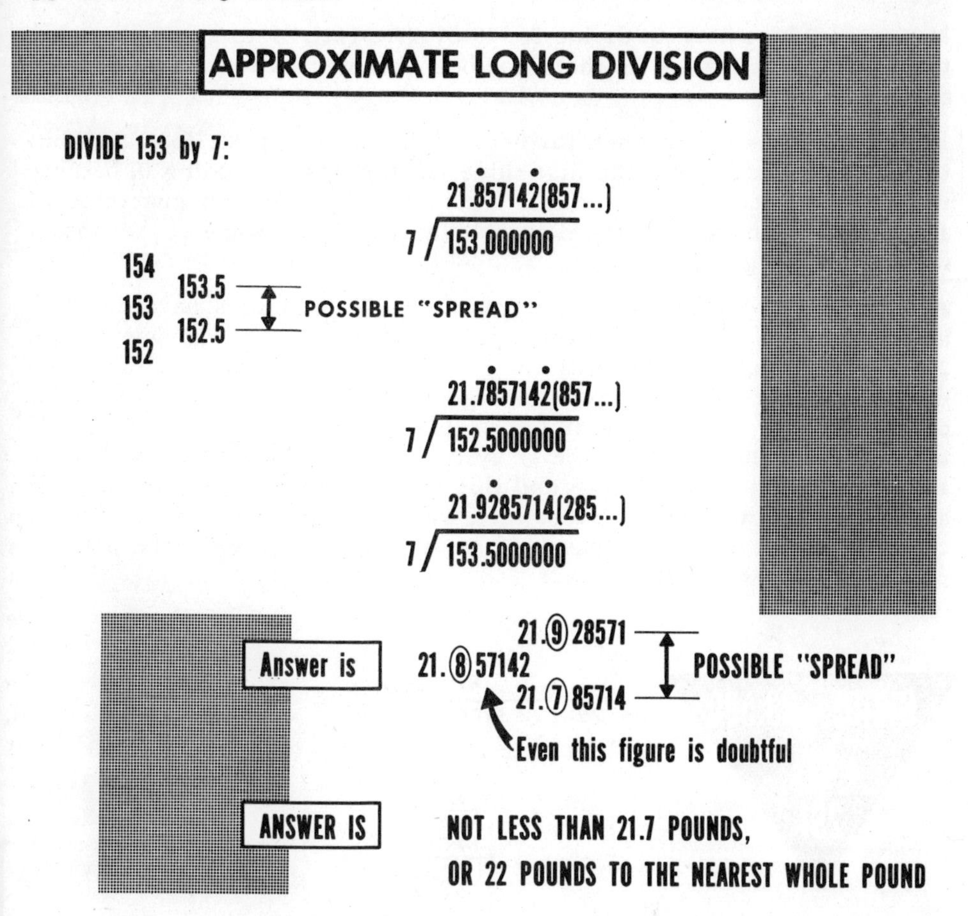

Suppose we have 153 pounds of material to be divided into 7 equal parts. This would lead to a recurring decimal: $21.\dot{8}5714\dot{2}$. If we gave this as the answer, we would be assuming that the original weight was 153 pounds *exactly*, and not a fraction of a dram more or less. But 153 pounds probably means "somewhere between 152.5 and 153.5." Dividing each of these by 7, we get $21.7\dot{8}5714\dot{2}$ and $21.9\dot{2}8571\dot{4}$. The only figures that are the same in all three answers are the first two: 21. The first decimal figure is 7, 8, or 9. The second decimal makes the number 21.85, with limits at 21.78 and 21.92. The only safe conclusion limits our answer to the first two figures: if we have to make sure to stay within the total quantity, we would make the answer 21 pounds; we could perhaps extend it to 21.7 pounds. But if we want the answer to the nearest pound, as it might show on the bathroom scale, we would write 22 pounds, because any of those answers are nearer to 22 than to 21.

But those figures show that a calculation is apt to lose accuracy. We started with 3 significant figures and our answer at the best has 2.

Approximate Long Division (contd.)

Now suppose we have to divide 23,500 by 291: each of these numbers has three significant figures, so that's the best that will mean anything for an answer.

We could divide it out much further (as shown: giving 80.75601 . . .) but the extra figures beyond the first three (in this case including 0, because it comes between other *significant* figures) would have no guarantee of accuracy. We can save ourselves trouble by leaving out some of the "meaningless" working.

After the first division by 291, the last significant figures have doubtful meaning; so we take the nearest figures, instead of bringing down more. 291 into the remainder 220 will not go even once, so knock off the 1 and divide by 29 for the next figure; this goes 7 times and leaves a remainder of 17. Now we "lose" another figure, but because this is 9, making 29 nearer 30 than 20, we divide the 17 by 3. 5 times 3 would be 15; 6 times 3 are 18; as the latter is nearest, and this is the last figure of even possible significance, we take the 6. To be safe, we should go back to three significant figures: as 6 is more than half, we increase the 7 after the decimal point to 8, and write the answer 80.8.

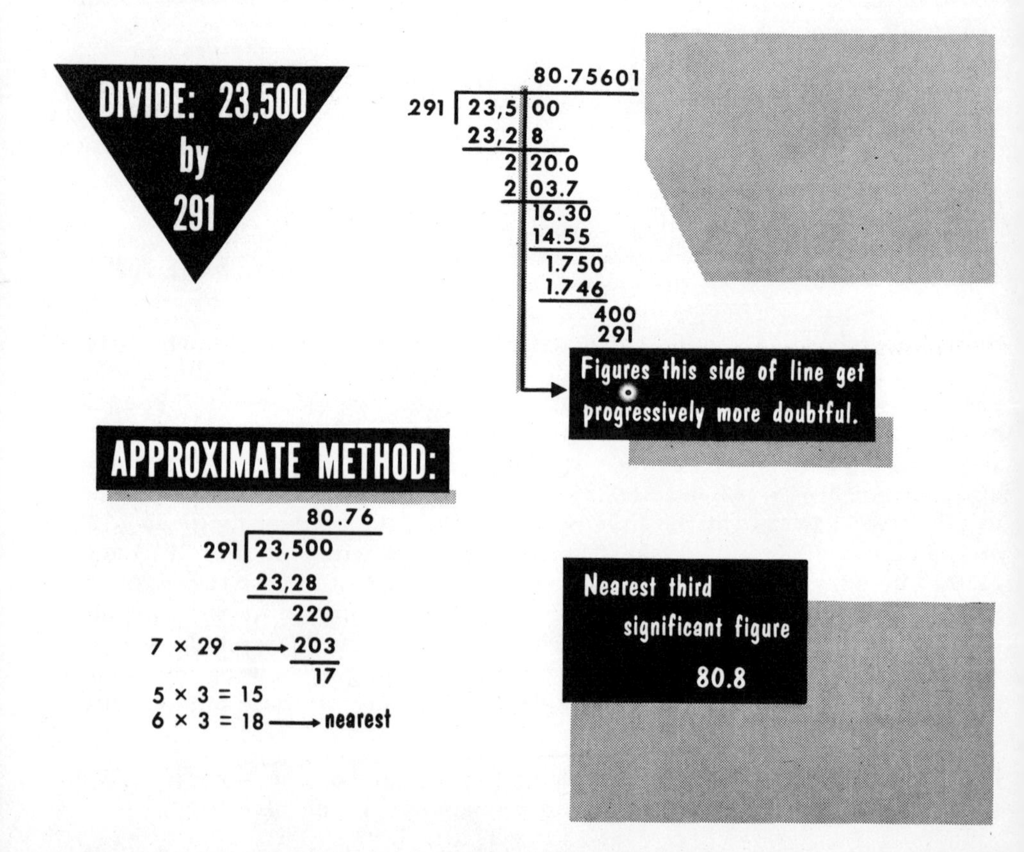

Approximate Long Division (contd.)

From the previous page, it looks as if 23,500 divided by 291 could be written as 80.8 without fear of serious error. But let's see. To find the limits, first we shall assume that 291 means something between 290.5 and 291.5, and that 23,500 is an exact quantity.

Dividing these out gives answers of 80.89 and 80.62. Notice that in dividing by a quantity with a decimal point in it, we find where to put the first figure of the answer by where the ones figure would come: 290 times 8 would be 2,320; 290.5 times 8 is 2,324.0; the ones figure (4 here) comes under the first zero following 235 in the line above, which is the tens place; so that is where we write the 8 in the top line answer.

But suppose now that we interpret 23,500 as only having three significant figures: it could mean something between 23,450 and 23,550. To find the limits of possible answers, we divide the larger by the smaller and vice versa: 23,550 by 290.5 and 23,450 by 291.5. The answers are 81.06 and 80.45. Now the only figure that doesn't change is the 8 in the tens place.

A reasonable approximate answer would be 81, because 80.8 is nearer to 81 than to 80. In the case of 23,500 being an exact number, the range of 80.89 to 80.62 really puts the "middle" figure at $80.75\frac{1}{2}$. But if you write 80.75, this implies an accuracy between 80.745 and 80.755, which is not what we mean at all; the answer comes between 80.62 and 80.89, so the third figure (6 or 8) is not definite even. So even here, as 6 and 8 are both more than 5, the nearest justifiable answer is 81.

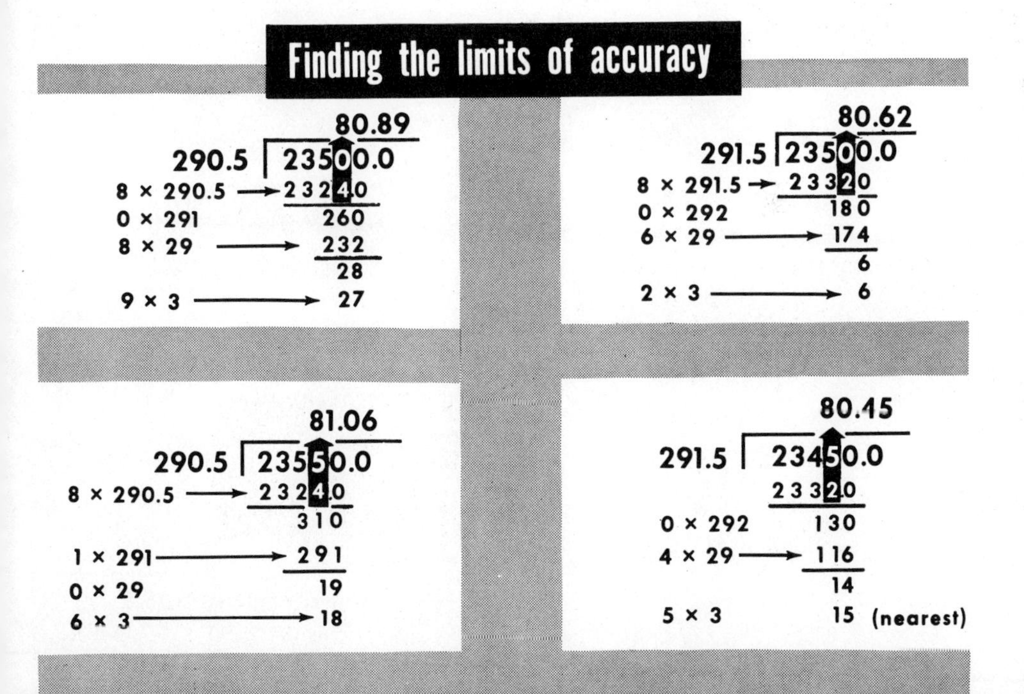

Approximate Long Multiplication

The same is true for multiplication. If we multiply two numbers with three figures each, we will have an answer with six or maybe seven figures. But, if each of the original numbers is only accurate to three significant figures, the last three or four are subject to doubt. So we can save ourselves the work of finding figures that may not be right anyway.

So we don't bother with figures beyond one more than our last final significant figure. Suppose we have to multiply 2.91 by 5.32. We can do this two ways. As a check, we have also multiplied it all out. But the last three figures are unreliable. In the first approximate method, we multiply 5.32 by 2; then 5.3 by 9, carrying 2 at the last figure, because 9 times 2 (the last figure had we used it) is 18, nearer 20 than 10. Finally we multiply 5 by 1 (as the remaining figures, 0.32, are less than half, we ignore them). Adding up, we get 15.48.

APPROXIMATE LONG MULTIPLICATION

Multiply 2.91 by 5.32

```
   2.91
   5.32
 ------
 14.555
   .873
    582
-------
15.4812
```

These figures are doubtful

Method 1:

	5.32
	2.91
2 × 5.32	10.64
0.9 × 5.3	4.79
0.01 × 5	5
	15.48

Nearest third figure 15.5

Approximate Long Multiplication (contd.)

The second method merely multiplies the other way around—5.32 by 2.91. Multiplying 2.91 by 5 gives the first line; the next line is 2.9 by 3 (actually 0.3); finally 3 (because 2.9 is nearer 3 than 2) by 2 (representing 0.02). Adding up, we get the same answer, 15.48. It is really a coincidence that the fourth figure is the same. The 8 is quite doubtful. So we write the answer, to three figures, as 15.5.

Maybe you are not sure that 8 is doubtful. To prove it, we've multiplied 2.905 by 5.315 and 2.915 by 5.325, which represents the extreme possibilities for this particular case; they come to 15.427—15.43 for four figures—and 15.509—15.51 for four figures. The range of possible answers for 2.91 multiplied by 5.32, bearing in mind the possible error that both 2.91 and 5.32 are not exact numbers, is 15.43 to 15.51. Obviously that 8 in the last place is doubtful. Even the 5 may be open to question, but it's much more likely to be 5 than 4.

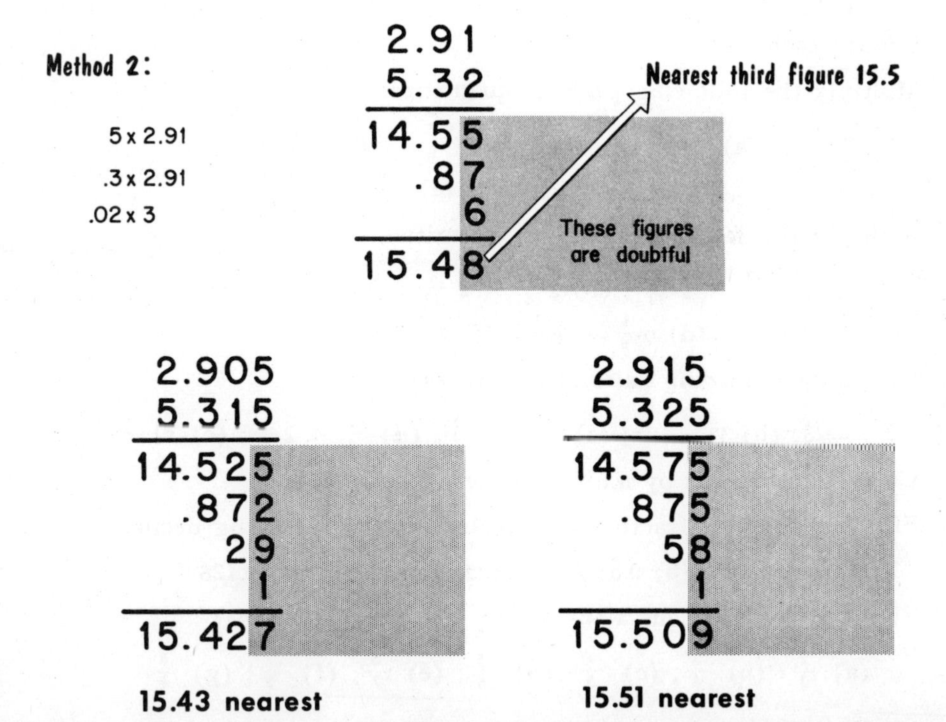

1. Arrange the following fractions in groups that have the same value:

$$\frac{1}{2}, \frac{1}{3}, \frac{2}{5}, \frac{2}{3}, \frac{3}{4}, \frac{3}{6}, \frac{4}{6}, \frac{4}{8}, \frac{3}{9}, \frac{4}{10}, \frac{4}{12}, \frac{8}{12}$$
$$\frac{9}{12}, \frac{5}{15}, \frac{6}{15}, \frac{6}{18}, \frac{9}{18}, \frac{8}{20}, \frac{10}{20}, \frac{15}{20}, \frac{7}{21}$$

2. Reduce the following fractions to their simplest form:

$$\frac{7}{14}, \frac{26}{91}, \frac{21}{91}, \frac{52}{78}, \frac{39}{65}, \frac{22}{30}, \frac{39}{51}, \frac{52}{64}, \frac{34}{51}, \frac{27}{81}, \frac{18}{45}, \frac{57}{69}$$

3. Without actually performing the divisions, indicate which of the following numbers divide exactly by 3, 4, 8, 9, or 11:

(a) 10,452, (b) 2,088, (c) 5,841
(d) 41,613, (e) 64,572, (f) 37,848

Check your results by actual division.

4. Using the rules on pages 1-75 and 1-76 and the tables on page 1-77, find the factors of the following:

(a) 1,829, (b) 1,517, (c) 7,387
(d) 7,031, (e) 2,059, (f) 2,491

Check your results by multiplying the factors together.

5. Add together the following groups of fractions:

(a) $\frac{1}{5} + \frac{1}{6} + \frac{4}{15} + \frac{3}{10} + \frac{2}{3}$; (b) $\frac{1}{8} + \frac{1}{3} + \frac{5}{18} + \frac{7}{12} + \frac{4}{9}$
(c) $\frac{1}{4} + \frac{1}{5} + \frac{1}{6} + \frac{1}{10} + \frac{1}{12}$; (d) $\frac{4}{7} + \frac{3}{4} + \frac{7}{12} + \frac{8}{21} + \frac{5}{6}$

Reduce each to the simplest form.

6. Multiply the following pairs of quantities:

(a) $\frac{3}{4} \times \frac{4}{5}$ (b) $\frac{37}{73} \times \frac{5}{6}$ (c) $\frac{51}{57} \times \frac{19}{26}$
(d) $\frac{55}{111} \times \frac{37}{44}$ (e) $\frac{19}{119} \times \frac{17}{57}$

7. Multiply the following pairs of quantities:

(a) $2\frac{3}{5} \times 1\frac{7}{13}$; (b) $3\frac{1}{6} \times 2\frac{4}{19}$; (c) $7\frac{4}{7} \times 8\frac{5}{8}$;
(d) $6\frac{1}{8} \times 7\frac{1}{7}$; (e) $1\frac{2}{3} \times 3\frac{4}{5}$

8. Divide the following pairs of quantities:

(a) $2\frac{1}{4} \div 3$; (b) $3\frac{1}{3} \div 5$; (c) $7\frac{1}{7} \div \frac{5}{7}$; (d) $\frac{3}{4} \div 2\frac{1}{4}$; (e) $30 \div 4\frac{7}{2}$

Check your results by multiplication.

9. Find the simplest fractional equivalent of the following decimals:

(a) 0.875; (b) 0.6; (c) 0.5625; (d) 0.741; (e) 0.128

10. Find the decimal equivalent of the following fractions:

(a) $\frac{2}{3}$; (b) $\frac{3}{4}$; (c) $\frac{4}{5}$; (d) $\frac{5}{6}$; (e) $\frac{6}{7}$; (f) $\frac{7}{8}$; (g) $\frac{8}{9}$

11. Find the decimal equivalent of the following fractions, and thus check the answers in question 10, by adding corresponding quantities that should make 1:

$$(a)\ \frac{1}{3};\ (b)\ \frac{1}{4};\ (c)\ \frac{1}{5};\ (d)\ \frac{1}{6};\ (e)\ \frac{1}{7};\ (f)\ \frac{1}{8};\ (g)\ \frac{1}{9}$$

12. Find the fractional equivalent of the following recurring decimals:

   (a) $0.41\dot{6}$; (b) $0.\dot{2}\dot{1}$; (c) $0.\dot{1}8\dot{9}$; (d) $0.\dot{5}7142\dot{8}$; (e) $0.\dot{9}0\dot{9}$; (f) $0.\dot{0}9\dot{0}$

   Check each by dividing back to decimal form again.

13. The following interesting number sequence is sometimes shown as "mathematical magic":

$$142,857 \times 2 = 285,714;\ 142,857 \times 3 = 428,571;$$
$$142,857 \times 4 = 571,428;\ 142,857 \times 5 = 714,285;$$
$$142,857 \times 6 = 857,142$$

   Each has the same numbers, in the same order, but starting at a different point; but 142,857 × 7 = 999,999. Can you explain this from work learned in this section? (See page 1-89 for hint.)

14. What is meant by significant figures? To illustrate, show the limits of possible meaning for measurements given as 158 feet and 857 feet.

15. Using the approximate method, divide 932 by 173. Then by dividing (a) 932.5 by 172.5 and (b) 931.5 by 173.5, show how many of your figures are justified. Noting that 932 and 173 each have three significant figures, what conclusion would you draw from this calculation?

16. **Divide 93,700 by 857, using an approximate method. Then by dividing 93,750 by 856.5 and 93,650 by 857.5, show how many of your figures are justified. Can you shorten up the approximate method still further, to avoid putting down meaningless figures? (Bear in mind that you have to get as many figures as possible correct, and know where the decimal point comes.)**

17. Multiply 4,856,000 by 2.375, obtaining an approximate answer, because each of these numbers has only four significant figures.

18. Another magic number sequence is the following: take the number 769,230; subtract 692,307: it leaves 76,923—the first number without the final zero. Can you explain this rearrangement trick? (See page 1-90 for hint.)

19. Divide 3,520 by 7, and give the result correct to three significant figures.

AREA: THE SECOND DIMENSION

Scales of Length — Units and Measurement

So far, we have been mainly concerned with various aspects of counting. We have applied our counting to things, money, weights, measures, and also distances or lengths. But we have just concerned ourselves with adding, subtracting, multiplying, and dividing any of these things, just as we might count any other things.

You can't multiply ORANGES by PEARS ... or inches by gallons, or tons by miles

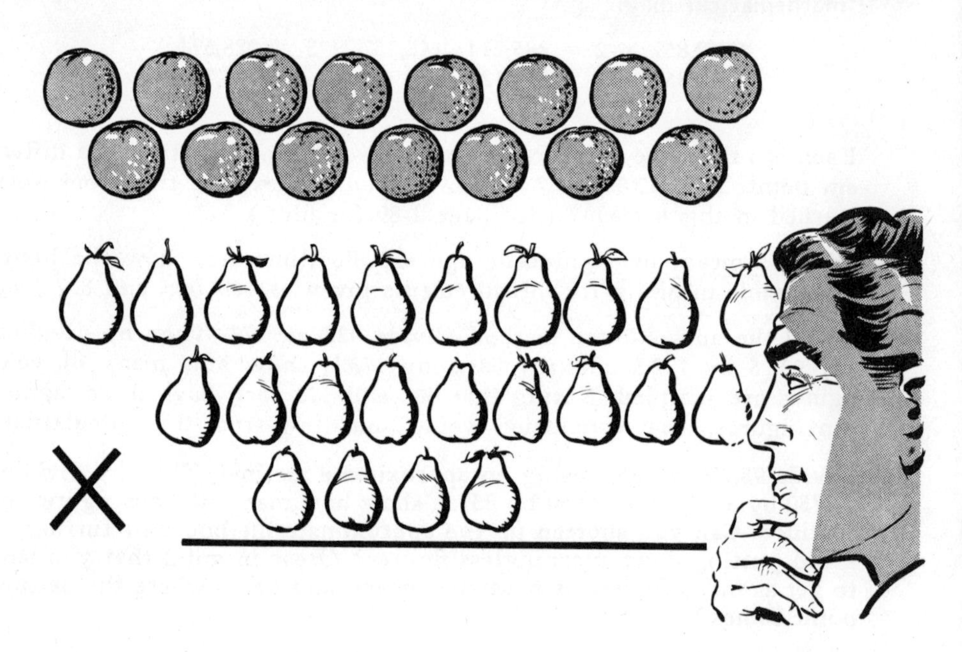

We stacked things, discs, balls, squares, or cubes in rows, squares, and cubes, but merely as a convenient way of counting them. If we multiplied 35 articles by 7, the result was 245 articles, still the same variety as at first. Oh yes, we did consider change of units, from inches to feet, or pints to gallons, but always we used something that was a multiple or submultiple—the same kind of unit: inches and feet are both measures of length; pints and gallons are both measures of quantity; cents and dollars are both measures of money.

Now we start to see how arithmetic can help us when we relate different measures together. What happens if we multiply a length by a length, instead of by a number?

If someone asked you to multiply 17 oranges by 23 pears, you could multiply 17 by 23, but the answer is 391 what? It does not make sense. But multiplying a length by a length can make sense, as we shall see.

Length Times Length is Area

You've possibly guessed already that multiplying a length by a length gives an area. If you have a length of wallpaper 27 inches *wide* and 108 inches *long*, its *area* is 27 inches times 108 inches, and the answer is in square inches. We could deduce that from the way we began with counting; laying articles in rows and thus building up squares or areas of other shapes.

If you lay 27 square inches to a row, and then line up 108 rows of 27 square inches, the total area, which will be that of the wallpaper in the question, is 27 times 108 square inches. From what we have learned, you can figure that out to 2,916 square inches.

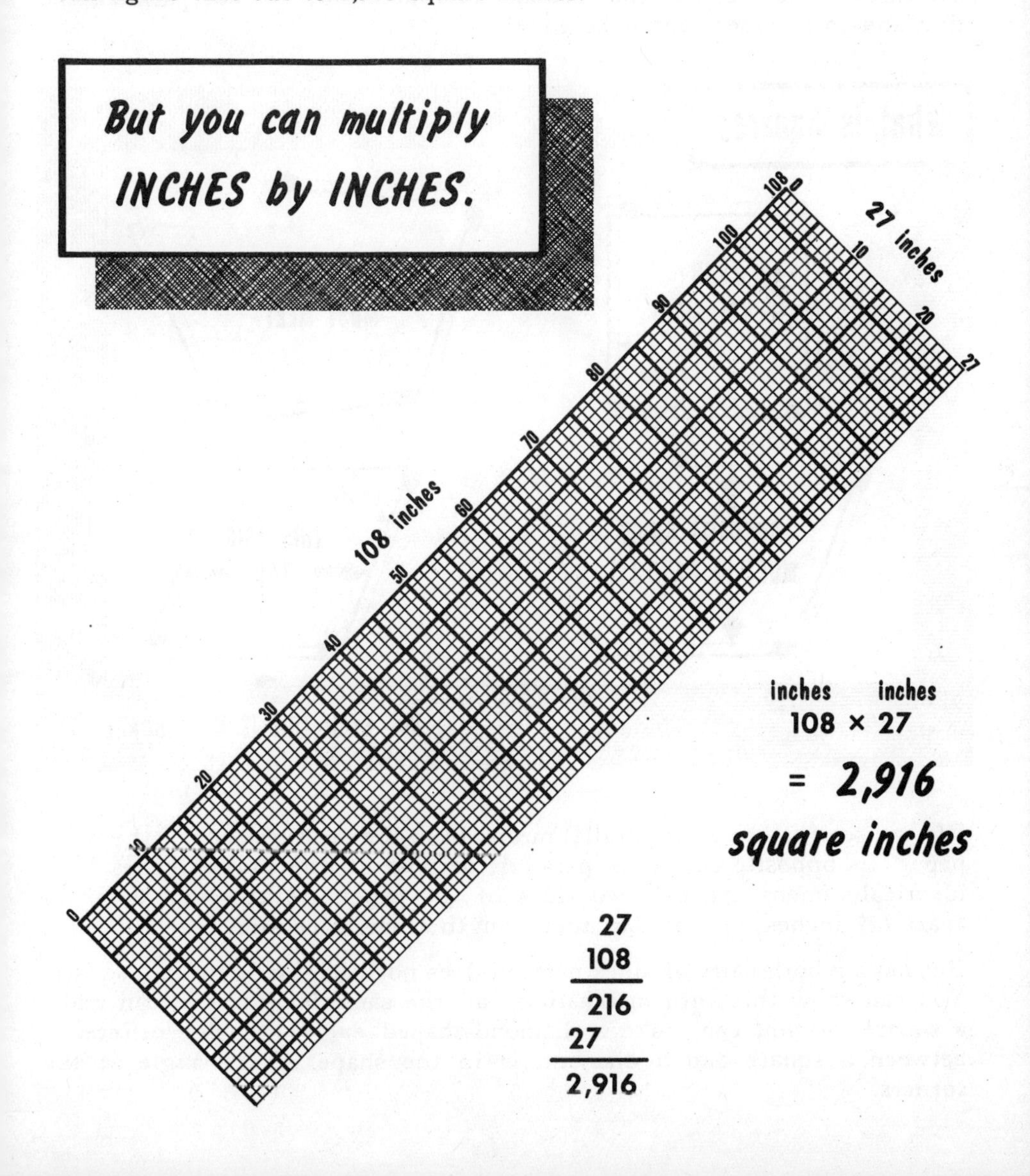

What Is Square?

We are so used to the shape we call square that we've probably never bothered to define it. In working with those square inches, we just thought of them as measuring 1 inch "each way." But if you measure 1 inch along four edges, you may not end up with a square. For one thing, the fourth side must end up where the first side began.

A requirement for this is that opposite sides (the first and third and the second and fourth) must be parallel. If they are not, the square will not work out. If the first and third side are not parallel, the fourth side will have to be more or less than the second side, instead of the same length, for the ends to meet. If the second and fourth side are not parallel, the first and third sides cannot be equal.

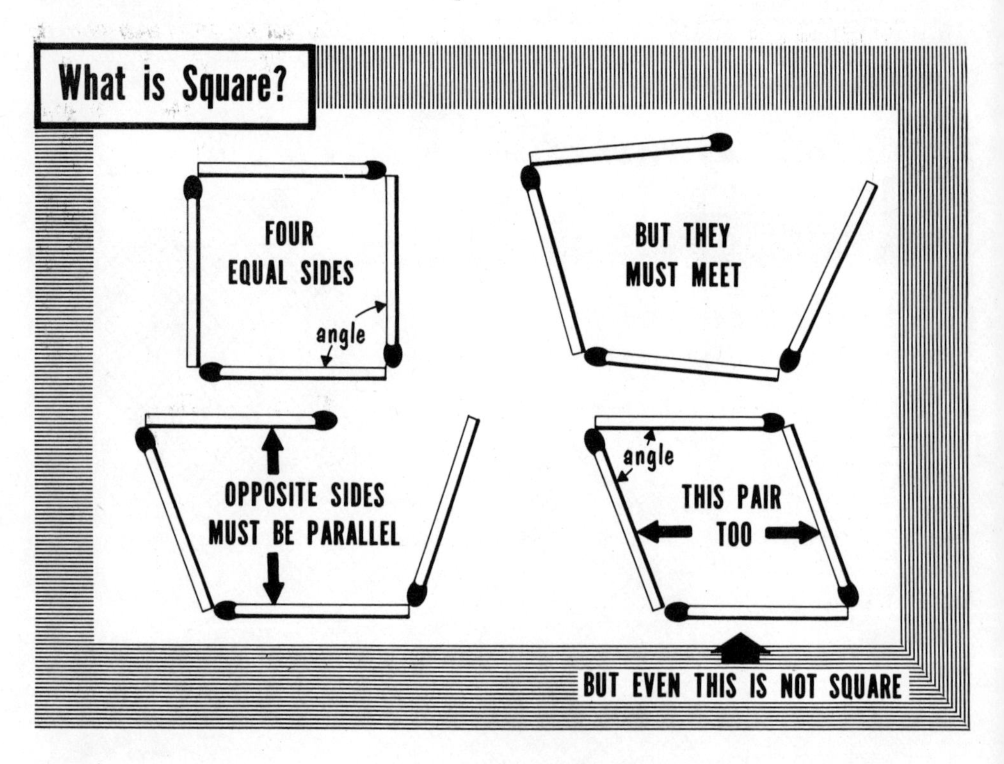

We can see further what parallel means from the measurement of the wall-paper. Its opposite edges are parallel; because all the square inches have identical dimensions, the two sides of the paper are at equal distances apart (27 inches) throughout their length: that is parallel.

But having both pairs of sides parallel does not necessarily make a square. You can show this with matchsticks, all the same length. You can make a square, or you can make a diamond-shaped enclosure. The difference between a square and a diamond is in the shape of the angle at the corners.

The Right Angle

While you can fit diamonds together to make a solid area, you have to be careful to lay them all the same way; when you use squares, each way around is the same. Fitting 4 square corners together fills in a solid area, with no gaps and no overlapping. In a square, all 4 angles are the same, and exactly 4 of them fit together at a point. This is because each of them is the "right" angle.

So a square corner is one that uses the *right angle*.

Another way to view it can be understood from the way a carpenter might build a table. He wants the top level, so he uses legs all the same length. Then he fixes the legs to the underside of the table top. If they are not at the right angle, any weight on the top will make the table tend to tip. If it's the wrong angle one way, it will tip one way. If it's the wrong angle another way, it will tip that way. Only if it's the right angle, with no tendency to "lean" any way, will the table be secure from falling over.

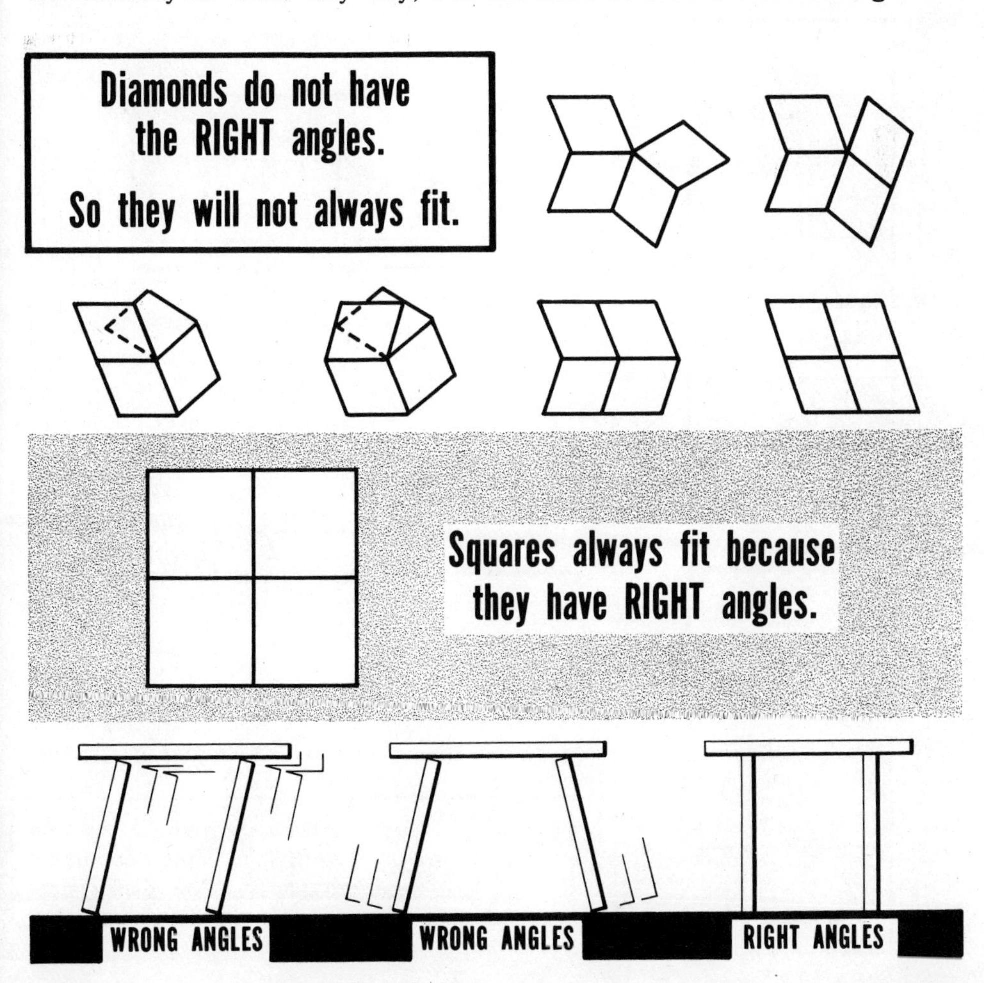

Different Shapes with the Same Area

Suppose we have a piece of drawing paper 22 inches by 30 inches: we could cut this across and rejoin it to be 44 inches by 15 inches; this will be the same area, because it's the same paper just rearranged. The area in either case is 22×30 (or 44×15) $= 660$ square inches. One way to check this is to rule it off in inches each way and count the square inches (or inch squares).

We could rearrange the same number of square inches into almost any number of shapes having the same total area.

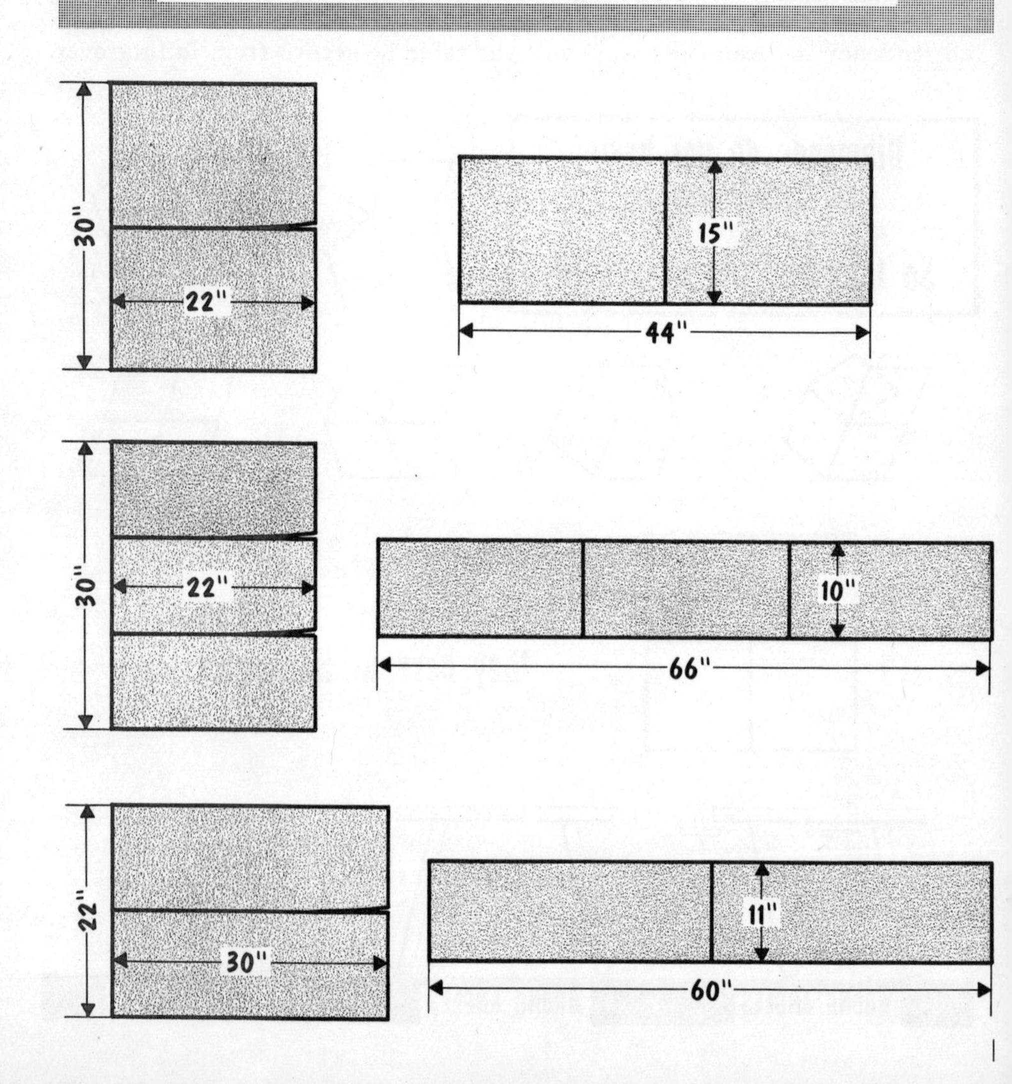

Square Measure

We know that there are 12 inches to a foot and 3 feet to a yard; they are established standards of length measurement. But how many square inches to a square foot, or square feet to a square yard?

This we can easily figure out. When we were learning to count, we found that 10 rows of 10 made a hundred. By similar arrangement, we find that a square 12 by 12 contains 144 one-unit squares, and a square 3 by 3 contains 9 one-unit squares. From this we know that 144 square inches make 1 square foot and 9 square feet make 1 square yard.

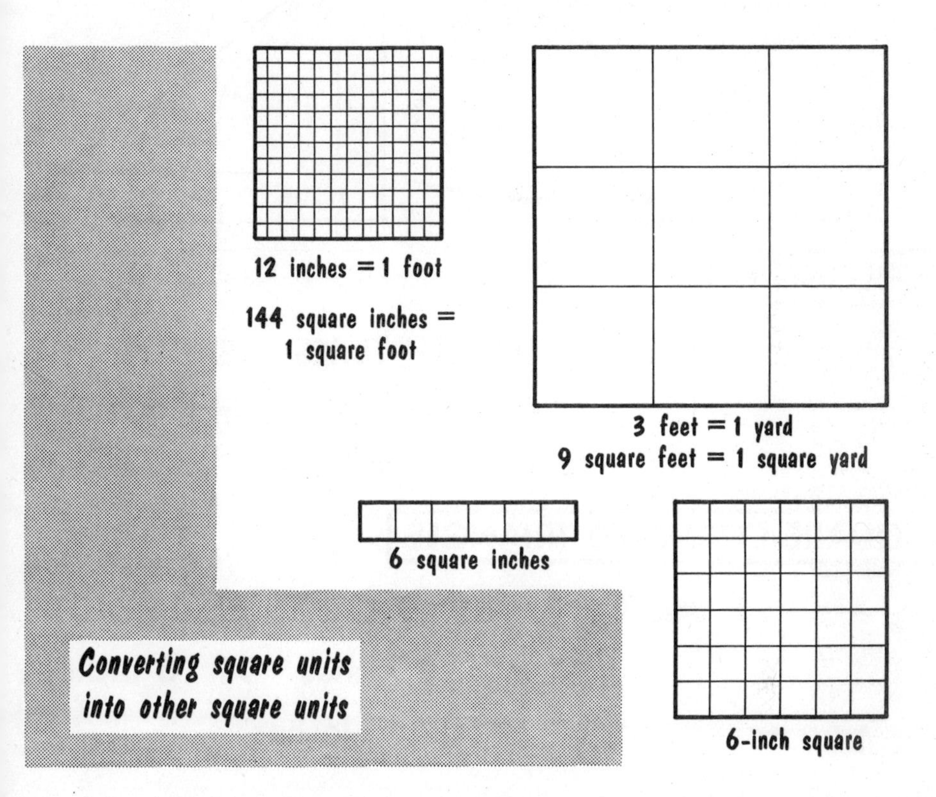

We could extend this to 1,760 times 1,760, or 3,097,600 square yards make 1 square mile. For real estate measure, there is a unit called an *acre,* which is 4,840 square yards. Dividing this into 3,097,600 shows that a square mile contains 640 acres. As 4,840 is not an exact square (4,840 does not appear on our table of squares), an acre cannot be defined as so many yards each way; the nearest, using round numbers (complete yards) for each dimension, would be a plot 55 yards by 88 yards. It should be remembered that an acre is essentially a square, or area measure.

Here it may be pertinent to mention the distinction between, say, 6 square inches and a 6-inch square: a *6-inch square* is a square, each of whose sides is 6 inches long, and thus contains 36 *square inches.*

From Oblongs to Triangles

So far we have considered areas of four-sided shapes with square corners, because these are simple. The common name for shapes in which the two pairs of sides are not equal is *oblong;* mathematical books usually call them *rectangles*. The next shape to find the area of is a square-cornered (or right-angled) *triangle*.

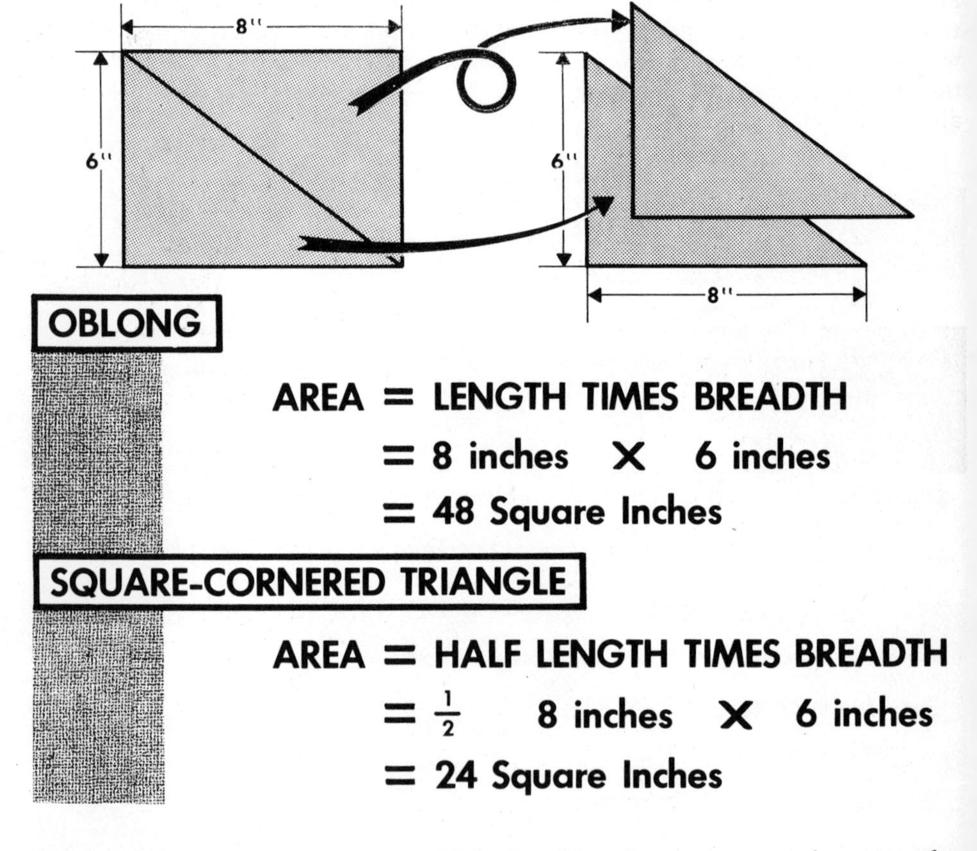

Suppose we have an oblong in which the sides that come together to make the square corner are 6 inches and 8 inches long. Its area would be 6 times 8 or 48 square inches. Now we could lay a ruler from corner to corner, diagonally, draw a line, and thus cut the oblong in two. If we take the two pieces and rotate one of them, we can lay one on top of the other and they should exactly coincide, which means they have equal areas. Since we have cut the oblong exactly in two, each square-cornered triangle with 6- and 8-inch sides, cut from the original 6- by 8-inch oblong, must have half the area of the oblong: 24 square inches.

So a square-cornered triangle has an area equal to *half of the sides which make up the square corner, multiplied together*.

Parallelograms

This is a word to describe any four-sided shape whose opposite sides are parallel both ways. Beside the *square* and *oblong*, each of which has all square corners, the *diamond* (also called a *rhombus* in geometry books), and a shape like an oblong knocked out of square, called a *rhomboid*, are all parallelograms.

Squares and oblongs are usually called by their own names, although they also happen to be parallelograms, and the diamond will be called either that or a rhombus. This leaves only the rhomboid type of parallelogram without its own specific name. So the word parallelogram is generally taken to mean one that is not a square, oblong, or diamond, and hence could also be called a rhomboid.

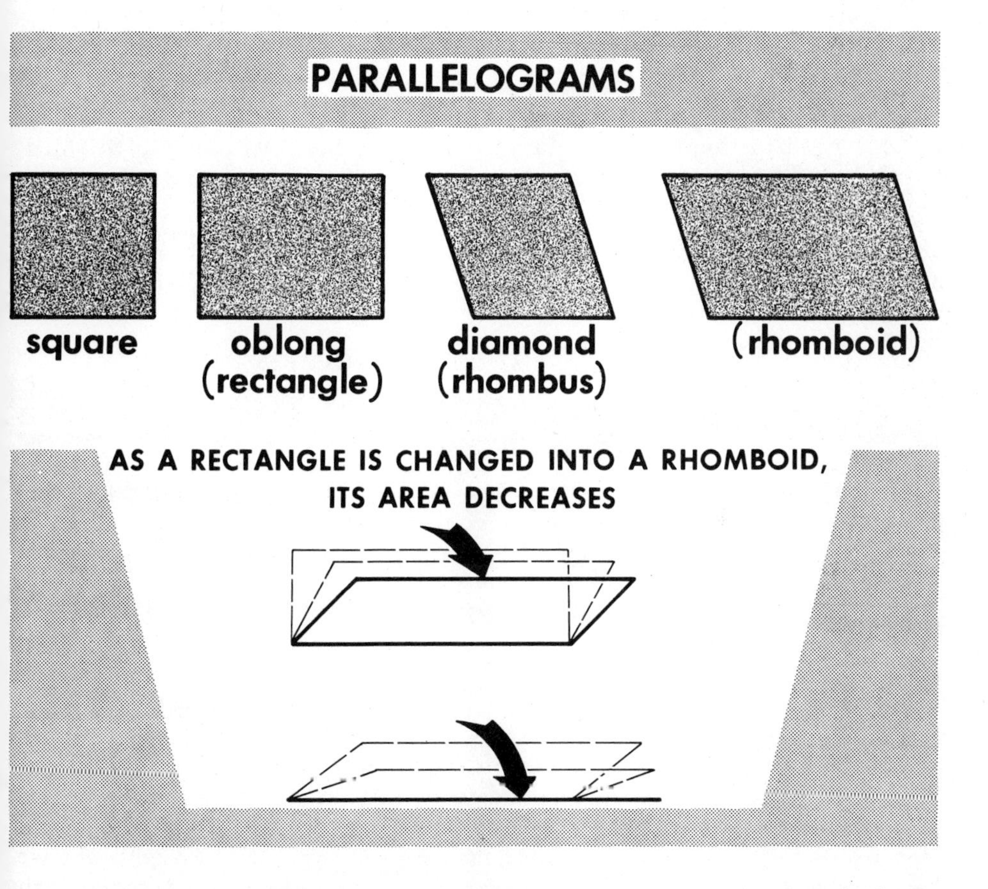

If we think of a parallelogram as an oblong with its corners knocked out of square but still having the same sides, it is fairly obvious that, as the corners get further away from being square, the area of the shape must diminish. When two corners are flattened "shut" and the other two "open," there is no area left; the shape has been squashed into a straight line.

Area of Parallelograms

The way to get at the area of a parallelogram is to take it from a different oblong than the one having the same sides before the corners were changed. A parallelogram can be changed back to an oblong by making a square cut at one corner so as to remove a triangle. When this triangle is fitted on the other end of the parallelogram, it becomes an oblong, with all square corners. This is the oblong we use to find the area of the parallelogram.

Because the change is made just by moving a triangular piece of it from one place to another, without any gaps or overlap in either case, the area of the oblong must be the same as that of the parallelogram.

Actually, you don't need to make the cut to measure or calculate the area. But this trick shows how to make the calculation. The area of the oblong is the *length of the side of the parallelogram that is not changed, multiplied by the distance to the opposite side, measured squarely.*

Suppose a parallelogram has two sides 15 inches long and two sides 10 inches long. But the distance measured squarely between the 15-inch sides is 8 inches. The area is found, by multiplying 15 times 8, to be 120 square inches.

This could also be found by using the other pair of sides and the distance measured squarely between them. These sides are 10 inches long, and the distance between them is 12 inches. Multiplying together gives 120 square inches, the same answer.

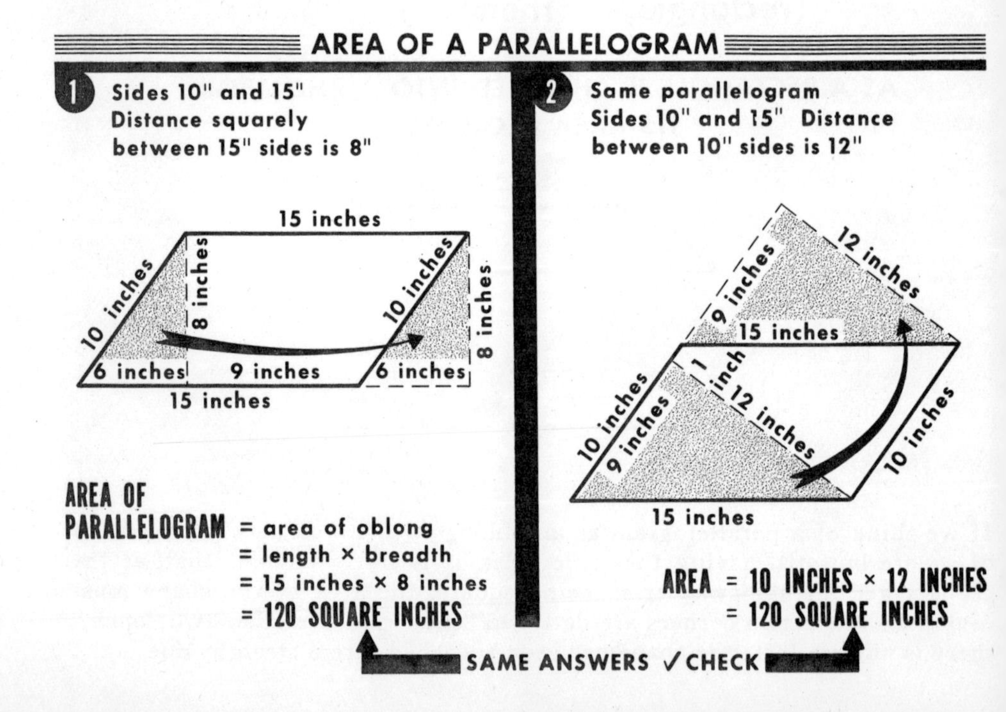

Area of Acute Triangles

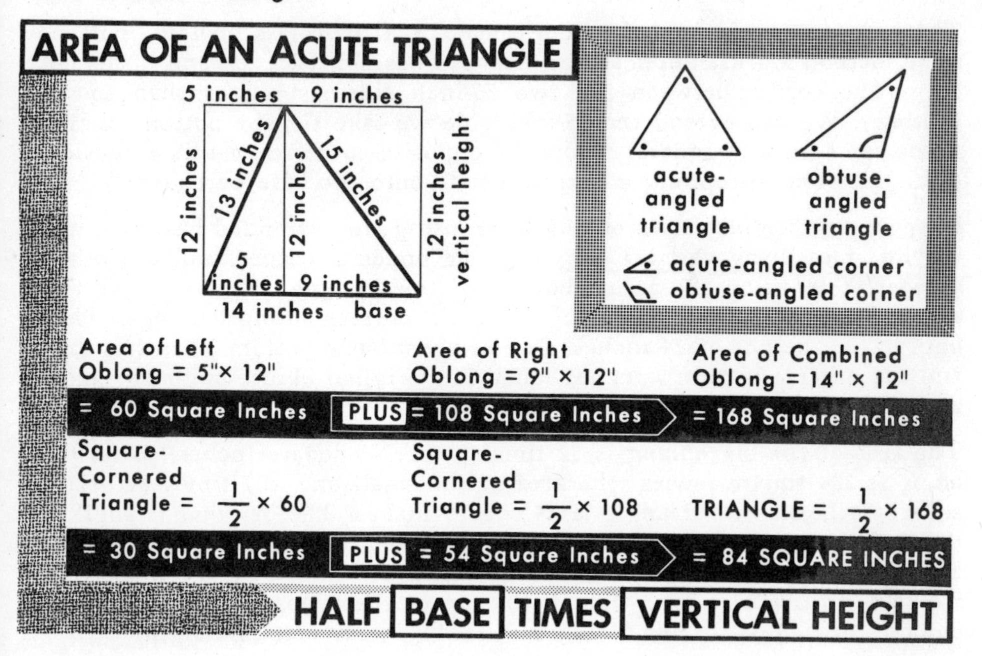

The same idea can be used for finding the area of a triangle when none of its corners are square (right angles). In most triangles, all the corners are smaller (or sharper) than squares and are called *acute angles.* In a few, one (only) of the corners may be bigger (or more open) than square; this is called an *obtuse angle.*

Carefully draw an oblong with one side the same as one side of the triangle and the opposite side just touching the opposite corner of the triangle. Now you have a triangle sitting inside an oblong. Next draw a line from the top corner of the triangle, square to the bottom of the triangle. This line follows the vertical or perpendicular *height* of the triangle. It also divides both the triangle and the original oblong into two triangles and oblongs.

Each of these is a square-cornered triangle, with its associated oblong. So each part triangle has half the area of its oblong. This means that the whole original triangle, made up of the other two, must have half the area of the whole oblong.

If the sides of the original triangle have lengths 13, 14, and 15 inches, all the corners are smaller than square, and vertical height from the 14-inch side is 12 inches. The whole triangle has an area of *half the bottom multiplied by the height:* half of 14 times 12, or 84 square inches.

The perpendicular divides the bottom into parts 5 inches and 9 inches long. You can check that the two part triangles have areas 30 and 54 square inches, which add up to the same total—84.

Area of Obtuse Triangles

The broader, obtuse-angled triangle may be a little less obvious, but the same method works. Suppose the triangle has sides 25, 25, and 40 inches long. The corner between the two 25-inch sides is bigger than square (obtuse). We can extend the 25-inch side we take for the bottom so that a line can be drawn squarely from the opposite corner onto this extension. (This is called "dropping a perpendicular onto the base extended.")

Now we can complete two oblongs, one using this extended base line and the line measuring vertical height to the opposite corner, and the other, as part of it, using the actual bottom of the triangle. We now have two square-cornered triangles sitting in their corresponding oblongs. They both have a height of 24 inches. One of them has a bottom 32 inches long and the other a bottom 7 inches long. Our original obtuse-angled triangle uses the difference—a bottom 25 inches long.

The area of the big oblong is 32 times 24 or 768 square inches, so its triangle is 384 square inches; the area of the small one is 7 times 24 or 168 square inches, so its triangle is 84 square inches. The original triangle is the difference, or 300 square inches. The oblong on the same bottom and having the same vertical height is 25 times 24, or 600 square inches. So the same rule works, even though the top of the triangle goes outside its oblong. Its area is *half the bottom multiplied by the vertical height.*

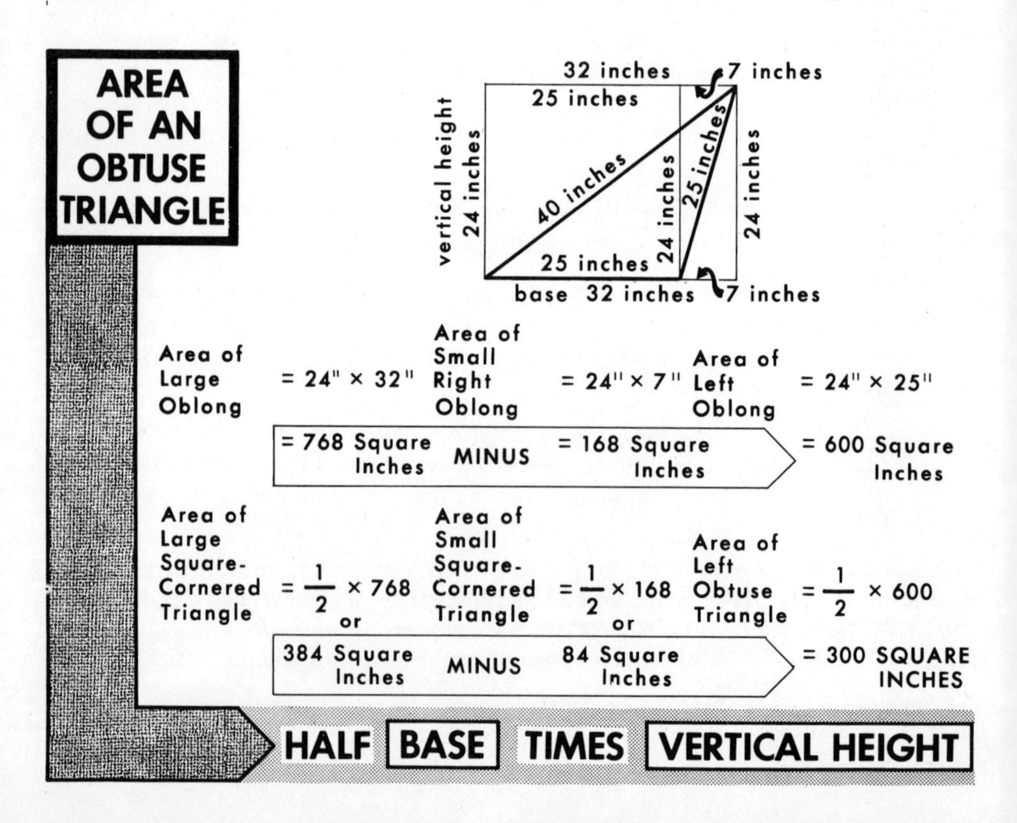

Area of Obtuse Triangles (contd.)

If one of the short sides of that last triangle is used as bottom, it has the top go beyond the oblong on the same bottom and keeps the same height. But by using the third or longest side, the original method of page 1-111 will work.

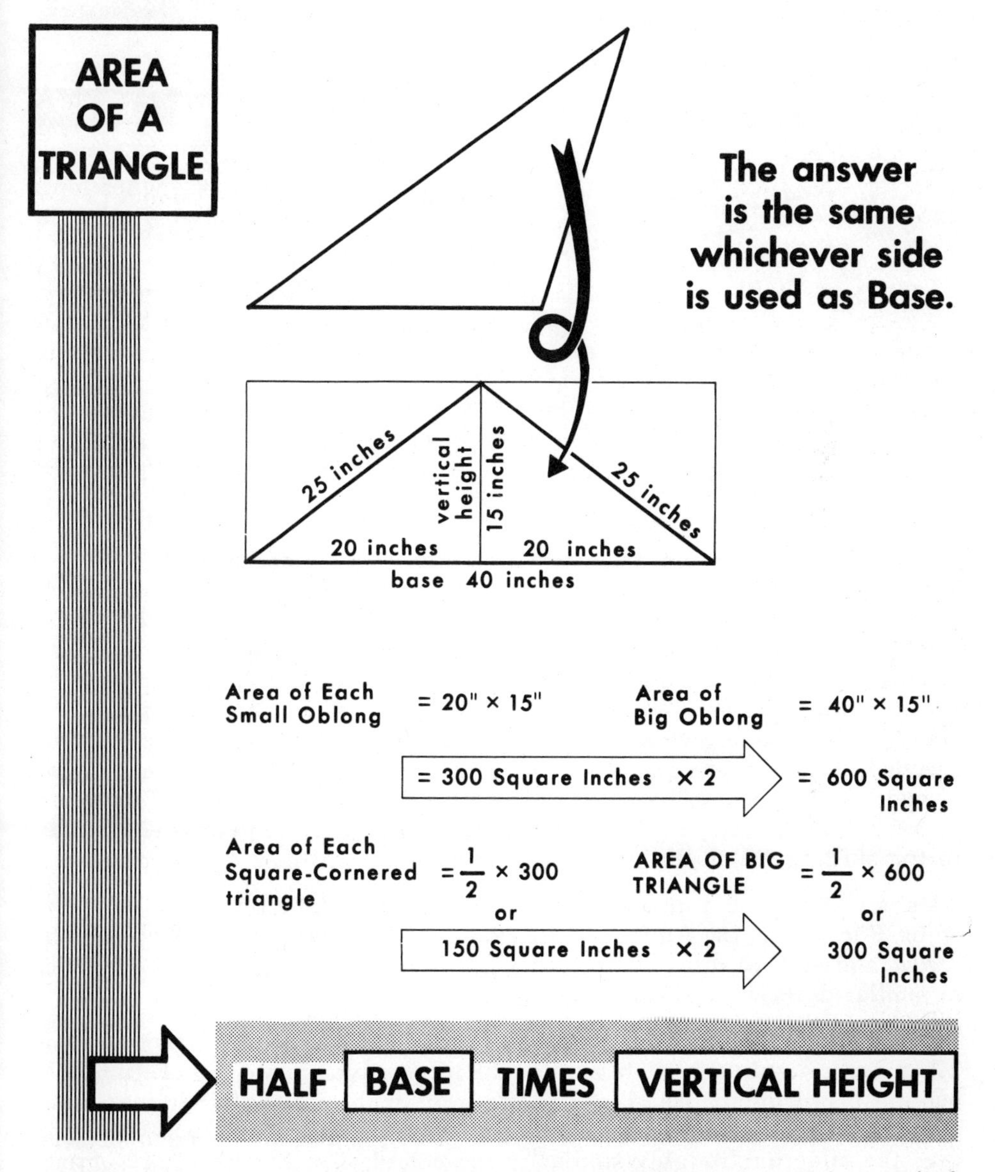

Taking the same triangle: its bottom is now 40 inches long and its vertical height 15 inches. So its area is half 40 times 15, or 300 square inches, which is the same answer.

Metric Measure

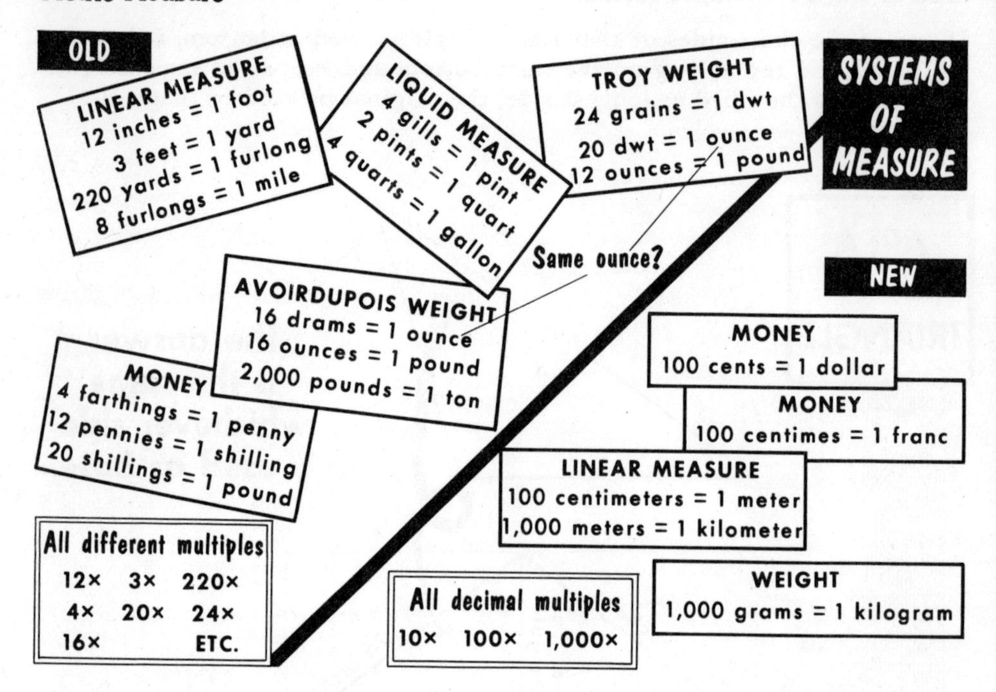

For many years, the inconsistency of systems of measurement has been a nuisance to people learning arithmetic: 12 inches to the foot, 3 feet to the yard, 1,760 yards to the mile (which incidentally, came from the Latin 1,000 paces—no one knows why it changed to 1,760 yards); in measures: 2 pints to the quart, 4 quarts to the gallon; in weights (avoirdupois): 16 drams to the ounce, 16 ounces to the pound, 28 pounds to the quarter, 4 quarters to the hundredweight, 20 hundredweight to the ton (in the English system). But there are also precious metal weights and other systems, with 12 ounces to the pound (is it the same ounce? That takes some finding out); in money (again the English system): 4 farthings to the penny, 12 pennies to the shilling, 20 shillings to the pound, or 21 shillings to the guinea.

This is what led to a new system, based on decimal, or ten-times relationships. For money, the American system uses 100 cents to the dollar; French, Swiss, and several other European systems use 100 centimes to the franc, or similar units with different names.

For lengths, the meter is roughly similar to a yard; 1,000 meters is a kilometer, roughly similar to a mile; the meter divides into 100 centimeters, making a centimeter roughly similar to an inch, etc. In other measures, similar systems have been adopted on the European continent: weight uses the kilogram, roughly similar to the pound, dividing into 1,000 grams, roughly similar to the dram; measures use the liter, roughly similar to the quart. But all these measures come in multiples and submultiples (or parts) of 10 times, 100 times, 1,000 times, etc.

Metric System

The metric system had to be devised so the new units had simple relationships. So it was not possible to make the conversions from the old units simple as well. Although the meter is roughly similar to the yard, it is actually 39.37 inches, where the yard is 36 inches.

As a meter contains 100 centimeters, and a yard contains only 36 inches, it is obvious a centimeter must be a smaller unit than the inch. The meter is 39.37 inches; the centimeter must be one-hundredth of this, or 0.3937 inch. Dividing this into 1 (which is taking the "reciprocal") shows that there are 2.54 centimeters to the inch (use the approximate method for this).

Square measure uses the same units. If there are 2.54 centimeters to an inch, there will be 2.54 times 2.54 square centimeters to a square inch, or 6.45. (Again the approximate method can be used.)

Don't try to memorize these conversions. Most of the time you'll either use the old system or the new (metric). We've concentrated on the old system, because it's still used and is the more difficult. Most scientific work uses the new system, but everyday work sticks to the old.

When you do need to make conversions, which does happen occasionally, you can always check the conversion factor from an appropriate table; if it's in an exam, the proper conversion factor will be given.

If you have to convert from inches to centimeters, remember that the centimeter is a smaller unit, so you will have more of them: multiply by 2.54. If you are converting from centimeters to inches, the inch is a larger unit, so you will have less of them: divide by 2.54.

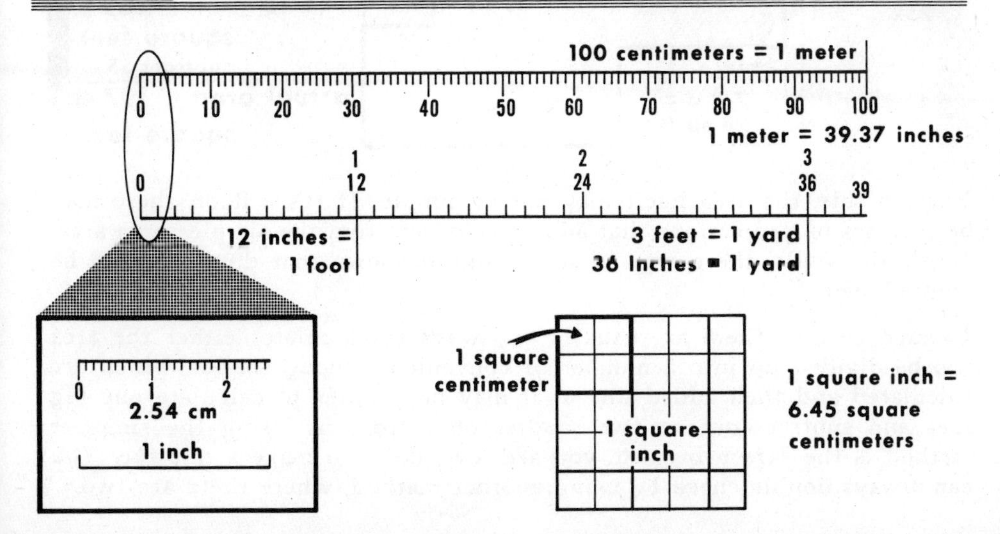

Area Problems

The simplest kind of area problem is concerned with just the amount of area, in whatever units are convenient. For example, if a type of paint on a certain kind of surface covers 5,000 square feet to the gallon, all we need to know is the number of square feet involved to find how much paint is needed.

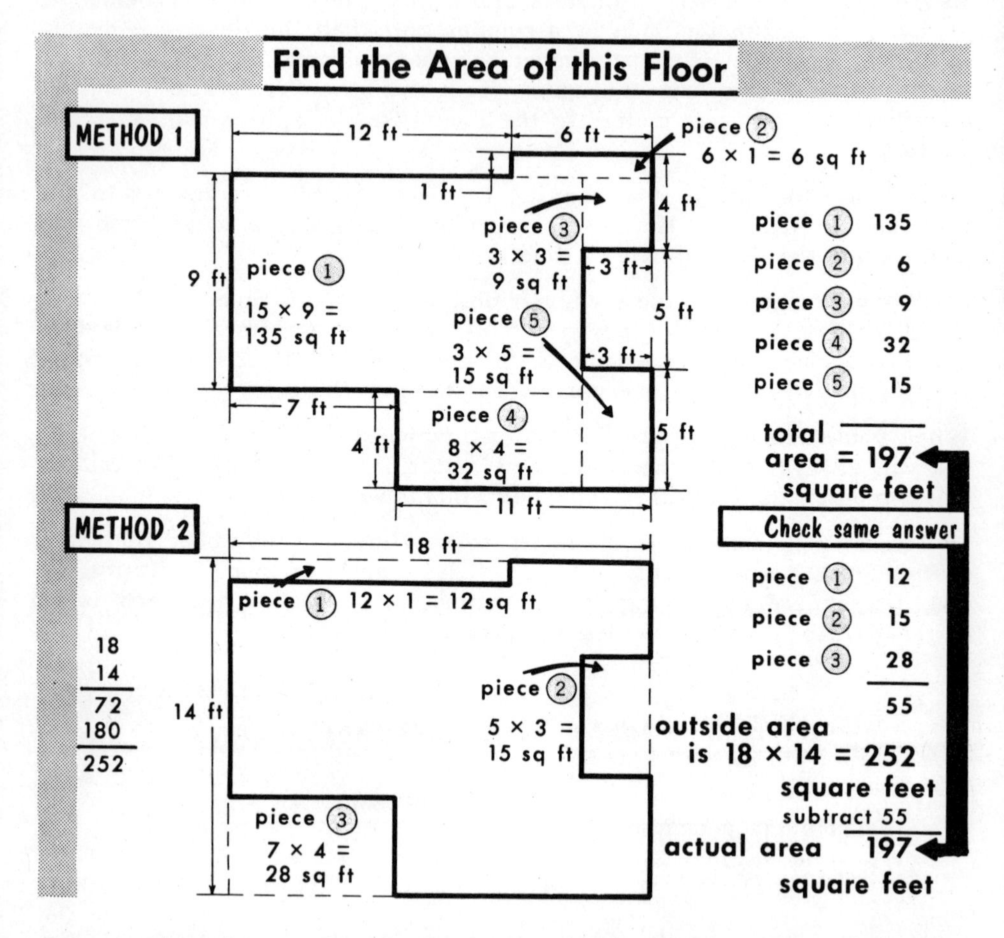

Even in this, the area itself may not be simple. If it's a floor, there may be recesses or projections that add or subtract from the simple room area. If it's the walls, there may be doors and windows that don't have to be painted over.

In such an area there are usually two ways to calculate: either the area can be divided up into a number of convenient oblong shapes, which are calculated and then added up; or it may be simpler to calculate one big area and subtract one or two smaller ones from it. Using the simplest method is the safest, because you are less likely to make a mistake. You can always double check by using another method, where there are two.

Area Problems (contd.)

Area problems can be further complicated by having to fit certain shapes into the area. If it is wallpaper, the paper comes in strips of a certain width; you need to find how many rolls of paper are needed by finding out how many strips are needed. This may be quite simple if the pattern is simple, but with more complicated patterns the pattern may have to be matched, involving more waste.

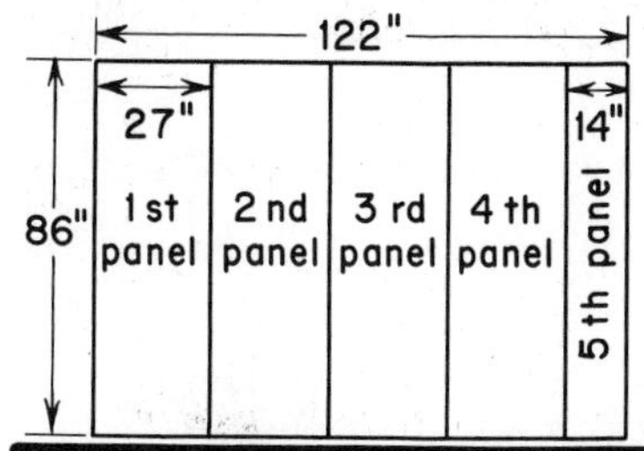

Papering a Wall ...

Five panels must be allowed Each 86" long.
Total 430" or 35 feet 10 inches
Avoid joins in panels. If 30-ft rolls are used (360"), this will do 4 panels: 344".
Last panel must start new roll.

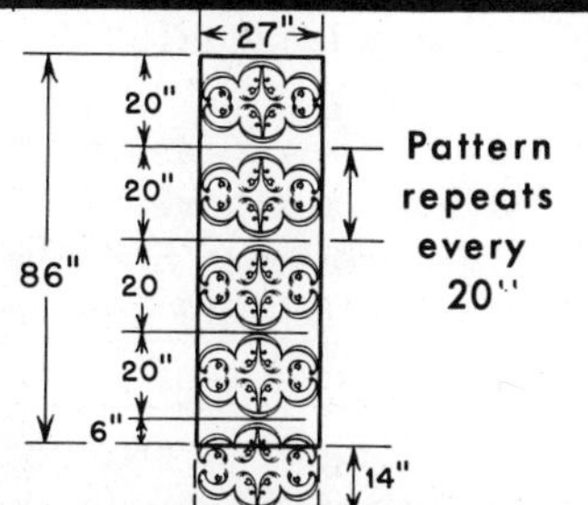

... when there's a pattern

If pattern has to match, length must be allowed to next larger complete pattern length. 80" is not enough. Needs 100" so 30-ft roll will only do 3 panels (300").

Remaining 60" is waste.

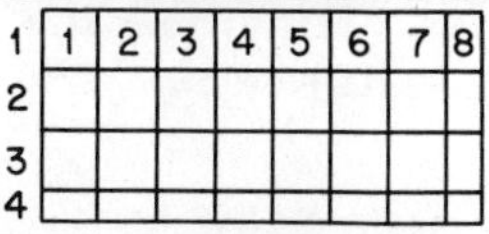

Tiling a Floor ... with square tiles

All pieces must be counted as well as whole tiles
8 × 4 = 32 tiles needed.

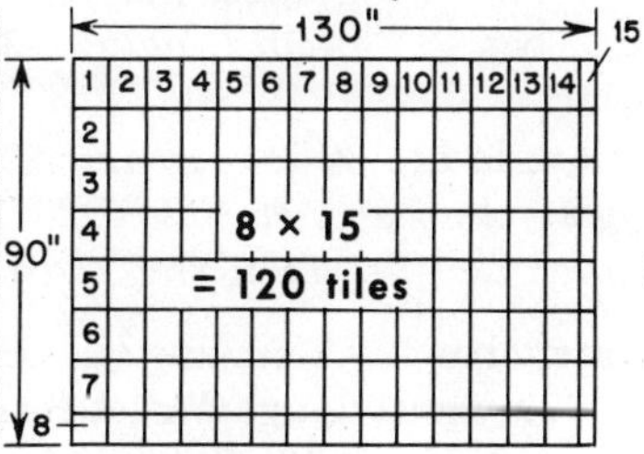

... with oblong tiles

Area 90" × 130"
Tiles 9" × 12"

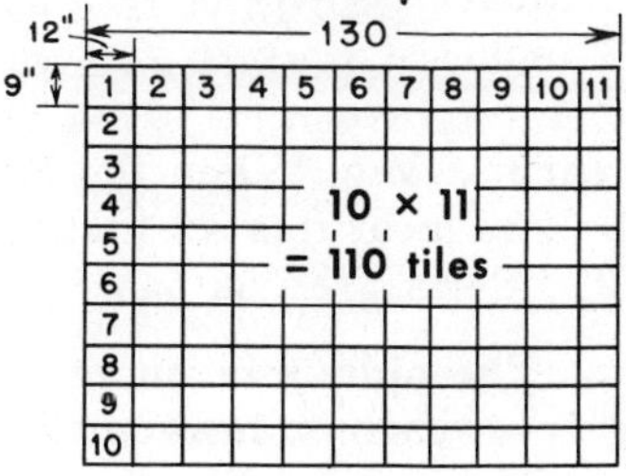

1st way: 130, 12", 9", 90" — 10 × 11 = 110 tiles

2nd way: 130", 15 — 8 × 15 = 120 tiles

1st way saves 10 tiles over 2nd way.

Another variation is when the "material" comes in standard pieces, such as ceiling or floor tiles. Then you have to see how many complete tiles "go" each way and how many parts you have to use. If the tiles are square, they can be laid either way. But if they are oblong, one way may fit the area more economically than the other. The only way is to make trial calculations.

1. Find the area of the following oblongs:

   (a) 54 inches by 78 inches; (b) 13 feet by 17 feet;
   (c) 250 yards by 350 yards; (d) .3 miles by 7 miles
   (e) 17 inches by 5 feet; (f) 340 yards by 1 mile

2. What is a right angle? Why is it so named?

3. Starting with a piece of paper 36 by 25 inches (which you may draw using $\frac{1}{8}$ inch to represent 1 inch), cut it into three pieces that can be rearranged to prove that 37 $\frac{1}{2}$ by 24 inches has the same area.

4. How many square feet are there in (a) 5 square feet, (b) a 5-foot square?

5. Find the area of square-cornered triangles, where the sides by the square corner have the following dimensions:

   (a) 5 inches by 6 inches; (b) 12 feet by 13 feet
   (c) 20 yards by 30 yards; (d) 3 miles by 4 miles
   (e) 20 inches by 2 feet; (f) 750 yards by 1 mile

6. A field has four straight sides. Opposite pairs of sides measure 220 yards and 150 yards, respectively. But the field does not have square corners. A measurement between the opposite 220-yard sides finds the straight-across distance is 110 yards. Find the area of the field in acres (1 acre is 4,840 square yards).

7. A parallelogram has sides 20 inches and 15 inches long. The straight-across distance between the 20-inch sides is 12 inches. Calculate the straight-across distance between the 15-inch sides. (Hint: use the fact that area can be calculated two ways. See page 1-110.)

8. Find the area of the following triangles:

   (a) base 11 inches, height 16 inches
   (b) base 31 inches, height 43 inches
   (c) base 27 inches, height 37 inches

9. Two sides of a triangle are 39 inches and 52 inches long. When the 39-inch side is used as the base, the vertical height measures 48 inches. What is the vertical height when the 52-inch side is used as base?

10. A piece of property has two square corners. The side joining these square corners is 200 yards long. Measuring from each square corner, the two adjoining sides are 106.5 yards and 256.5 yards. The fourth side, joining the ends of these two sides, is 250 yards long. What is the acreage of this property? (Hint: treat this area in two parts, an oblong and a square-cornered triangle.)

11. A large piece of property measures 330 yards by 440 yards. The owner wants to keep a piece in one corner that measures 110 yards by 44 yards, and sell the rest. What is the area he wants to sell?

12. A farmer has 60 6-foot lengths of portable fencing, with which to fence off an enclosure. What is the largest area he can enclose? (Hint: try different shaped oblongs that exactly use the 360 feet of fencing he has, and see which gives the biggest area).
13. Find the area of the floor shown in the drawing.

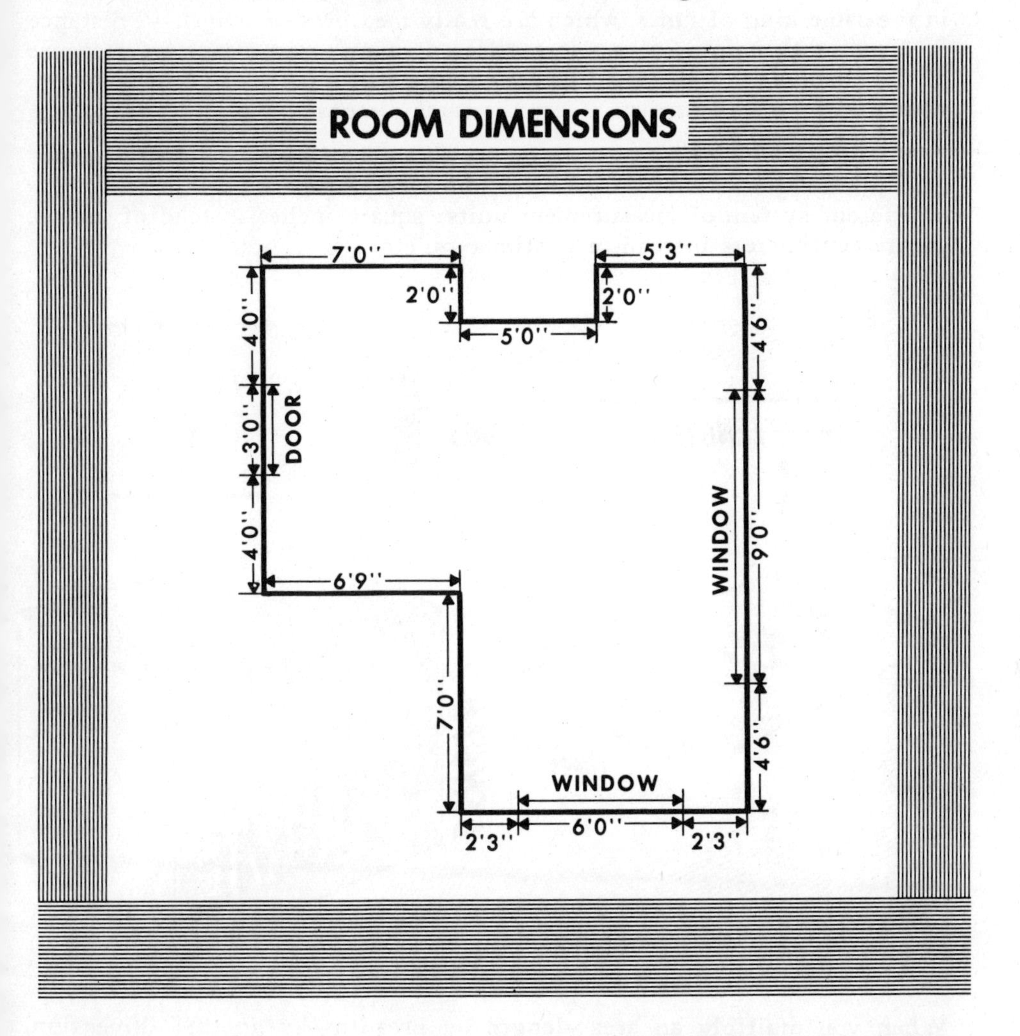

14. The walls of the room in question 13 are 7 feet high. Doors and windows at positions shown run from floor to ceiling. How much wallpaper, in 30-foot rolls 27 inches wide, will be needed to paper the room, if the pattern on the paper repeats every 22 inches? Don't allow for the strip of wallpaper turning a corner.
15. How many tiles will be needed to cover the ceiling of the same room, using the most economical way with 9- by 12-inch tiles? How many tiles can you save over the less economical way?

What is Dimension?

We can measure things with different scales. For example, we may use inches or centimeters to measure length; but whichever we use, it is still length we are measuring: that is the *first dimension.* Of course we also speak of breadth, depth, height, width. But any of these we would measure in the same kind of units, which are really measures of length—a distance from point to point. Calling it a different name only means we measure off the distance in a different direction: it's still a point-to-point distance, which arithmetically means it has the same dimension.

Now suppose we multiply length by breadth: That's two *length* dimensions multiplied together—an area. This is the *second dimension.* For it, we use a different system of measurement units: square inches instead of inches, square centimeters instead of centimeters, etc.

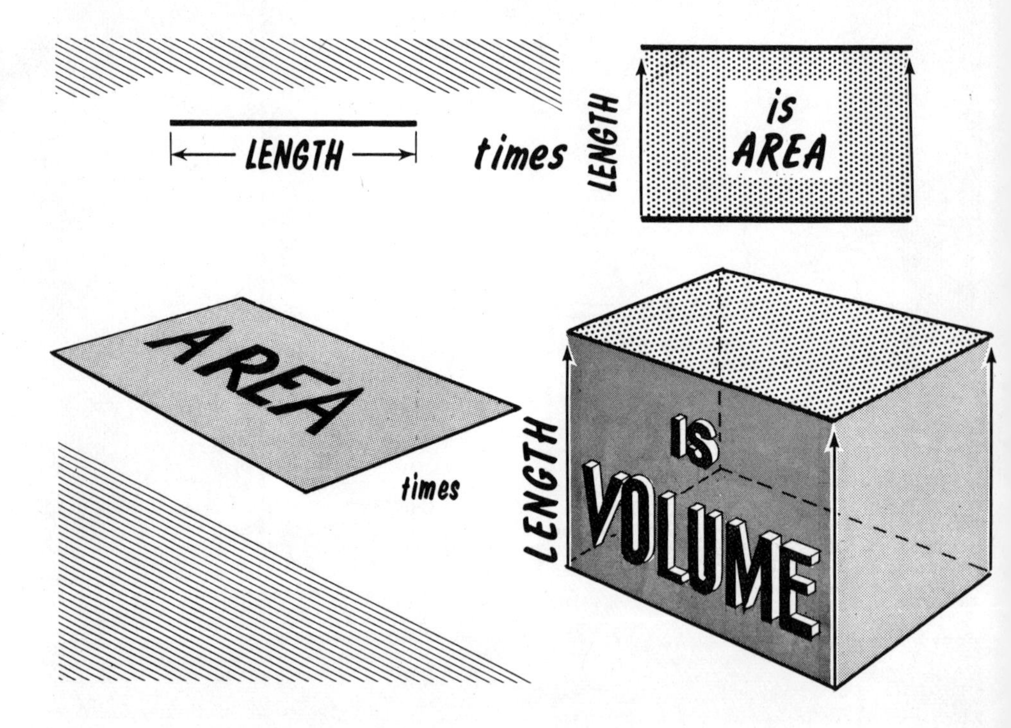

When you multiply an area—length by breadth—by another dimension, which we could call depth or height, we have *volume*—the *third dimension.* We used this in illustrating how to count. After using rows (length) to build a square (area), we stacked up squares to build a cube (volume).

For this dimension we use cubic inches, cubic feet, or cubic meters and cubic centimeters; but we will not be doing that yet. Later on, we will also be finding that volume is related to measure and weight, but for the moment there is a simpler kind of dimension we want to grasp. It involves what is usually called the "fourth dimension."

The Fourth Dimension — Time

How can time be a dimension? Well, we use a variety of means to measure it. The ancients used sand in a hourglass. We use clocks and watches, or electronic chronometers. All these are related to dimensions we have already established: the hourglass measures off so much sand through a small hole and that represents so much time. Watches and clocks count the number of swings a pendulum makes, or a balance wheel, and mark that off in time.

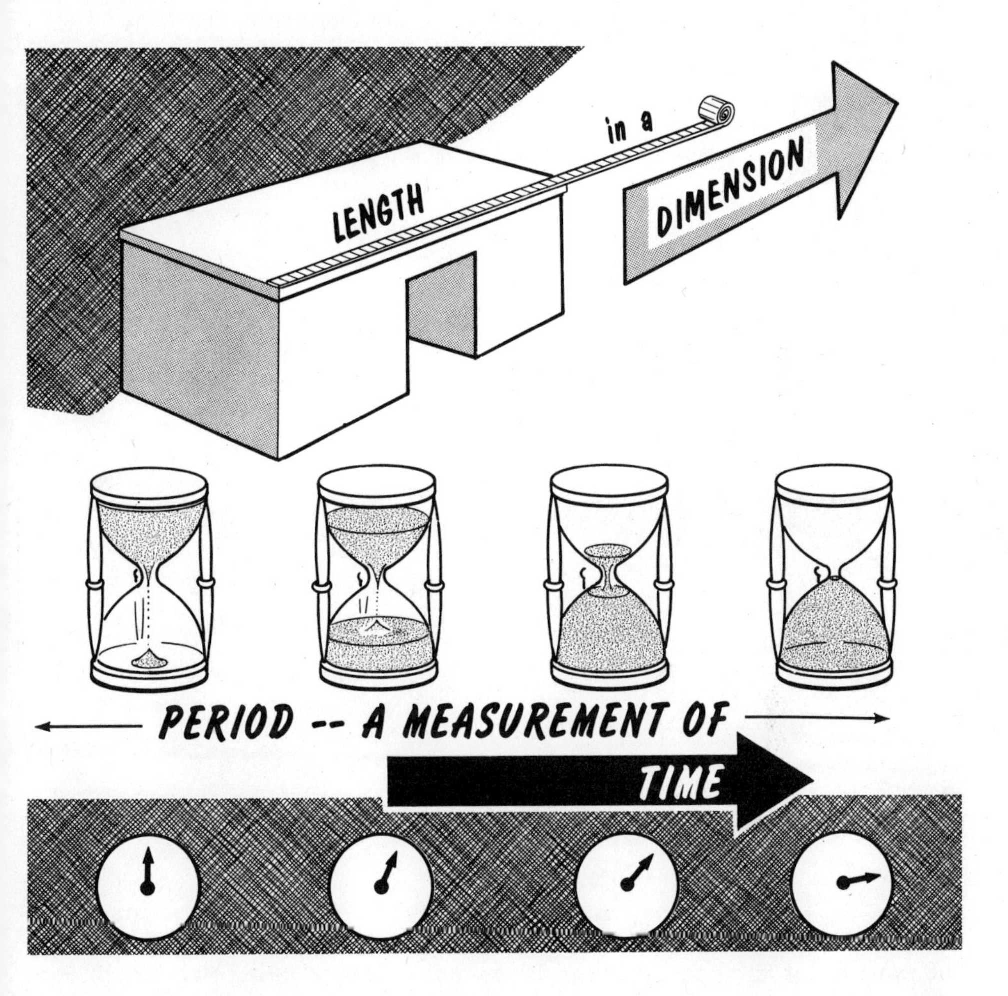

If I use a ruler to measure my desk, I find its dimension in inches. But that is not the end of space in the direction I measure. What I have found is how much space my desk occupies in that direction—that is a dimension.

When sand runs through the hourglass, or when a watch spring runs down, time does not stop. It continues although we may not be measuring any further. So time is a dimension.

Using Time to Build More Dimensions

We combine length one way with length another way to make an area. In similar ways we can combine time with length, or distance, to derive speed. Suppose we walk at a steady rate and with even pace, so as to cover a mile in 15 minutes. If we don't change our pace, we shall cover another mile in the next 15 minutes. If we continue for an hour (60 minutes) we shall go 4 miles. Our steady speed is 4 miles an hour (mph).

If we could keep it up, we would travel 4 miles in the next hour, and so on. So, to find the distance traveled, we should *multiply speed by time.*

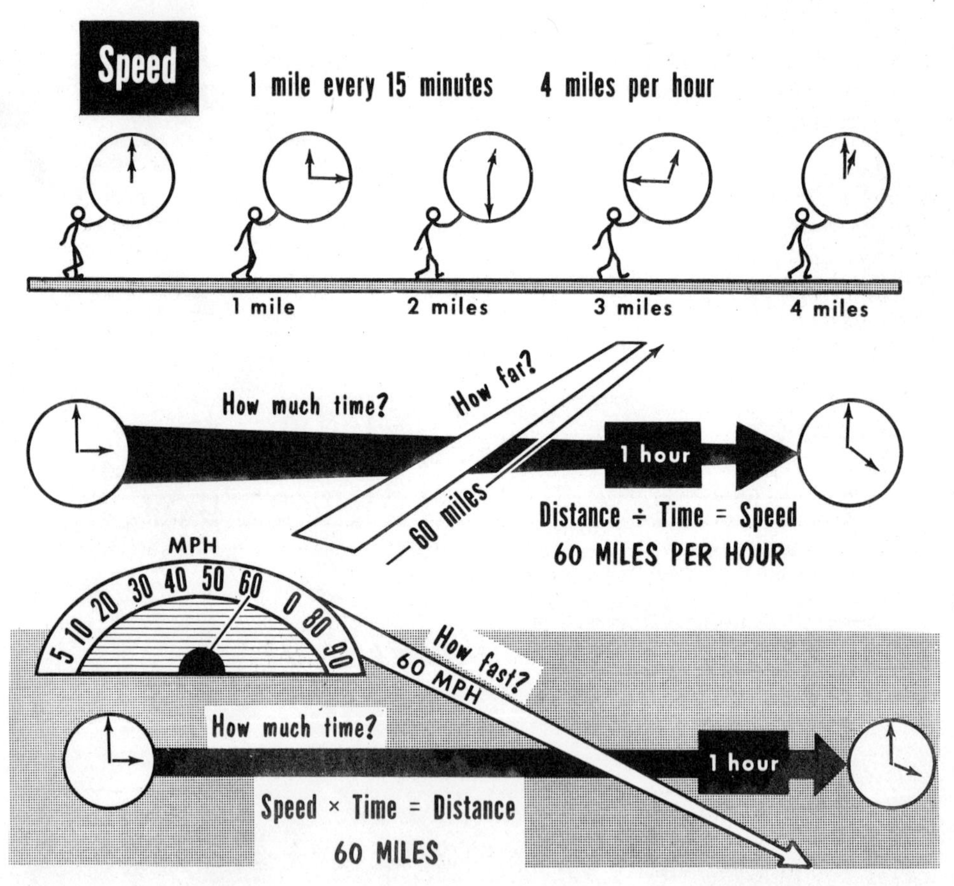

The same thing is true of driving. If we drive so as to cover 60 miles in an hour, we must go 1 mile every minute. Then, in 60 minutes (1 hour), we shall cover 60 miles.

To know speed, we need to know how far in how much time. If we travel 300 miles in 6 hours at a steady speed, we must be doing 50 miles every hour. Six hours at 50 miles each hour makes 300 miles. So to find speed, we need to *divide distance* (a length dimension) *by time.*

Average Speed

In our previous statements about speed, we assumed that it was steady. But it isn't always. On a 300-mile journey, we may cover 30 miles the first hour, 45 miles the second, 60 miles the third, 55 miles the fourth, fifth, and sixth hours. We did a total of 300 miles in 6 hours, which makes our speed $\frac{300}{6} = 50$ miles per hour. Actually, it is reasonable to assume that we didn't travel at that steady speed anywhere along the journey. Sometimes we were faster, sometimes slower. This is what we call our *average speed.* It is the speed we should have needed to go *at a steady rate* to cover the distance in the same time.

If you watch your car's speedometer, you will find that very seldom can you go for a whole hour at a steady speed—or even for a few minutes. So actually, if we measure the distance covered every hour, we are only finding the average speed covered during that hour.

Instead of noting our distance every hour, we could note it every five minutes. This would show us a little more closely how our speed varied *during* each hour. Notice that unless the speed is steady, whatever our average speed is, some of the time it is less than average and sometimes it is more: we can only maintain an average speed, either by doing exactly that steady speed, or by going faster and slower than our average some of the time.

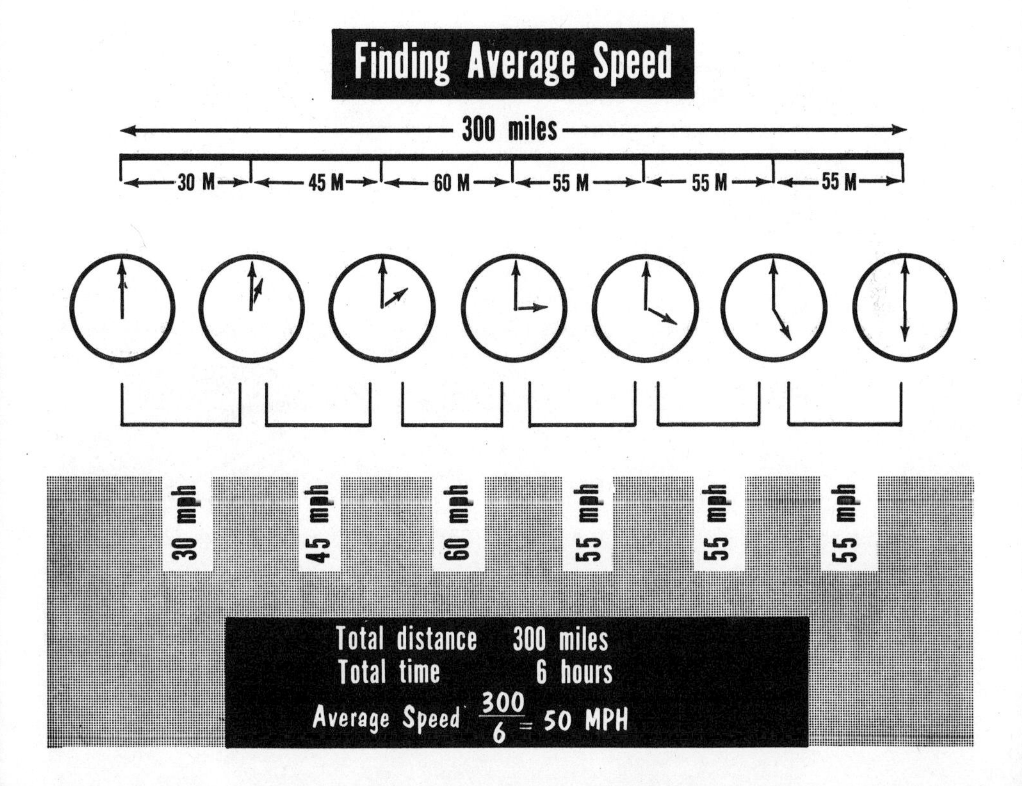

Average Speed (contd.)

That's one way to measure speed, probably the most obvious way. If you say 50 miles an hour, it means you cover 50 miles in an hour. But often, we need to know speed without waiting so long—speed over a short distance or over some specially known distance.

At a race track, for example, each lap may measure just 1 mile. Speed can be figured for each lap by measuring the time. If the lap is made in exactly 1 minute, the speed is 60 miles an hour. If it's made in 40 seconds, we should do $1\frac{1}{2}$ miles in 60 seconds, or 90 miles an hour. By dividing the time, as a fraction of one hour, into the distance, we get the speed in miles per hour.

If the lap were 3 miles and the time 2 minutes, this is $\frac{1}{30}$ of an hour. Dividing 3 miles by $\frac{1}{30}$ gives the speed as 90 miles an hour.

FIGURING SPEED FOR A SPECIFIC DISTANCE

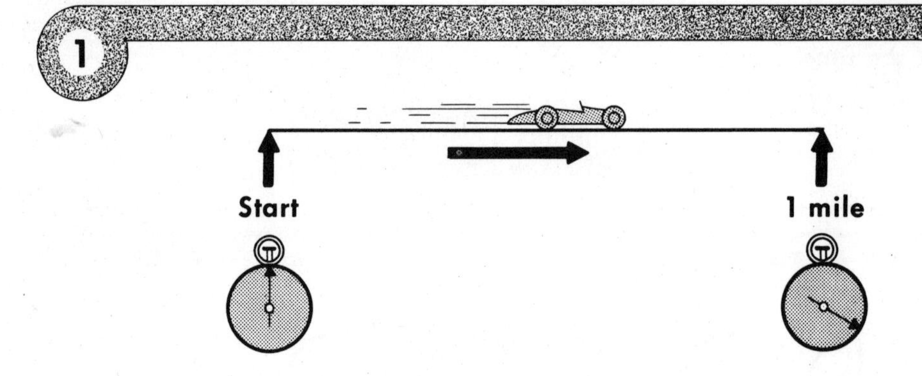

1 mile in 1 minute   60 miles in 1 hour (60 minutes)

1 mile in 40 seconds $60 \div \frac{2}{3} = 90$ mph

($\frac{2}{3}$ minute)

2

Lap is 3 miles; time is 2 minutes ($\frac{1}{30}$ hour)

Speed is $3 \div \frac{1}{30} = 90$ mph

Average Speed (contd.)

Now let us suppose we are timing a race: it's a 50-mile race, made by running 10 laps on a 5-mile course. The times made by one driver for the ten laps were 6, 5, 4, 3.5, 4, 3.5, 5.5, 4.5, 4, and 4 minutes. The total time for the 50 miles was 44 minutes. This was an average speed of 68.17 miles per hour.

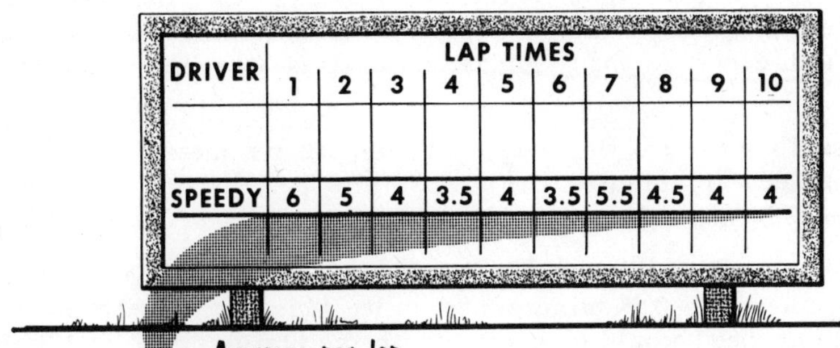

DRIVER	LAP TIMES									
	1	2	3	4	5	6	7	8	9	10
SPEEDY	6	5	4	3.5	4	3.5	5.5	4.5	4	4

Averages per lap

Lap number	Time	Miles	Miles per hour		Average of speeds
1	6	5	50	÷ 10 =	5
2	5	5	60		6
3	4	5	75		7.5
4	3.5	5	85.7		8.57
5	4	5	75		7.5
6	3.5	5	85.7		8.57
7	5.5	5	54.5		5.45
8	4.5	5	66.7		6.67
9	4	5	75		7.5
10	4	5	75		7.5
Complete run	44	50	68.17		70.26

WHICH IS THE RIGHT AVERAGE?

If we figure out the average speed for each lap, we get figures of: 50, 60, 75, 85.7, 75, 85.7, 54.5, 66.7, 75, 75. As each one of these represents the speed for $\frac{1}{10}$ of the distance, should not the average be found by adding $\frac{1}{10}$ of **each** of these figures? But that comes to 70.26.

Which is the right average speed—68.17 or 70.26 mph? Or wasn't our calculation accurate enough?

The Reference Quantity

Speed, or movement, involves two dimensions—distance and time. Which is the more important? Usually, time is. We want to get to a certain place, but we want to know *when*. Time will pass whether we go or not; whether we go fast or slow. So we use time as the reference—miles *per hour*.

The method of timing the race on the previous page uses distance as the reference quantity: time is measured every 5 miles, rather than distance being measured every so many minutes. That is why the discrepancy occurs.

We don't usually measure this way, but suppose we measured slowness (instead of speed) in minutes per mile (time per distance, instead of distance per time): the figures would be 1.2, 1, 0.8, 0.7, 0.8, 0.7, 1.1, 0.9, 0.8, and 0.8 minute per mile. Now take the average, by adding $\frac{1}{10}$ of each of these ten together: it's 0.88 minute per mile. This agrees with 50 miles in 44 minutes, so speed would now agree with the first figure of 68.17 miles per hour.

Lap Number	Time	Miles	MINUTES PER MILE		Average of minutes per mile
1	6	5	1.2	÷ 10 =	0.12
2	5	5	1		0.10
3	4	5	0.8		0.08
4	3.5	5	0.7		0.07
5	4	5	0.8		0.08
6	3.5	5	0.7		0.07
7	5.5	5	1.1		0.11
8	4.5	5	0.9		0.09
9	4	5	0.8		0.08
10	4	5	0.8		0.08
Complete Run	44	50	68.17		0.88

0.88 minutes per mile
= 0.88 × 50 = 44 minutes for 50 miles.

THE REFERENCE QUANTITY:

MILES PER HOUR (TIME)
or
MINUTES PER MILE (DISTANCE)

Changing the Average

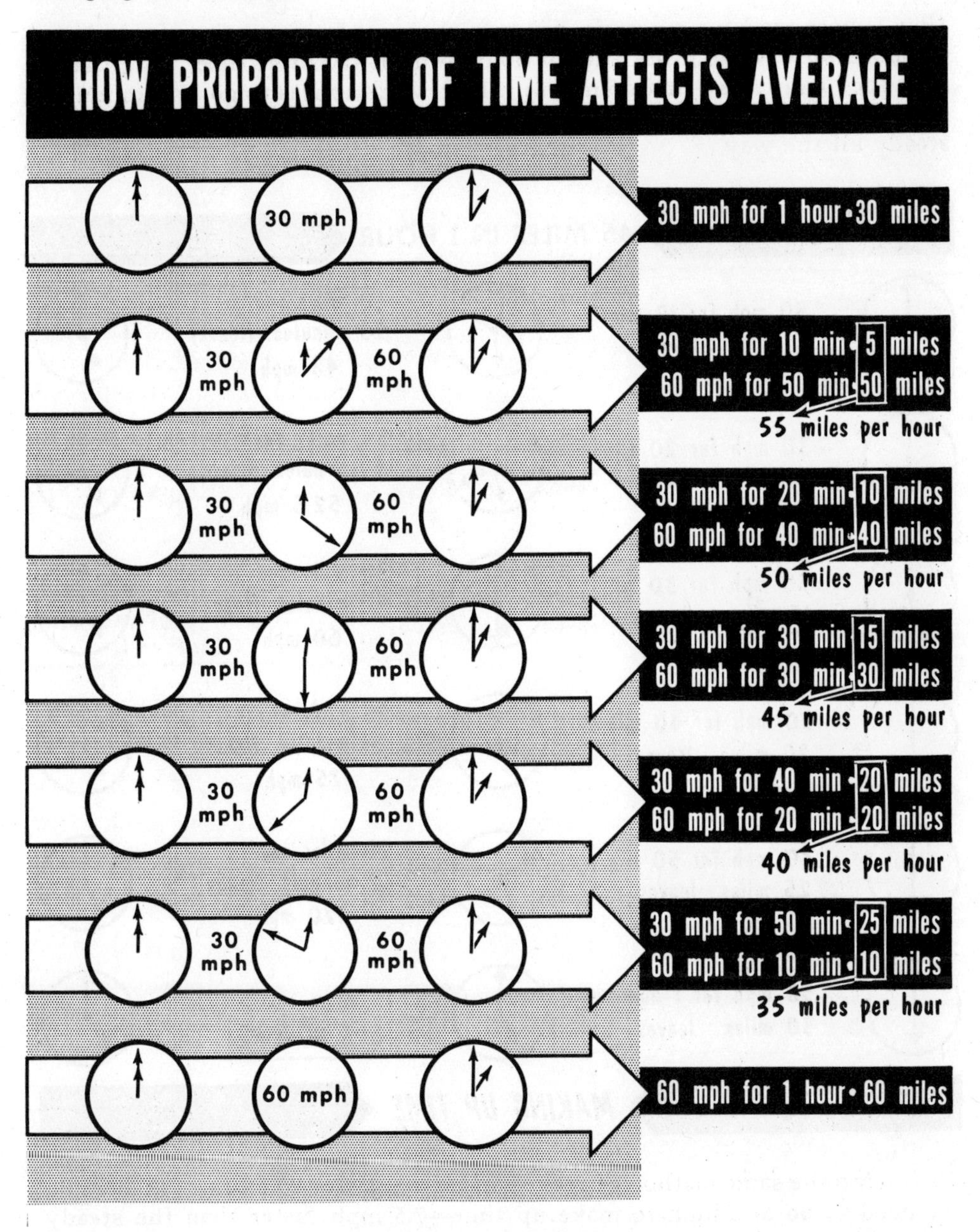

Now suppose we travel for a fixed time—say, 1 hour. First assume that we go at 30 mph for the whole hour: we shall go 30 miles. Next suppose that, for the last 10 minutes, we go 60 mph: now we shall go 25 miles at 30 mph and 10 miles at 60 mph, a total of 35 miles. So the average is 35 mph. We can calculate a progressively higher average rate as progressively more time is traveled at the higher speed.

Making Up Time

Now supose we have a certain distance to go, and a fixed time to do it in. Suppose we have 45 miles and an hour to do it in. First time, we go at 30 mph for 10 minutes—that's 5 miles; it leaves us 40 miles to go in 50 minutes, so we need to go at 48 mph to do it. Just 3 mph faster than if we had gone steady all the way.

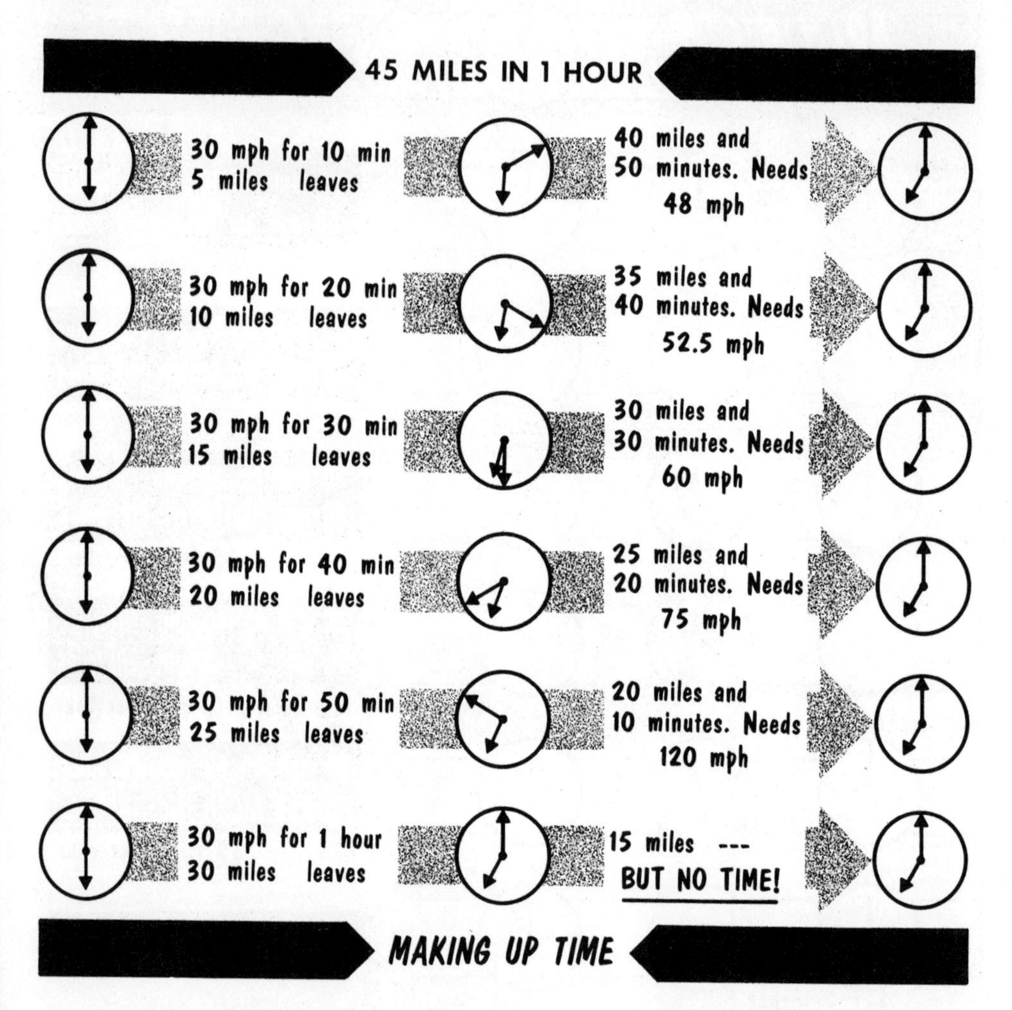

Following the same method of reckoning, if we go for 20 minutes at 30 mph, we need to do 52.5 mph to make up time—7.5 mph faster than the steady speed. If we go for 30 minutes at 30 mph, we need to do 60 mph to make up time—15 mph faster. For 40 minutes at the slower speed, we need to do 75 mph to make up time, while for 50 minutes at the slower speed, we need to do 120 mph to make it up. Finally, if we went for the full hour at 30 mph, we'd have 15 miles left to do, and no time left. It couldn't be done any more without being in two places at the same time.

Rate of Growth

Speed and rate of growth are similar ideas, if you can compare the hare and the tortoise method of travel. Growth is often imperceptible in terms of minutes or hours, but if you measure time in days or weeks, you can measure growth in inches or feet.

But the idea of rate of growth raises the question of the reference quantity again: if a seedling is 2 inches high today, and tomorrow it's 10 inches high, you would think that fast growth. But if a tree is 30 feet high, and tomorrow it's 30 feet and 8 inches, you'd have to look twice to make sure it had grown overnight at all. When you add 8 inches to 2 inches, that's a big growth, but added to 30 feet, 8 inches doesn't amount to much.

Fractional Increase

The seedling is growing 180 times as fast as the tree!

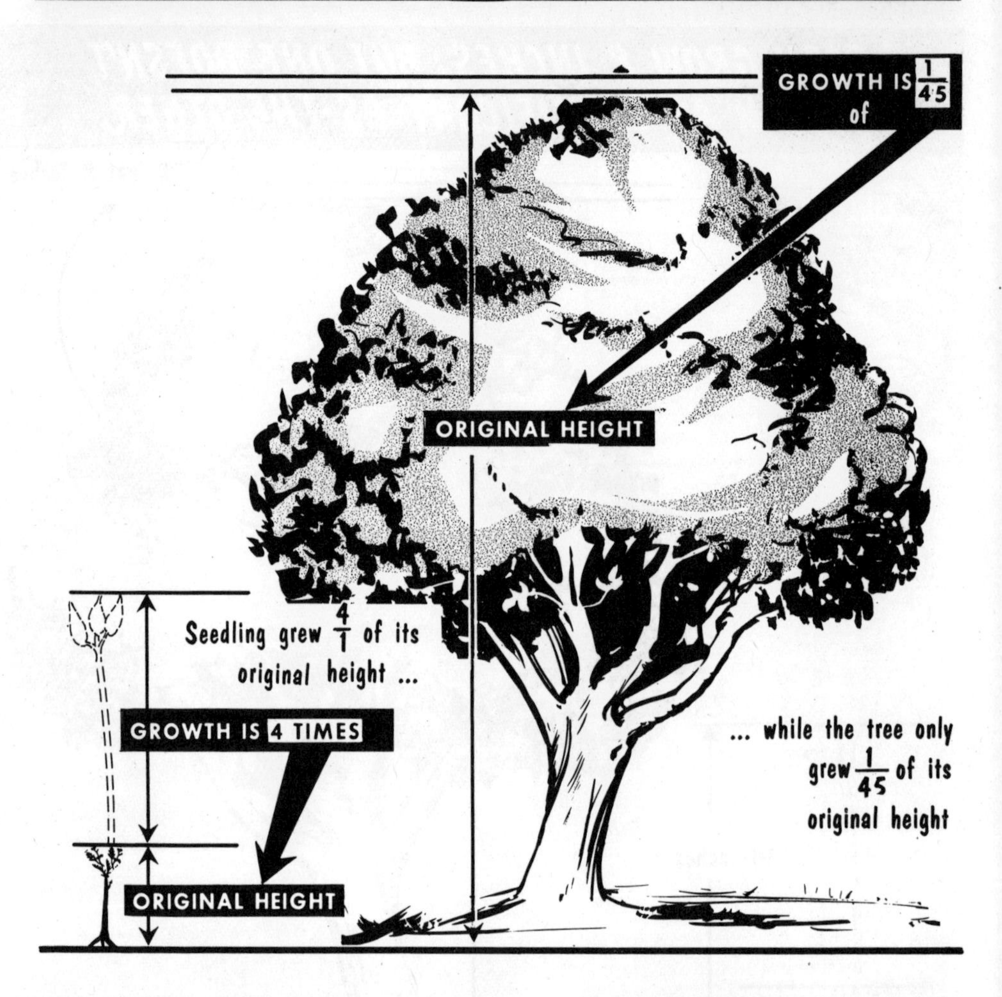

The seedling that grew from 2 inches to 10 inches increased its height 5 times, or added 4 times its height of yesterday. But the tree of 30 feet high added $\frac{2}{3}$ of a foot (8 inches is $\frac{2}{3}$ of 12 inches), which is only $\frac{2}{3}$ divided by 30, as a fraction of the height of the tree: $\frac{2}{90}$ or $\frac{1}{45}$.

So if we consider it on the basis of *fractional* increase, the seedling adds 4 times its height, while the tree only adds $\frac{1}{45}$ of its height, although both happen to be 8 inches. Using the fractional increase form of reference, the seedling is growing 180 times as fast as the tree.

Percentages

Percentages are a standard way of expressing things as a fractional reference. It seems to have started before decimals, in an attempt to make working in fractions a little easier. Nowadays, decimals might be easier to understand directly, but percentages have been used so long that they have become a habit for many purposes.

WHICH IS BIGGER? $\frac{2}{5}$ or $\frac{3}{8}$

1 BY FRACTIONS. COMMON DENOMINATOR IS $5 \times 8 = 40$

$$\frac{2}{5} = \frac{2 \times 8}{5 \times 8} = \frac{16}{40} \qquad \frac{3}{8} = \frac{3 \times 5}{8 \times 5} = \frac{15}{40}$$

THIS IS BIGGER THAN THIS

2 BY DECIMALS.

$$\frac{2}{5} = 0.4 \qquad \frac{3}{8} = 0.375 \qquad 5\overline{)2.0} = 0.4 \qquad 8\overline{)3.000} = 0.375$$

3 BY PERCENTAGES.

$$\frac{2}{5} = \frac{2 \times 20}{5 \times 20} = \frac{40}{100} = 40\%$$

$$\frac{3}{8} = \frac{3 \times 12.5}{8 \times 12.5} = \frac{37.5}{100} = 37.5\%$$

Like decimals, percentages were started because fractions could be so clumsy. For example, if someone asked you which is the bigger fraction, $\frac{2}{5}$ or $\frac{3}{8}$, could you say, just by looking at them? But convert to decimals, and it's easy to see: $\frac{2}{5}$ is 0.4 and $\frac{3}{8}$ is 0.375. As 0.4 is 0.025 bigger than 0.375, you know $\frac{2}{5}$ is that much bigger than $\frac{3}{8}$.

With percentages, they started with the notion of using a big denominator —100—so the numerator could be a simple number in many cases. The fraction $\frac{2}{5}$ is $\frac{40}{100}$, so we'd call it 40% (percent). The fraction $\frac{3}{8}$ is $\frac{37}{100}$ and $\frac{5}{1{,}000}$ (as we know from decimals) or $\frac{1}{200}$. This fraction $\frac{1}{200}$ is half of $\frac{1}{100}$, so the fraction $\frac{3}{8}$ can be written as $37\frac{1}{2}\%$ or 37.5%.

You can see that percentages, like decimals, make it easier to see how fractions compare at a glance: 40% is obviously $2\frac{1}{2}\%$ more than $37\frac{1}{2}\%$.

Percentages (contd.)

PERCENTAGE ALWAYS RELATES TO STARTING FIGURE

STARTS AT 2 INCHES; GROWS TO 10 INCHES

Growth is 8 inches which is 4 times starting height

4 times is $\frac{400}{100}$ or **400 %**

STARTS AT 30 FEET; GROWS 8 INCHES MORE ($\frac{2}{3}$ FOOT)

Growth is $\frac{2}{3} \div 30 = \frac{2}{90} = \frac{1}{45}$

$$\frac{\frac{100}{45}}{100} = \frac{\frac{20}{9}}{100} = \frac{2\frac{2}{9}}{100} = 2\frac{2}{9}\%$$

One reason for preferring percentages is that they automatically relate, or refer, to the starting size or number. If you say something grew 8 inches, you don't know whether to think that is fast or slow growth, unless you know how big it *was*. But if it grew 8 inches from 2 inches, you know that four times its starting size has been added to it: we call that 400%, because 4 is $\frac{400}{100}$.

On the other hand, if it grew 8 inches from 30 feet, it is a fraction of $\frac{1}{45}$, which is $2\frac{2}{9}$%—much smaller than 400%.

Percentages with Money

Of all places where percentages are used, probably money is the most common. When railway or airline fares go up, or down, it's usually figured on a percentage basis. Profits are paid in dividends by percent. This enables everything to be divided fairly.

If the railway company has to raise fares because of increased costs, it would not be fair to charge everyone $1 more. A fare that was previously 5¢ would now be $1.05, and one that was $30 would only go up to $31. Similarly, if profits among 200 stockholders are $10,000, one could share it out at $50 per stockholder. But one stockholder may have invested only $1 of his money, while another may have invested $100,000. It would hardly be fair to give the man who put in only $1 a full $50 profit—the same as the man who put in $100,000.

So these things are worked out on a percentage basis. If the total railway costs have gone up from $100,000,000 to $110,000,000, this is a 10% increase. To get this back from the fares charged, each should go up 10%. The 5¢ fare would then only go up to $5\frac{1}{2}$¢—possibly they would make this 6¢—while the $30 fare would go up to $33.

Similarly, if the profits were $10,000 on a total investment of $2,000,000, this is 5%. The stockholders who invested $1 gets 5¢, while the one who invested $100,000 gets $5,000 dividend.

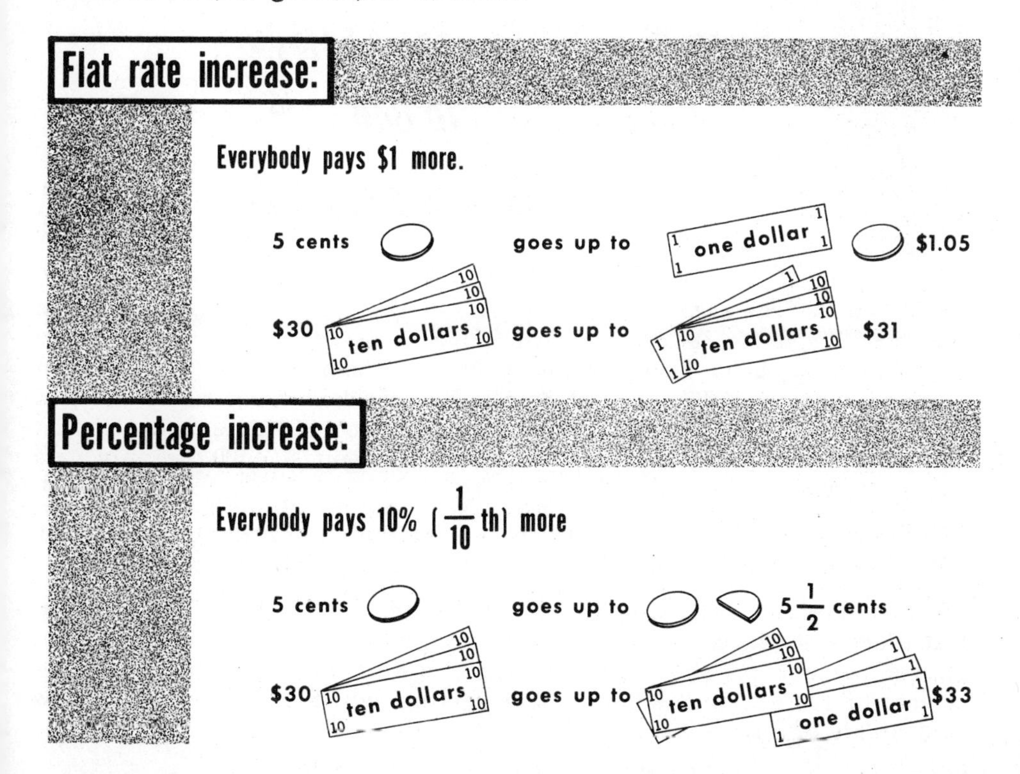

Percentages Up and Down

There is one thing to watch with percentages: *always take the starting figure of a transaction or calculation as the 100% reference.* Let us illustrate.

A man buys property for $10,000. Its value goes up and he sells it to another man for $12,500. He's made 25% profit on the deal: it cost him $10,000 and he has recovered his $10,000 with another $2,500 more.

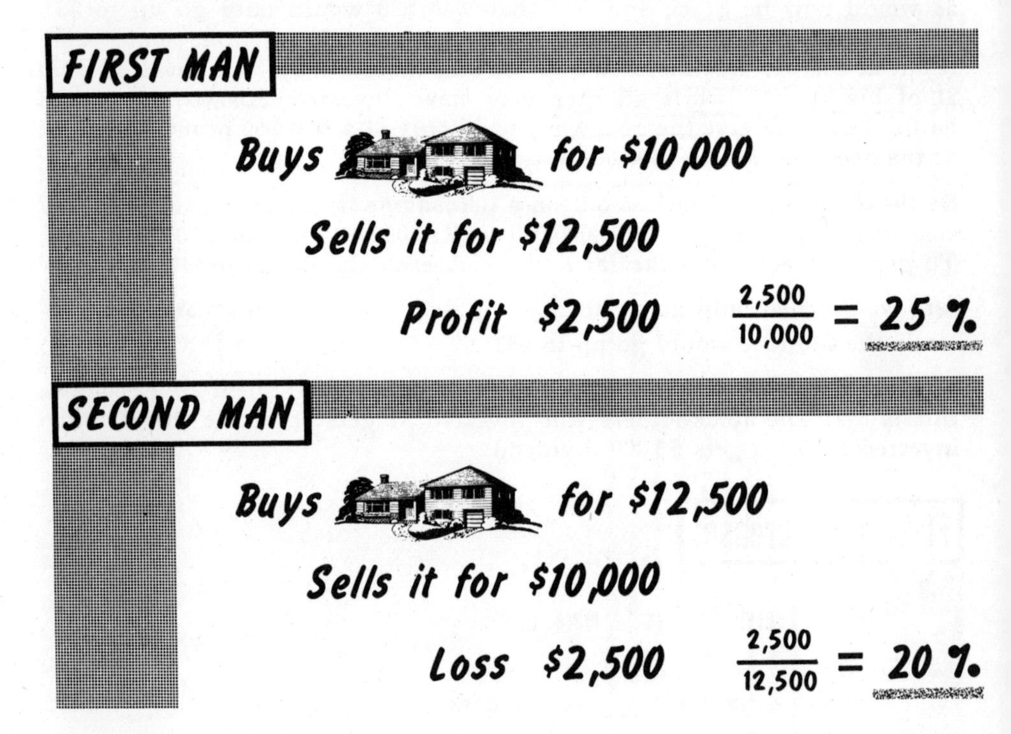

Now suppose the second man keeps it, but this time its value goes down and he sells it for its original price $10,000. Since it is now back to its original price, after having gone up 25%, we should think that it must now have dropped 25%. But it hasn't. The second man is not concerned about what the first man paid for it. The price he's concerned with is what he paid for it—$12,500. Of his original investment, $12,500, he only gets back $10,000.

This is still a loss of 2,500, but it now is a fraction, or percentage, of $12,500. This makes it a 20% loss.

So 25% increase is the same fractional change, in reverse, as 20% decrease. Smaller percentages come nearer to meaning the same, either way. But larger percentages show a much bigger difference. For example, an increase of 100% means doubling; but halving, which is the reverse, means a decrease of only 50%.

Graphical Representation of Facts

Visual presentation of statistics is very common these days. Commercials use it all the time—even if their "facts" may be questionable! The reason is that comparison by eye conveys an impression more quickly and more effectively or accurately than a statement of numbers usually can.

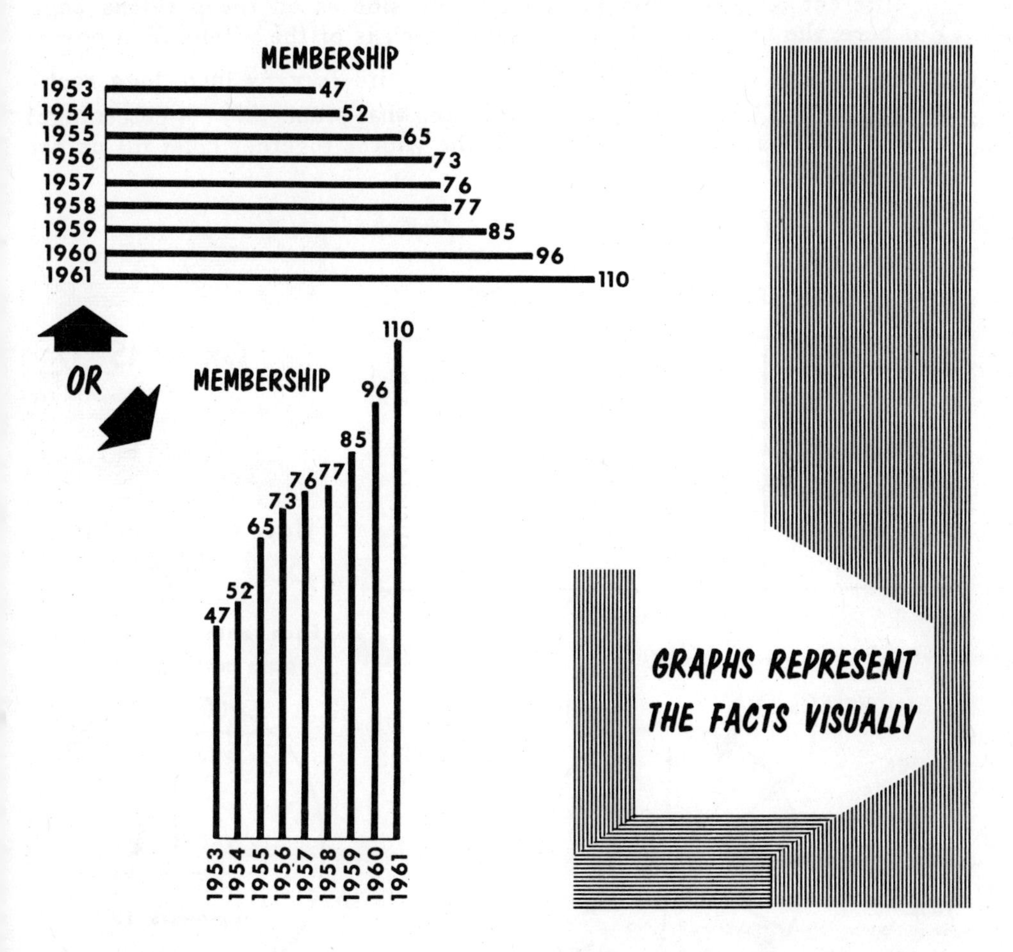

So the *graphical* presentation is used. Lengths are used to replace numbers. Suppose you want to show growth in membership of a certain club: its figures, for successive years, are: 47, 52, 65, 73, 76, 77, 85, 96, 110.

To do this, you draw lines, or blocks, to represent the number of members for each year. If you make each member take up $\frac{1}{16}$ inch of line, 110 members (the highest) will need $6\frac{7}{8}$ inches. Having drawn the lines, equally spaced, to represent uniform 1-year time intervals, you have a visual picture of the membership growth. You can put the lines either horizontally or vertically.

Graphs

Visual presentations can help in many ways. For example, a society may want to show how many of its members belong to certain groups: engineers, doctors, lawyers, salesmen, factory workers, shop assistants, truck drivers, musicians, etc. They could give these as percentages, or a number of lines of different lengths could be put side by side as on the previous page. But here, the idea is to show how much each is of the whole. So a box of suitable width can be marked off in 100 units (say $\frac{1}{16}$ inch long each), and each group is given a space representing that proportion (in percentage) of the total. As the total is 100%, all the widths together must fill up the box.

MEMBERSHIP COMPOSITION

ENGINEERS 13%
DOCTORS 19%
LAWYERS 15%
FACTORY WORKERS 18%
SHOP ASSISTANTS 13%
TRUCK DRIVERS 8%
MUSICIANS 11%
SALESMEN 3%

OR

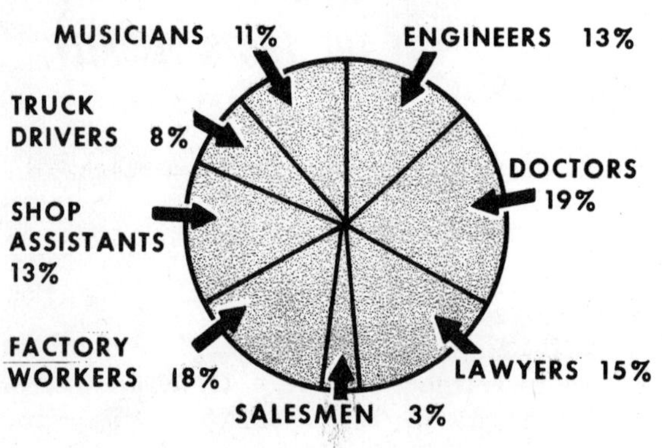

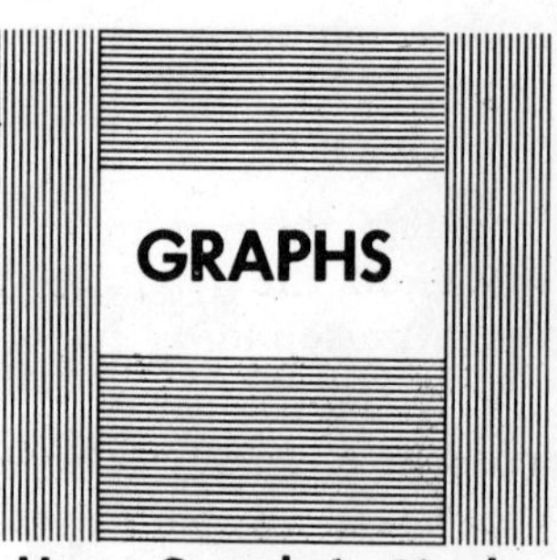

How Graph is Made

Each tenth divides by ten again making 100 parts

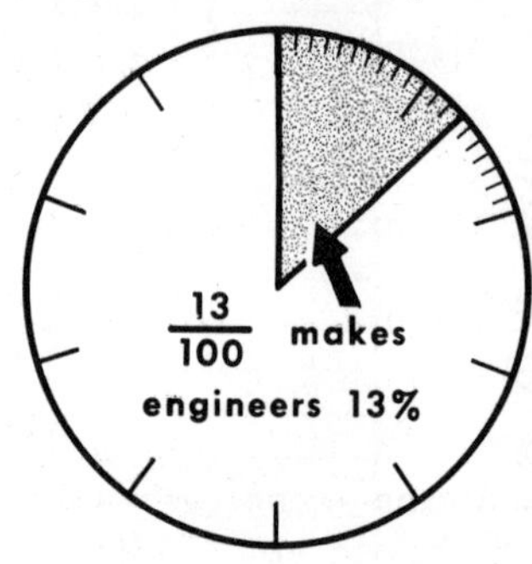

Circle divides into 10 parts (each 36° on a protractor)

Another way, sometimes favored for this, is to divide a circle up in the same way. Its circumference is divided into 100 parts (we have shown 10, to make it clearer—each of these can then be divided into 10 again). Then the circumference is divided according to the percentages in the groups, and lines drawn from each marker to the center.

Graphs (contd.)

But the use of graphs is not confined to statistical things. They can be used to help calculations. Suppose for example, some tests were made on an electric motor, to see how much electrical power is needed for different mechanical jobs the motor has to do. Electrical power is measured in watts and mechanical power in horsepower. The results are tabulated, giving the electrical power needed when the motor is running "light"—no mechanical output—and the power for various horsepower outputs.

Now we may have a job for the motor that needs an amount of horsepower not listed. How do you calculate the amount for this new job? A graph makes the job easier and more reliable. By marking off points on squared paper to show all the figures tabulated, then joining the dots made, you have a curve showing all the possible input and output powers. You don't even need to be an electrical engineer to do this, or know anything about electricity.

You find the amount of electrical power needed for the new job by reading it off the graph, or curve, you have made. In textbooks, this is given the high-sounding name of *interpolation.*

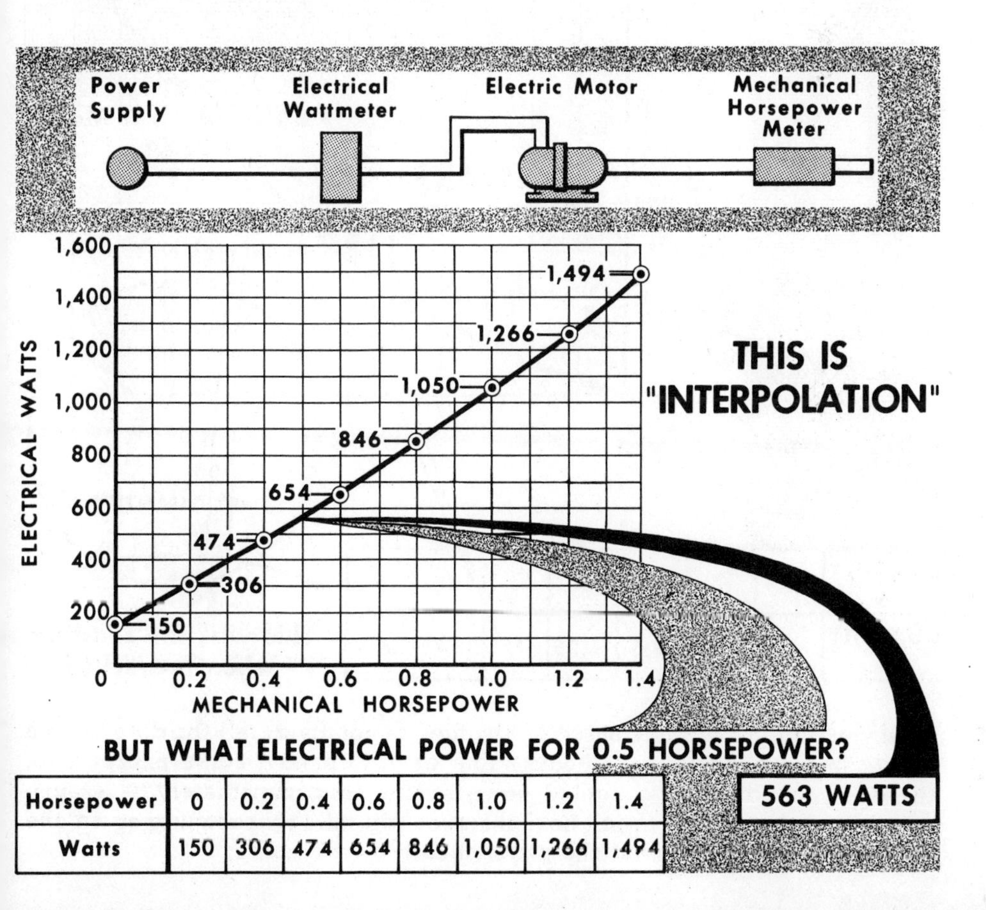

Horsepower	0	0.2	0.4	0.6	0.8	1.0	1.2	1.4
Watts	150	306	474	654	846	1,050	1,266	1,494

Graphs (contd.)

Graphs can show us a lot of things that may not be obvious from the figures used to make them, as you may begin to see. But graphs also serve as a useful check on figures. Maybe you made the tests on which the figures were based. You had to read meters to write down the figures. A meter may have numbers on its scale at 20 and at 30, with 9 marks in between, but no numbers. Suppose the reading should be 23, but you copy it down as 27 by mistake. But you have all the other readings correct.

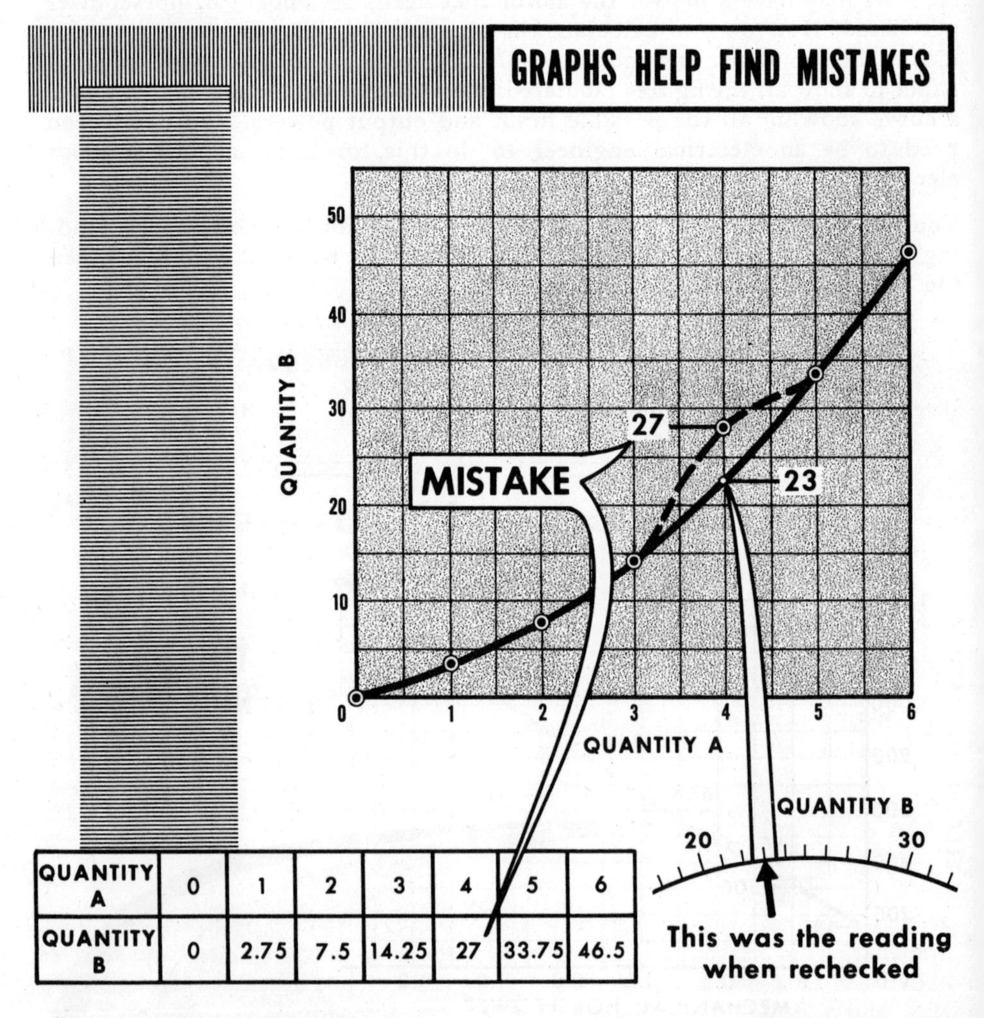

QUANTITY A	0	1	2	3	4	5	6
QUANTITY B	0	2.75	7.5	14.25	27	33.75	46.5

Now you plot your graph, based on the figures you have. All the dots (called *points* in mathematics text books) line up into a nice curve except one: the one you erroneously copied down as 27. This immediately gives you an inkling where there might be a mistake; you take that reading again and find out that you had read the meter incorrectly.

Graphs (contd.)

The same basic information can often be presented in a number of different ways. As an example, look at that race track record on page 1-125 again. One driver made the ten laps in 6, 5, 4, 3.5, 4, 3.5, 5.5, 4.5, 4, and 4 minutes.

Each lap represents 5 miles, so we could set this up to show how he progressed along the 50-mile race, in terms of elapsed time as each lap is completed.

Maybe rather than knowing how the race is going at different stages, the important statistic is how fast he went each lap. So a graph can show it that way, or rather two ways. It can either show the time taken for each lap, or the speed at which each lap was covered, as average.

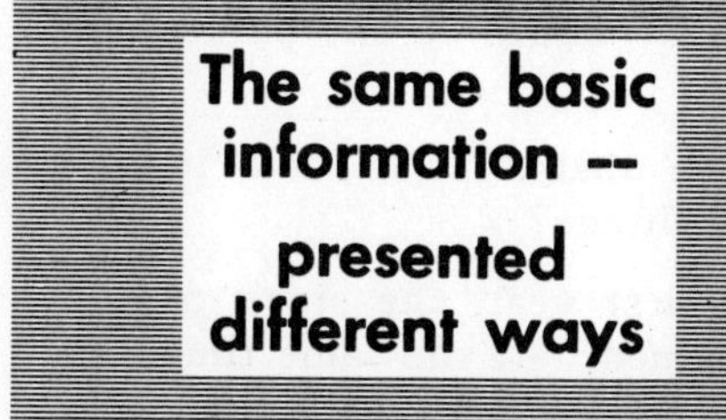

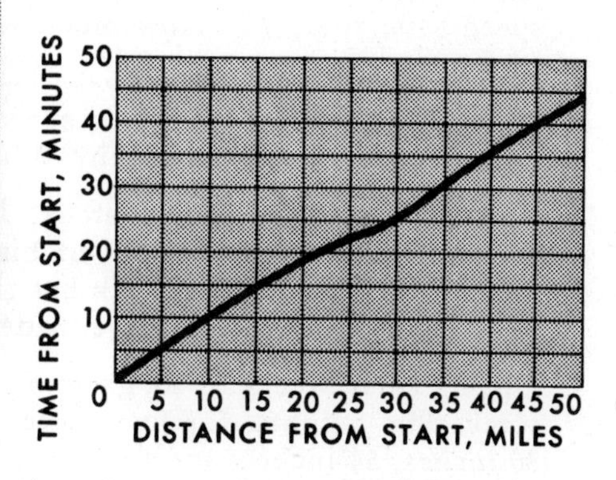

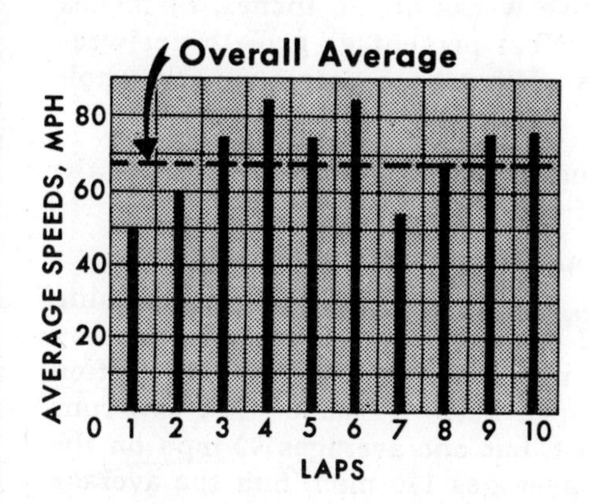

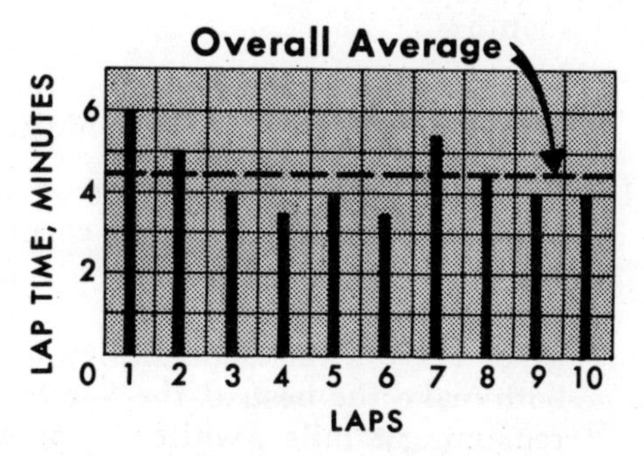

If you want to, you can figure out the average, either lap time or speed, and mark this on the scale, so you can see how much of the time he was above and how much of it he was below his average speed or lap time. By this, and a knowledge of other details about individual laps, he can better judge his performance: how much it was affected by changes in weather, if any; interference from other drivers crowding him; etc.

As we go on in later books, we shall find many more things for which graphs can be useful.

1. How far will a car go traveling at 35 mph for 36 minutes?

2. A riverboat makes a water speed (the speed at which the motor propels it) of 10 mph. The river has a downstream current flowing at 2 miles per hour. How fast does the boat go (a) upstream? (b) downstream?

3. How long will the riverboat in question 2 take to make a journey of 96 miles (a) upstream? (b) Downstream?

4. Traveling at a water speed of 10 mph, the riverboat burns half a ton (1 ton is 2,000 pounds) of fuel per hour. How much fuel does the boat take on its 96-mile journey (a) upstream? (b) Downstream?

5. If the boat slows down so as to make the downstream journey in the same time as the upstream one, and if the fuel burned is stricly according to the water speed she makes, (a) will the reduced downstream speed save fuel? (b) How much? (c) What would be the percentage saving?

6. If the boat reduces its water speed on the upstream run, will it save fuel or use more? How much? What percentage?

7. A man invests $50,000 in stock. In the first year, the stock pays a dividend that represents 5% of his investment. At the same time, the value of this amount of stock has risen to $60,000. If he sells the stock, how much profit will he have made (a) in cash, (b) in percentage?

8. During early weeks of its growth, the height of a tree is recorded each week. The heights, for five successive weeks are 16 inches, 24 inches, 36 inches, 54 inches, and 81 inches. What percentage growth per week is this, for each of the four weeks? What percentage for the whole month?

9. Make a graph of the growth for the month and from it estimate the height of the tree in the middle of the second week.

10. A certain race track consists of an 8-mile lap. The lap is made up of 5 miles with many hairpins, corners, and grades, while the remaining 3 miles is made up of straights and banked curves. The best time any car can make on the 5-mile part is 6 minutes, but the remaining section gives drivers the opportunity to "open up." Assume that two runs both make the best of the 5-mile part, but one averages 90 mph on the remaining 3 miles, while the other averages 120 mph, find the average each makes on the whole lap.

11. A car is checked for mileage per gallon and found to go 23 miles per gallon on straight turnpike driving. How far will it go on a tankful, if the tank holds 18 gallons?

12. A company needs printed circuit boards made for which two processes are available. The first needs a tool made that costs $2,000, after which each board costs 15¢ to make. The second process requires a setup procedure that costs $200, after which each board costs 65¢ to make.

Find the cost per board, assuming that the total quantity ordered is: 100, 500, 1,000, 2,000, 5,000, or 10,000 boards.

13. Plot a graph of the cost per board by the two processes (question 12) for quantities between 1,000 and 10,000 boards. At what quantity would the cost of both processes be the same?

14. Driving a certain car at a steady speed of 40 mph gets a mileage of 18 miles per gallon; driving the same car at 60 mph steady speed reduces the mileage obtained to 16.5 miles per gallon. On a journey of 594 miles, how much gas will be saved by going at the slower speed, and how much longer will the journey take?

15. A man pays $20,000 for some property, which is its market value. After a year, its value has risen 25%, but he does not sell. During the next year its value drops 10%, after which he sells. What profit did he make on his original investment (a) in cash, (b) in percent? Why was it not $25 - 10 = 15\%$ profit?

16. After all proper allowances and deductions have been made, a man's taxable income is $7,000. How much tax will he have to pay, at 20% on the first $4,000 and 22% on the next $4,000?

17. A square-cornered triangle with 12-foot and 16-foot sides which make up the square corner has the same area as a parallelogram with opposite pairs of sides 10 feet and 16 feet long. What is the distance between the 16-foot sides?

18. On a certain flight, an aircraft gains altitude at a steady rate of 1,000 feet per minute. How long does he take to climb to his flying altitude of 22,000 feet? If his forward ground speed while climbing is 360 mph, how far does he travel during the climb?

19. The same aircraft in level flight flies at the speed of 420 mph, but consumes fuel at half the rate (per minute) compared with climbing. How far can the plane fly level, using an amount of fuel equal to that used to reach 22,000 feet?

20. How much further would the plane of the previous two questions get on the same total fuel, if he leveled off at 11,000 feet instead of 22,000 feet, assuming that altitude does not affect speed or fuel consumption and ignoring wind effects?

INDEX TO VOL. I